PENGUIN BOOKS
860

THE PRIESTLEY COMPANION

J. B. PRIESTLEY

THE PRIESTLEY COMPANION

A SELECTION FROM THE WRITINGS

OF J. B. PRIESTLEY

WITH AN INTRODUCTION BY

IVOR BROWN

PENGUIN BOOKS
IN ASSOCIATION WITH
WILLIAM HEINEMANN

FIRST PUBLISHED 1951

MADE AND PRINTED IN GREAT BRITAIN
FOR PENGUIN BOOKS LTD
HARMONDSWORTH · MIDDLESEX
BY C. NICHOLLS AND COMPANY LTD

CONTENTS

PARTIES

PASTIMES AND PLEASURES

PEEPSHOWS

PEOPLE

CONTENTS

PERSONS · PLEASING OR PECULIAR

PLACES

POLEMICAL

The 'Postscripts' that I delivered for the B.B.C. in 1940 were never meant to be read but only to be heard, but as they found their way into print and seem to be a part of so many people's wartime memories, I have included a small selection of them here. Almost from the first, I was accused, by a small but noisy and aggressive section of the listening public, very well represented in the Press, of being too political. But *Where, When* or *How* was never explained to me, and to this day I do not know what such people had in their minds.

POSTSCRIPTS

PROCEEDINGS

PURELY PERSONAL

INTRODUCTION

By Ivor Brown

To read the samples of J. B. Priestley's work that are here collected, and then to remember his plentiful achievement as a journalist and dramatist, is surely to be convinced that he is the best all-round writer of English in our time. All-round is not a graceful adjective, I admit, but it does effectively suggest that Priestley's mind has windows on every side.

He looks out on Tahiti and Anzouc as well as on Bruddersford and the Isle of Wight, on the fabric of social life as well as on the foibles of individual people; he is a metaphysician concerned with the mystery of Time as well as a Radical politician who investigates the roots of our economy and has abundant ideas about weeding and replanting it. He conceives himself, almost boasts himself, to be a major Grumbler (see the charming essay on this point in the section called Purely Personal). But, compared with most of the writers younger than himself, he is a rollicking hedonist and an enjoyer on a tremendous scale. He cannot look out of any of his multitudinous windows without seeing at least one thing grotesquely amusing or fantastically beautiful, whereas his peevish juniors analyse the same object only to find that it wickedly exemplifies nothing but social inequality or psychological disintegration. It is significant that his self-portrait as a Grousing Ogre is the first of many essays on the good times and lustrous moments that have come his way. This is a frank and laughing self-exposure. His grievances emerge from his gusto and his furies are part of his fun.

So you may view him as an all-round man, copious, energetic, uncannily swift in perception and reaction. He is a sculptor of scenes, a hewer of ideas, not a polisher of words. It is true that he has written an essay in his volume called *Delight* on the glory of lying smoking in a bath and in this he playfully ridicules the idea of his being energetic and calls himself lazy and self-indulgent. Certainly he likes his pleasures, though he finds them as a rule in simple activities, like home-made music or frying sausages at picnics. Having tasted the most luxurious forms of travel and catering he has nicely described himself and his supposedly sybaritic companions as 'lotus-eaters clean out of lotus'. But it is impossible to look at his list of publications and then to regard him as a man of dalliance. Once out of that hot bath he claps to it with a vigour and application that most of us do not begin to possess.

When his writing glistens with a brilliant aptness of adjective and felicity of metaphor it is not because he has retired to a chalet in the mountains or a Florentine villa. He has not tied a scented towel round his head or sat fiddling for a whole morning with the cut of a sentence or the cadence of a line. He has simply been smoking a pipe and tapping on a typewriter; no exquisite, museum-worthy manuscripts emerge from Priestley; his handwriting is bad enough to be unusable and he rarely uses it. He is a worker who employs the machinery of his trade and has a friendly feeling for those clickety-clack contraptions which others regard as odious utilities.

I was staying with him in the Isle of Wight when he was writing one of his most typical books, *English Journey*, so observant, so lively, so poignant in its picturing of hard times in the 'thirties and yet so well balanced in its blend of humour and indignation. It seems to be now, on re-reading it, a model of composition, with style and subject in happiest union. But that book fairly poured out of him, as, I believe, does all his best work. Away, upstairs in a study with windows as capacious as his own mental outlook, he was tap-tap-tapping with his characteristic precision as well as his own rhythm of pace. There is little, as a rule, to revise.

That he was thus prolific did not mean that he was abstracted or fussily dedicated to his work. He played his tennis, went about the island, talked and played games at night, and was a genial social figure; he is very happy as a host. Most of the greatest writers have been able thus to mix life and letters, none more so than the abounding, oratorical, play-acting, party-going, platform-loving Dickens. The great Victorians did not miss their dinners or their whist at the club in order to finish off a chapter; but finished it was. And so with Priestley.

It was insisted by the Roman professors of oratory who laid down rules for the eloquence then deemed proper to a gentleman's education that the speaker should have *copia*, plenty. The adjective 'fatal' has frequently been prefixed to the word fluency and everybody knows what a nuisance the chatterbox can be, whether he prattles or scribbles. But the best story-tellers and playwrights have usually been copious. Dickens, Scott, Balzac, Thackeray, Trollope, and, in our time, Wells and Maugham did not sit in ivory towers elaborating perfection at the rate of one sentence to the hour. I am not demeaning those who prefer the status of the *petit maître*, as Sir Max Beerbohm confessedly does. E. M. Forster, through paucity of output, is another who can hardly be set among the big masters, however high you rank his too rarely shown qualities. James Agate, himself a most copious man, felt very strongly that the genius too thrifty of his art was to be censured for a parsimony or an idleness. He was robbing the public of what it had a fair claim to receive. Shakespeare, to turn to the summit of English writing, was a busy, multifarious man, acting, managing, and investing as well as writing, copious in all, and, as the fertile artist must be, fast. 'His hand and mind went together,' said his colleagues and editors, Heminge and Condell. 'What he thought he uttered with the easiness that we have scarce received from him a blot in his papers.'

Accordingly this all-roundness, this easy outflow, and mental restlessness of Priestley's will be charged against him only by the devotees of preciosity. Such fluency, which it is absurd to call fatal, can be, perhaps must be, fallible. Priestley has passed for print more than posterity will want to remember. But what great author has not? Ranging minds experiment and experiment means mingling failure and success.

One weakness of his, as many think, is the weighting of stories and more especially of plays with an excess of 'message' and this may have led to some public resentment. But failures are merely incidents in any big career. There is far too much brooding over and harping upon mishaps, especially in the theatre. 'He's had a flop.' So the town gossips, while jealous eyes sparkle. The decent man's attitude to the 'flops' of the great is to forget them. To be uneven is the very nature of grandeur in man as in nature. Who wants a range of mountains to be all the same height?

Whether Priestley dips or soars (in your judgement) in his plays, his novels, and his admirable 'point-of-view' books such as *Midnight on the Desert* or *Rain Upon Godshill*, there are certain abiding qualities. He is always lucid. He has written myriads of passages with which large numbers of people can reasonably disagree; but he has never written anything which a normal person cannot understand. He has cultivated simplicity because he believes that to be the obvious business of anybody who believes in his own ideas and therefore wishes to spread them. In that he is running counter to the wiseacres of our time who make the most reverent salaams to unintelligible poetry and generally regard 'difficulty' as the first qualification of a 'progressive' master in any of the arts. In this connexion the included essay called 'Too Simple' might very well be taken first and read as a Priestleyan foreword. It states a position that I myself would strongly support; far more important, it is an epitome of Priestley's attitude to his own creed and craft.

There will always be artists who, whether or not they use or accept the label Progressive, prefer to work for the few and to use an idiom which baffles the many. They may thus achieve the kinds of truth and beauty that they have in mind; furthermore, their aims and methods may in time work outwards from the clique to the community and so affect the general conduct of their art. They cannot expect wide immediate appreciation any more than the plain-speakers, especially the plain-speakers who, like Priestley, have a huge public, can look for the plaudits of the cliques. The clear, straightforward writer with a large appeal, especially when he is well into middle-age, is certain to be airily dismissed by the young as being in his dotage and he will be rudely snubbed by the critics whose appeal is only to the few. Priestley has had plenty of that, just as he has had plenty of abuse from those who cannot abide his politics.

Broadcasting, by bringing opinions and personality right to the armchair, has created popularities and animosities with a rapidity and intensity quite unknown when writers merely wrote. H. G. Wells was a prickly and voluble Socialist who poured out on paper opinions which were more advanced and more obnoxious to the popular feeling of his time than anything Priestley has said in recent years. But Wells's books, like Shaw's plays, did not reach the Tory fireside. Broadcasts do, and so broadcasts have a peculiar power to infuriate as well as to charm. You do not expect to answer back at a book; but you do look for a chance to answer and confute a conversational speaker. But suddenly you are being deluged, *via* the air, with chat that you cannot interrupt and opinions that you strongly dislike. The consequent frustration and rage may lead to all sorts of distortion of what was actually said; thus Priestley became a kind of ogre to a large number of ears.

To anybody reading the general mass of his work or such political elements as are included in this *Companion* Priestley will appear, I think, as a rather disillusioned Socialist who remains a robust Radical and would therefore rather vote on the Left than on the Right. His boyhood embraced the flamboyant, chivalrous, Merry Englandish Socialism that flourished on the platforms and in the pamphleteering of forty years ago. The Bradford lad who saw the ugly mess that unfettered capitalism had made of the North would hardly be able to foresee the dreary, form-ridden routine that 'National Board' Collectivism is widely creating, to the increasing dismay of those Socialist workers who thought they had voted themselves into the larger air of a Wellsian Utopia.

There is a touch of the anarchist in most Englishmen and especially in most English Socialists. In the days when Socialism was unpopular, they had to be independent of mind and lonely pioneers if they were to go that way at all. There is a rich vein of this anarchism, this loathing of formulae and of the bureaucrats who delight in them, in the mental make-up of Priestley. Like so many Radicals of to-day, he realizes intellectually that a good deal of interference is necessary to clear up old muddles and injustices, and yet he is instinctively inimical to the interfering hand. 'I am the kind of man', he has written, 'whom nearly all senior Civil servants dislike on sight; and indeed some of them dislike me, I gather, even without seeing me.' This leads to a playful essay on 'The Joy of Frightening Civil Servants', but beneath the banter of this amusing piece is a deposit of essential truth. Priestley, like many who were boy-Socialists when he was a Bradford boy on the first rungs of a wool-trade career, is profoundly sceptical of the instruments which are creating Socialism in our time. He likes neither the bureaucracy nor the rigid, obstructive Trade Unionism that cannot wake up to the creative challenge of Full Employment and Short Supplies and is still dreaming about unemployment in a world of plenty. It seems a long way now from William Morris, Robert Blatchford of *The Clarion*, and the gay journalistic pirouettings of Shaw and Wells in a dance of wits with Chesterton and Belloc. But these were the jovial background of my own juvenile politics and of Priestley's too.

His political writings, like those of H. G. Wells, have a kaleidoscopic fascination. He is prolific in general criticisms and general suggestions; the committee-work and routine of research that go to turn party programmes from slogans into practical propositions could hardly be accommodated, even if he had the appetite for them, into a life that is teeming with novels and plays, with the consequent castings and rehearsals, with film-scripts and film-business, with family affairs, with hospitality, and with quite a deal of travel. As readers and play-goers we can be very thankful that Priestley never did settle down to the exacting business of a workaday politician and that he just missed getting into Parliament as an Independent for Cambridge University in 1945. True, University seats did not involve quite so much drudgery as an ordinary one, but there would have been Commissions and Committees and many entanglements which might have robbed us of so characteristic a story as *Bright Day* or so poignant a play as *The Linden Tree*.

The *Companion* reveals in brief the range of his personal experience. Boyhood in Bradford, four-and-a-half years of war, a career at Cambridge, then a rapid climb up the literary ladder with the usual first steps of reviewing and reading for a publisher, John Lane, who had a long tradition of discoveries behind him. Cambridge has yielded surprisingly little to Priestley's writing. To me, just free of a conventional Public School, to breathe the larger air of Oxford was emancipation indeed. But ex-service men, who have already been at grips with the Universe in its toughest aspects, usually find less excitement in a University. They have wasted precious years; they are eager to be through and to 'get cracking' with a civilian career. Yet I am surprised that the beauty of Cambridge does not come glittering more often into Priestley's category of delights.

Time and again, however, we find Priestley's memory and fancy returning to Bruddersford and its characters, its local loyalties, and its warm, genial domesticity. He was brought up in a schoolmaster's home where there was not much money. But that was in years when a little money bought a lot and in a town where, without money, you could create abundant pleasures of your own. You had the freedom of the moors at the end of a tuppenny tram-ride: indoors it was still the age of the happy amateur who made his own music and whose parties owed nothing to the B.B.C. and its top-line professional entertainers. Cheap food permitted 'open house' and, for outings, a gallery seat at the Theatre Royal cost little enough. Books could be bought by scrimping lunches and by bludgeoning a lusty young appetite with something sickly instead of by serving it sensibly with a 'cut from the joint and two veg.' Priestley, viewing the vast, new suburbs and bungaloid ribbon developments on the rim of our wider-sprawling cities, thinks that these myriads of radio-fed and possibly car-owning families are missing much that he and his kind relished when they went on thrifty picnics and created their own concerts or found that foreign travel was possible with only a pound or two (and no passport) in your pocket. I fancy that he underrates the amount of getting together that goes on in new suburbs where he sees so much isolation of spirit in proximity of bodies. Perhaps, too, he sees boyhood's first adventures in affection, in the arts, and in discovery of people and places through a certain rosiness of retrospect; we all do.

In any case all his Yorkshire reminiscences in his essays or the reconstruction of them in play or novel are tremendously alive. His parties (see 'Boxing Day at Mr Joseph Ackworth's') are authentic bliss; Herbert Leaton at the piano in Joe's house is the fireside maestro to perfection. Youth in those years, even with little in its purse, entered a kingdom of 'good stoof' and Mr Ramsbottom in *Faraway* carried the doctrine of 'good stoof' across the oceans. Behind the good Bradford overcoats and the good Yorkshire hams and steaks was a wilderness of 'bad stoof' in the way of Northern slums and also in the Midland squalor which he so eloquently denounces in the passage called 'Rusty Lane'. But, whereas so many writers of to-day can see only the dismal chaos of Rusty Lane and forget the genuine goodness and unquenchable jocularity of the Rusty Laners, Priestley has got the thing in proportion. His sense of character is never soured by political prejudice. Because he would have society very much improved he does not have to pretend that all its members are sadists or sufferers, tramplers or trampled.

It was said, with some justice, of Arnold Bennett that, when he left the Five Towns and the Staffordshire of his youth and began to write of London, his descriptive genius and his grip of character dwindled. But Priestley has as nice a grip on *Angel Pavement* in the City or on a home in a London suburb as on the offices and parlours of Bruddersford. Take that 'Dinner at the Dersinghams'. Now the events in this are routine; the nerves of the hostess, the collapse of the maid, the spilled cutlets and so on show no particular invention; but the commonplace nature of the factual comedy is gloriously overridden by the sharp actuality of the characters engaged. This *is* the London gathering of edgy, all-assorted types with which the luckless wives of professional or commercial husbands have occasionally to cope for their men's supposed advancement.

The section called 'People' and the following one called 'Persons' in this anthology contain multitudes in small space. But these people and persons flow out far beyond their own section and are the life and soul of many other excerpts. The 'Peepshow' passages are concerned with events and institutions, but events and institutions arrive in our world only because people make them do so. The clubs and dinners and hostels and cafés there on view are most persuasively real, chiefly because the people inside them are the creations of a realist. Take that 'Dinner at Soho' in a restaurant which was 'determinedly foreign in a denationalized fashion as though the League of Nations had invented it.' The ghastly place and its gruesome menu seem to have got the reader right inside and settled at one of the tiny tables, not least because of the aloof waiters who project the gluey fodder at their victims. All the factory scenes in *Daylight on Saturday* would be very little were it not for the driving actuality of the industrial workers.

I began with allusion to the 'all-roundness' of Priestley and with that I shall close. He is too big, too copious to be labelled and stuck in a 'school'. Writers of genuine fluency in fancy and in word defy the categories: Dickens is a superb mixture of the unquenchable romantic and the man-on-the-spot realist. What Boz so acutely saw Charles could magnificently magnify. So, too, there is the 'Boz' Priestley with his perception pin-pointed on the social scene and the J.B.P. who wanders into metaphysics with the enraptured tread of a small boy discovering a new wood and a rivulet undreamed. The Socialist, as I said, is part-Anarchist and there are lots of old things that the Radical would never eradicate. In that same paradoxical way the exact recorder of the Bruddersford landscape with its funerals and its football, its markets and its feasts, its music and its neighbouring dales, its 'cards' and its queer company, is a mystic who is continually ready to have Nature take him by the throat and shake him into ecstasy.

Read him on 'The Grand Canyon' of the Colorado River with its incredible pageantry of sunlight and chasm. 'Perhaps it is not size nor the huge witchery of changing shapes and shades that fill us with awe, but the obscure feeling that we have of an instantaneous vision of innumerable eons ... As I peered over the far edge of all familiar things and I saw the storm clouds roll and flash in the gulf below, the rainbows tangled in the hanging woods, the sunlight turning to mist and drifting smoke and the vast shadowy walls into ruined empires, I kept muttering to myself that it had been set there as a sign. I felt wonder and awe, but at the heart of them a rich deep happiness. I had seen his handiwork and I rejoiced.'

That might have been written by a Christian or Theist mystic with a gift of words as well as a depth of vision. But you would not expect your voluble mystic to be also the consummate word-painter of commercial travellers laying into chops and steaks. And Priestley in his books about English or foreign journeys can make these astonishing jumps from the continent of fancy free into the parishes of flesh and blood. 'Buried deep in me', Priestley has confessed 'is a tiny Wordsworth or Thoreau, crying reedily to be let out.' If all his world were to be ruins and he a shambling old wreck, Nature would still be there, he claims, to set him 'chuckling in senile joy'. 'And delight shall soar into ecstasy when a great shaft of late afternoon sunlight reaches the upper downland, bright against a sky of pewter, and my rheumy eyes seem to stare at the fields of Paradise. Patience, patience, my minikin Wordsworth, my foetal Thoreau: your turn will come.'

I am not aware that Priestley ever set up in business as a poet; certainly, he did not need to, since he can out-distance most of our poets when he is merely writing his prose. But that kind of bardic J.B.P., the minikin Wordsworth, has to be remembered along with the Bruddersford reporter, the technician of films and plays and handler of the absurd, tetchy, and yet glorious people who act them. There is the restless Radical; there is the traveller with an eye ranging 'far over the edge of all familiar things' and yet as certain in its scrutiny of gross acquaintance and the cordialities of common clay. It is scarcely for me to prove my assertion that Priestley is this nation's best all-round writer of our time. If my claim be doubted, try the book that follows.

AUTHOR'S NOTE

THIS book is made up of passages I have selected myself from my novels, essays, pieces of autobiography. The sections into which it is divided – which suggest that I have been minding my P's if not my Q's – should not be taken too seriously. Within the sections I have aimed at some sort of chronological order. For various good reasons, not all my books are represented here. Some older readers may be sorry to find no examples of the literary criticism I was producing about the middle 'twenties, and may miss a favourite passage or two from my earlier essays and first attempts at fiction. But – to be honest – I had no such older readers in mind when I made this selection. I hope some of them will enjoy it, but still more do I hope that it will be bought and read by the youngest generation of adult readers, those who began to read for themselves during the war years, when so many of the books represented here were out of print and hard to obtain. (They have now been – or are being – reprinted by Messrs Heinemann.) I have a notion that I can get along nicely with their generation, in spite of the gap of thirty years or so between us, just as I can with my own contemporaries; and far better than I ever could with the generation that comes between mine and theirs, the readers who grew up between the wars and often preferred something colder and harder than anything I could offer. Here I may be deceiving myself – I often do – but it made me jump at the chance, possible only in a *Penguin* edition, of assembling this fine big bag of tasting samples, to be sold at a price most younger people can still afford. I am told I have a fairly strong flavour of my own;

and if they dislike that flavour, then they need waste no more time and money on me. And friendly older readers might like to enjoy, within one light cover, some characters and scenes that gave them pleasure years ago. Now and again the shadow of the Great Depression of the early 'thirties falls on these pages; and I cannot help feeling that it will do both sets of readers no harm to meet that shadow for a few minutes. We live in hard times, but so did some other people, not twenty years ago. And just as there was sunlight for brave hearts then, so there is now.

My thanks are gratefully offered to Mr Ivor Brown for his generous Introduction, to my friend Mr W. E. Williams for his initial encouragement of this enterprise, and to Messrs Heinemann, the publishers of all the books represented here, for their co-operation.

J. B. P.

PARTIES

The Royal Standard at Rawsley

INIGO threw open the dining-room door. 'Ladies and gentlemen,' he roared. 'Miss Trant.'

A stir, a quick sigh, a buzz of welcome and a clapping of hands; and she stood for a moment or two in the doorway, looking at them all, half embarrassed, half delighted, no longer that familiar and only-to-be-expected figure, Miss Elizabeth Trant, who had stayed at the Old Hall so long that her youth had slipped by and all her bright looks been dimmed, but a mysterious Miss Trant who had popped up, come from nowhere, to save the show, and whose entrance lit up the room just as it lit up her face. As she stood there, she felt for a moment that she was a vivid and rather delightful person, one that even a busy Scots doctor might remember with pleasure. It was a moment well worth the whole six hundred pounds that had fallen to her last week out of the blue.

'And, if you'll allow me to say so, Miss Trant,' said Mrs Joe, otherwise Miss Stella Cavendish, sweeping forward impressively, 'as pretty an entrance as one could wish for. It takes me back in a flash,' she told the company, 'to the big scene in *The Rose of Belgravia*.'

'Take your seats, ladies and gentlemen,' Inigo called out.

'Now where are we going to sit, Jollifant?' asked Mr Morton Mitcham in his most dignified manner. 'Quite like old times, Mrs Brundit.'

'I should say so,' cried Miss Susie Dean. 'The good old times when we all played the baby in *East Lynne* – perhaps. Well, I'm going to sit next to Mr Oakroyd, because he's shy. Aren't ta, lad?'

'Noan too shy to gi' thee a bit of a slap, lass, if tha doesn't behave thysen,' replied the delighted Mr Oakroyd in his broadest accent. 'Yond's a coughdrop,' he announced to the room at large, and took his place beside her.

We have never heard that The Royal Standard in Rawsley is famous for its dinners, and as Mrs Tidby herself pointed out more than once during the evening, the notice was short, so that it would be absurd to pretend that the dinner Inigo gave that night was an exquisite and memorable repast. Nevertheless, it seemed so to the whole ten of them. There were special reasons why it should. Miss Trant enjoyed it without noticing what she was eating, not because she was not interested in food but simply because she was still excited about herself and everybody else. Inigo enjoyed it both as a meal (for his interior still remembered Washbury Manor School) and as a lark that would inevitably beget other and wilder larks. Mr Oakroyd was rather overawed and dubious at first; there were too many knives and forks for his peace of mind; but the company of the lively Miss Susie and the sight of a large glass of beer helped to reassure him, and soon he happily stared and grinned and ate like one who had suddenly found an appetite in fairyland. As for Mr Morton Mitcham and the other players, they enjoyed it because it was a splendid novelty, eating at that hour, and something of a novelty, perhaps, eating at all, certainly eating steadily through four generous courses. Miss Susie Dean, who confessed that she had been living entirely on tea and bread-and-butter and brawn and apples for the past week, declared she had forgotten there was so much food in the world, and was promptly asked not to be vulgar by her colleague, Miss Longstaff, who was so determined to be ladylike that she carefully left a little of each course at the side of her plate, which was otherwise clean enough. Mr Jerningham contrived to wear an expression of faint boredom throughout the dinner, but despatched it like an elegant wolf. Mr Joe Brundit, who joined Mr Oakroyd in his preference for a large glass of beer, demanded so many pieces of bread that he became an important figure in the waiter's reminiscences. But it was Mrs Joe and Mr Morton Mitcham who succeeded best in giving the dinner the air of being a prodigal feast. With them there seemed to be not four courses but fifty. The tomato soup, the mysterious little pieces of white fish, the boiled mutton, the blackberry and apple tart, were transformed by their histrionic gusto into a banquet of Lucullus, and they seemed to nod and smile at one another over the ruins of garnished peacocks' and nightingales' tongues. To see Mr Mitcham fill Mrs Joe's glass and then his own from the solitary bottle of Beaune was to catch a glimpse of the old mad bad days of the fine ladies and gentlemen who lived careless of the morrow, though the very tumbrils were rattling down the street. When they raised their glasses, the least you saw was a Viceroy or Governor-General of the old school and the Duchess of Dorking. It was a fine performance.

Even Mr Jimmy Nunn contrived to enjoy the dinner in his own way. It was not the soup and fish and toast, to which he restricted himself, that he enjoyed, but his abstinence. As he groaned 'Can't look at 'em – poison to me!' he did not seem to be refusing a little mutton and tart, but a gigantic host of dishes; waving away the very fat of the land. He referred to his stomach as if it were a haughty and eccentric guest he had brought with him. He crumbled his toast and sipped his whisky and soda ('Can't touch wine or beer') with a melancholy pride.

Dinner at the Dersinghams'

THE DERSINGHAMS, standing together now on their bear-skin rug, heard the first guest arrive. It must be either Golspie or the Trapes. It could not be the Pearsons, who, living in the maisonette above, always waited until they heard someone else arrive below, before they made their appearance. And Golspie it was, looking strangely unfamiliar to Mr Dersingham in a rather voluminous dinner jacket and a very narrow black tie. He had hardly been introduced to Mrs Dersingham before the Pearsons, who were just as anxious not to be late as they were not to be first, came in, breathless and smiling.

'A-ha, good evening!' cried Mr Pearson, as if he had found them out.

'And how are *you*, my dear?' cried Mrs Pearson to her hostess, in such a tone of voice that nobody would have imagined that they had met less than four hours ago.

The Pearsons were a middle-aged, childless couple, who had recently retired from Singapore. Mr Pearson was a tallish man, with a long thin neck on which was perched a pear-shaped head. His cheeks were absurdly plump, a sharp contrast to all the rest of him, so that he always appeared to have just blown them out. He was both nervous and amiable, and consequently he laughed a great deal at nothing in particular, and the sound he made when he laughed can only be set down as *Tee-tee-tee-tee-tee*. Mrs Pearson, who was altogether plump, had her face framed in a number of mysterious dark curls, and looked vaguely like one of the musical comedy actresses of the picture post-card era, one who had perhaps retired, after queening it in *The Catch of the Season*, to keep a jolly boarding-house. They were a lonely, friendly pair, who obviously did not know what on earth to do to pass the time, so that this was for them an occasion of some importance, to be looked forward to, to be referred to, to be enjoyed to the last syllable of small talk.

They were now all shouting at one another, after the fashion of hosts and guests in Barkfield Gardens and elsewhere.

'Found your way here all right then?' Mr Dersingham bellowed to Mr Golspie.

'Came in a taxi,' Mr Golspie boomed over his cocktail.

'That's the best way if you're going to a strange house in London, isn't it?' Mr Pearson shouted. 'We always do it when we can afford it. Tee-tee-tee-tee-tee.'

'And how's the little darling to-night?' Mrs Pearson inquired at the top of her voice, affectionately maternal as usual.

'Oh, we took the infant's temperature, and it was normal.

He's all right,' Mrs Dersingham screamed in reply, elaborately unmaternal as usual.

'I'm so glad, *so* glad.' And as she said it, Mrs Pearson looked all beaming and moist. 'I was so afraid there might be something really wrong with the dear kiddy. I was telling Walter that you thought it might be a chill. I'm *so* glad it wasn't, my dear. You can't be too careful with them – can you?'

'This Russian business looks pretty queer, doesn't it?' Mr Dersingham shouted.

'Very queer. What do you make of it?' Mr Pearson shouted in reply. He made nothing of it himself yet, because the evening paper had not told him what to make of it and he had heard nobody's opinion yet. On any question that had its origin west of Suez, Mr Pearson liked to agree with his company. When it was east of Suez, he sometimes took a line of his own, and when Singapore itself was actually involved, he had been known to contradict people.

'Well, I'll tell you, Dersingham,' said Mr Golspie, who as usual knew his own mind. 'It's all a lot of tripe, bosh, bunkum. I know those yarns. Fellows up in Riga trying to earn their money, they sent out that stuff.'

'That's terribly interesting, Mr Golspie,' Mrs Dersingham shrieked at him, suddenly looking like a woman of the world who had wanted to get to the bottom of this business for some time. 'Of course, you've been up there, haven't you?'

'Round about.' And Mr Golspie gave her a grin, at once sardonic and friendly. It seemed to tell her that she was all right, not a bad-looking girl, but she mustn't try to draw him, for that wasn't her line at all, not at all.

'It makes a difference when you've been there, doesn't it?' cried Mr Pearson. 'You know the facts. Tee-tee-tee-tee-tee.'

'And where do you live now, Mr Golspie?' Mrs Pearson inquired, rather archly and with her head on one side.

'Just got a furnished flat in Maida Vale,' replied Mr Golspie.

'Now I don't think I know that part,' Mrs Pearson said, girlishly reflective.

'There's a lot of London we still don't know. Tee-tee-tee-tee-tee.'

'You're not missing much if you don't know Maida Vale, from what I've seen of it,' Mr Golspie boomed away. 'Where I live seems to be full of Jews and music-hall turns. Old music-hall turns, not the good-lookin' young 'uns.'

'Tee-tee-tee,' Mr Pearson put in, rather doubtfully.

'Oh, you men!' cried Mrs Pearson, who had not lived at Singapore for nothing: she knew her cues.

'Tee-tee.' Triumphant this time.

Miss Verever was announced, and very resentfully, for already Agnes had had enough of the evening and she had not liked the way this particular guest had walked in and looked at her.

There is something to be said for Agnes. Miss Verever was one of those people who, at a first meeting, demand to be disliked. She was Mrs Dersingham's mother's cousin, a tall, cadaverous virgin of forty-five or so, who displayed, especially in evening clothes, an uncomfortable amount of sharp gleaming bone, just as if the upper part of her was a relief map done in ivory. In order that she might not be overlooked in company and also to protect herself, she had developed and brought very near to perfection a curiously disturbing manner, which conveyed a boundless suggestion of the malicious, the mocking, the sarcastic, the sardonic, the ironical. What she actually said was harmless enough, but her tone of voice, her expression, her smile, her glance, all these suggested that her words had some devilish inner meaning. In scores of small hotels and *pensions* overlooking the Mediterranean, merely by asking what time the post went or inquiring if it had rained during the night, she had made men wonder if they had not shaved properly and women ask themselves if something had gone wrong with their complexions, and compelled members of both sexes to consider if they had just said something very silly. After that, she had only to perform the smallest decent action for people to say that she had a surprisingly kind heart as well as a terrifying clever satirical head. This was all very well if people had booked rooms under the same roof for the next three months, but on chance acquaintances, wondering indignantly what on earth she had against *them*, this peculiar manner of hers had an unfortunate effect.

She now advanced, kissed her hostess, shook hands with her host, and then, pursing her lips and screwing up the rest of her features, said: 'I hope you've not been waiting for *me*. I'm sure you have, haven't you?' And, strange as it may seem, this remark and this simple question immediately made the whole dinner party appear preposterous.

'No, we haven't really,' Mr Dersingham told her, at the same time asking himself why in the name of thunder they had ever thought of inviting her. 'Somebody still to come. The Trapes.'

'Oh, I'm glad I'm not the last then,' said Miss Verever, with a bitter smile, which she kept on her face while she was being introduced to the other guests.

A minute later, the Trapes arrived to complete the party. Late guests may be divided into two classes, the repentant who arrive, perspiring and profusely apologetic, to babble about fogs and ancient taxis and stupid drivers, and the unrepentant, who stalk in haughtily and look somewhat aggrieved when they see all the other guests, their eyebrows registering their disapproval of people who do not know what time their own parties begin. The Trapes were admirable specimens of the unrepentant class. They were both tall, cold, thin, and rather featureless. Trape himself was an Old Worrellian and a contemporary of Dersingham's. He was a partner in a firm of estate agents, but called himself Major Trape because he had held that rank at the end of the War and had become so soldierly, training the vast mob of boys who were conscripted then, that he could not bring himself to say good-bye to his outworn courtesy title. He was indeed so curt, so military, so imperial, that it was impossible to imagine him letting and selling houses in the ordinary way, and the mind's eye saw him mopping up, with a small raiding party, all flats and bijou residences, and sallying out with an expeditionary force to plant the Union Jack on finely timbered, residential and sporting estates. His wife was a somewhat colourless woman, very English in type, who always looked as if she was always faintly surprised and disgusted by life. Perhaps she was, and perhaps that was why she always talked with a certain ventriloquial effect, producing a voice with hardly any movement of her small iced features.

Leaving them all to shout at one another, Mrs Dersingham now slipped out of the room, for it was imperative that dinner should be announced as soon as possible. She returned three minutes later, trying not unsuccessfully to look as if she had not a care in the world, a sort of Arabian Nights hostess, and then, after the smallest interval, Agnes popped her head into the room, thereby forgetting one of her most urgent instructions, and said, without any enthusiasm at all: 'Please m'. Dinner's served.'

Mrs Dersingham smiled heroically at her guests, who, with the exception of Mr Golspie, looked at one another and at the door as if they were hearing about this dinner business for the first time and were mildly interested and amused. Mr Golspie, for his part, looked like a man who wanted his dinner, and actually took a step or two towards the door. Then began that general stepping forward and stepping backward and smiling and hand-waving which take place at this moment in all those unhappy sections of society that have lost formality and yet have not reached informality. There they were, smiling and dithering round the door.

'Now then, Mrs Pearson,' cried Mr Golspie in his loudest and most brutal tones. 'In you go.' And, without more ado, this impatient guest put a hand behind Mrs Pearson's elbow, and Mrs Pearson found herself through the door, the leader of the exodus. They crowded into the small dining-room, where the soup was already steaming under the four shaded electric lights.

'Now let me see,' Mrs Dersingham began, as usual, feeling that these guests were not people now but six enormous bodies of which she, the wretched criminal, had to dispose. 'Now let me see. Will you sit there, Mrs Trape? And Mrs Pearson there?' And then, having disposed of the bodies, she had time to notice that the soup looked horribly greasy.

*

The soup was bad, and Miss Verever left most of hers and contrived to be looking down at it very curiously every time

Mrs Dersingham glanced across the table at her. As there were eight of them, Mrs Dersingham was not sitting at the end of the table, opposite her husband. Mr Golspie was there, and very much at his ease, putting away a very ungentlemanly quantity of bread under that great moustache of his. On Mr Golspie's right were Mrs Dersingham, Major Trape, and Mrs Pearson, and on the other side were Miss Verever, Mr Pearson, and Mrs Trape.

'And how,' said Miss Verever to Mrs Dersingham, 'did you enjoy your Norfolk holiday this summer? You never told me that, and I've been dying to know.' The smile that accompanied this statement announced that Miss Verever could not imagine a more idiotic or boring topic, that you would be insufferably dull if you answered her question and terribly rude if you didn't.

'Not bad,' Mrs Dersingham shouted desperately. 'In fact, quite good, on the whole. Rather cold, you know.'

'Really, you found it cold?' And you would have sworn that the speaker meant to suggest that the cold had obviously been manufactured for you and that it served you right.

At the other end of the table, Major Trape and his host were talking about football, across Mrs Pearson, who nodded and smiled and shook her mysterious curls all the time, to show that she was not really being left out.

'Do you ever watch rugger, Golspie?' Mr Dersingham demanded down the table.

'What, Rugby? Haven't seen a match for years,' replied Mr Golspie. 'Prefer the other kind when I do watch one.'

Major Trape raised his eyebrows. 'What you a soccah man? Not this professional stuff? Don't tell me you like that.'

'What's the matter with it?'

'Oh, come now! I mean, you can't possibly – I mean, it's a dirty business, selling fellahs for money and so on, very unsporting.'

'I must say I agree, Trape,' said Mr Dersingham. 'Dashed unsporting business, I call it.'

'Oh, certainly,' Major Trape continued, 'must be amatahs – love of the game. Play the game for its own sake, I say, and not as these fellahs do – for monay. Can't possibly be a sportsman and play for monay. Oh, dirty business, eh, Dersingham?'

'I'm with you there.'

A sound came from Mrs Trape's face and it seemed to declare that she was with him too.

'Well, I'm not with you,' said Mr Golspie bluntly He did not care tuppence about it, one way or the other, but there was something in Trape's manner that demanded contradiction, and Mr Golspie was not the man to ignore such a challenge. 'If a poor man can play a game well, why shouldn't he allow that game to keep him? What's the answer to that? A man's as much right to play cricket and football for a living as he has to clean windows or sell tripe –'

'Tripe indeed! How can you, Mr Golspie?' cried Mrs Pearson, girlishly shaking her curls at him.

'My wife hates tripe,' said Mr Pearson. 'Tee-tee-tee-tee-tee.'

'I disagree,' said Major Trape, stiffer than ever now. 'Those things are business, quite different. Games ought to be played for their own sake. That's the proper English way. Love of the game. Clean sport. Don't mind if the other fellahs win. Sport and business, two diff'rent things.'

'Not if sport *is* your business,' Mr Golspie returned, looking darkly mischievous. 'We can't all be rich amachures. Let the chaps have their six or seven pounds a week. They earn it. If one lot of chaps can earn their living by telling us to be good every Sunday – that is, if you go to listen to 'em: I don't – why shouldn't another lot be paid to knock a ball about every Saturday, without all this talk of dirty business? It beats me Unless it's snobbery. Lot o' snobbery still about in this country. It pops up all the time.'

'What *is* this argument all about?' Miss Verever inquired. And, perhaps feeling that Mr Golspie needed a rebuke, she put on her most peculiar look and brought out her most disturbing tone of voice, finally throwing in a smile that was a tried veteran, an Old Guard.

But Mr Golspie returned her gaze quite calmly, and even conveyed a piece of fish, and far too large a piece, to his mouth before replying. 'We're arguing about football and cricket. I don't suppose you're interested. I'm not much, myself. I like billiards. That's one thing about coming back to this country, you can always get a good game of billiards. Proper tables, y' know.'

'I used to be very fond of a game of billiards, snooker, too,' said Mr Pearson, nodding his head so that his fat cheeks shook like beef jellies, 'when I was out in Singapore. There were some splendid players at the club there, splendid players, make breaks of forty and fifty. But I wasn't one of them. Tee-tee-tee –'

'We went to see Susie Dean and Jerry Jerningham the other night,' said Major Trape, turning to Mrs Dersingham. 'Good show. Very clevah, very clevah. You been to any shows lately, Mrs Dersingham?'

'That's true,' Mrs Pearson informed her host and anybody else who cared to listen. 'When we were out in Singapore, my husband was always going over to the club for billiards. And now he hardly ever plays. I don't think he's had a game this year. Have you, Walter? I'm just saying I don't think you've had a game this year.'

'And so what with one thing and another,' Mrs Dersingham told Major Trape, 'I've simply not been able to see half the plays I've wanted to see. Something has to go, hasn't it? We were out at the Trevors' – I think you know them, don't you? – the shipbuilding people, you know, only of course these Trevors are out of that – they're terribly in with all that young smart set, Mrs Dellingham, young Mostyn-Price, Lady Muriel Pagworth, and the famous Ditchways. Well, what with that, and then going to Mrs Westbury's musical tea-fight – Dossevitch and Rougeot *ought* to have been there and were only prevented from coming at the last minute, but Imogen Farley was there and played divinely. Oh, and then on top of all that, I went to see that new thing at His Majesty's – what's it called? – oh, yes – *The Other Man*. And so I haven't had a single moment for any other show.'

'No, by Jove, you haven't, have you?' said Major Trape, with whom this miracle of the social loaves and fishes worked every time. 'You're worse than Dorothy, and I tell her she overdoes it. Mustn't overdo it, you know.'

Mrs Dersingham, wondering how long Agnes was going to be bringing up the cutlets, shrugged her shoulders, and did it exactly as she had seen Irene Prince do it in *Smart Women* at the Ambassadors. 'It *is* stupid, I know,' she confessed charmingly, 'and I'm always saying I'll cut most of it out – but – well, you know what happens.'

Miss Verever, wearing her most peculiar smile, leaned forward, caught the eye of her hostess, and said: 'But what *does* happen, my dear?'

Mrs Dersingham was able to escape, however, by plunging at once into the talk at the other end of the table, as if she had not heard Miss Verever's inquiry. 'Oh, have you been reading that?' she cried across the table to Mrs Trape, who did not look as if she had spoken for weeks, but nevertheless had actually just conjured out several remarks. 'No, I *haven't* read it and I don't mean to.' But did Agnes mean to bring the cutlets?

The talk at Mr Dersingham's end, as we have guessed, had suddenly turned literary. Mrs Trape had just read a certain book. It was, she added, apparently throwing her voice into the claret decanter, a very clever book. Mr Dersingham had not read this book, and did not hesitate to say that it did not sound his kind of book, for after a jolly good hard day in the office he found such books too heavy going and preferred a detective story. Mrs Pearson was actually reading a book, had been reading it that very afternoon, had nearly finished it and was enjoying it immensely.

'And I'm sure it's a story *you'd* like, Mr Dersingham,' she cried, 'even though there aren't any detectives in it. I could hardly put it down. It's all about a girl going to one of those Pacific Islands, one of those lovely coral and lagoon places, you know, and she goes there to stay with an uncle because she's lost all her money and when she gets there she finds that he's drinking terribly, and so she goes to another man – but I mustn't spoil it for you. Do read it, Mrs Trape.'

The claret decanter murmured that it would love to read it, and asked what the name of the book was, so that it might put it down on its library list.

'I'll tell you the title in a moment,' and Mrs Pearson, bringing her curls to rest, bit her lip reflectively. 'Now how stupid of me! Do you know, I can't remember. It's a very striking title, too, and that's what made me take it when the girl at the library showed it to me. Now isn't that silly of me?'

'I can never remember the titles either,' Mr Dersingham assured her heartily. 'What was the name of the chap who wrote it? Was it a man or a woman?'

'I *think* it was a man's name, in fact, I'm nearly sure it was. It was quite a common name, too. Something like Wilson. No, it wasn't, it was Wilkinson. Walter, do you remember the name of the author of that book I'm reading? Wasn't it Wilkinson?'

'You're thinking of the man that came to mend the wireless set,' Mr Pearson replied, shooting his long neck at her. 'That was Wilkinson. You know the people, Dersingham – the electricians in Earl's Court Road?'

'Oh, so it was. How silly of me!'

'Tee-tee-tee-tee-tee.'

Mrs Pearson smiled vaguely but amiably, then said: 'So you see I can't tell you *now*, but I'll tell Mrs Dersingham in the morning and then she can tell you.'

A sudden silence fell on the table at that moment, perhaps because there was a sort of scratching sound at the door, which opened, but only about an inch or two. That silence was shattered by the most appalling crash of breaking crockery, followed by a short sharp wail. Then silence again for one sinking moment. The cutlets and the vegetables had arrived at last, and a brown stain, creeping beneath the door, told where they were.

'My God,' cried Mr Golspie to Miss Verever, as Mrs Dersingham dashed to the door, 'there goes our dinner.'

'Indeed!'

'You bet your life!' Mr Golspie, earnest and unabashed, assured her.

Miss Verever and Major Trape exchanged glances, which removed Mr Golspie once and for all from decent society and handed him over to the social worker and the anthropologist.

Meanwhile, Mrs Dersingham had disappeared through the doorway, and Mr Dersingham was trying to follow her example but could not do so because, what with cutlets, vegetables, gravy, broken dishes and plates, a weeping Agnes, and a panic-stricken Mrs Dersingham, there was no space for him. So he stood there, holding the door open, with his body inside the dining-room and his head outside.

'Oh, do shut the door, Howard,' the guests heard Mrs Dersingham cry.

'All right,' the invisible head replied hesitatingly. 'But I say – can't I – er – do anything? I mean, do you want me to come out or – er – well, what do you want me to do?'

'Oh, go-in-and-shut-the-door.' And there was no doubt that in another moment Mrs Dersingham would have screamed, for this was the voice of a woman in an extremity.

Mr Dersingham closed the door and returned to his chair. He looked at Major Trape, and Major Trape looked at him, and no doubt they were both remembering the good old school, Worrellians together.

'Sorry, but – er –' and here Mr Dersingham looked round apologetically at his guests – 'I'm afraid there's been some sort of accident outside.'

Immediately, Mrs Trape, Mrs Pearson, Major Trape, and Mr Pearson began talking all at once, not talking about this accident but about accidents in general, with special reference to very queer accidents that had happened to them. Miss Verever merely looked peculiarly at everybody, while Mr Golspie finished his claret with a certain remote gloom, as if he were a man taking quinine on the summit of a mountain.

Then the door, which had not been properly fastened, swung open again, to admit a mixed knocking and gobbling and guggling noise that suggested that Agnes was now lying on the floor, in hysterics, and drumming her feet. Then came a new noise, very hoarse and resentful, and this voice declared that it was all a crying shame, even if the girl was clumsy with her hands, and that one pair of hands was one pair of hands and could not be expected to be any more, and that while notices were being given right and left, *her* notice could be taken, there and then. In short, the cook had arrived on the scene.

Mr Dersingham arose miserably, but whether to shut the door again or to make an entrance into the drama outside we shall never know, for Mrs Pearson, fired with neighbourly solicitude, sprang up, crying, 'Poor Mrs Dersingham! I'm sure I ought to do something,' and was outside, with the door closed behind her, before Mr Dersingham knew what was happening.

And Mrs Pearson, once outside, did not simply intrude, did not gape and hang about and get in the way, but took charge of the situation, for though Mrs Pearson may have been a foolish table-talker, may have worn mysterious curls, and been old-fashioned and monstrously girlish and affectionate, she was a housewife of experience, who had weathered the most fantastic tropical domestic storms in Singapore.

'I *knew* you wouldn't mind my coming out,' she cried, 'and I felt I must help, because after all we are neighbours, aren't we, and that makes a difference.'

'It's too absurd,' Mrs Dersingham wailed. 'This wretched girl's smashed everything and ruined the dinner and now she's going off into a fit or something out of sheer temper. And it's all her own fault. I engaged her sister to come and help her to-night, and then when her sister couldn't come, at the last minute of course, she wouldn't let me get anybody else, she said she could do it herself.'

Mrs Pearson was looking at Agnes, who was still guggling and drumming on the floor. 'Only stupid hysterics. Get up at once, you silly, silly girl. Do you hear? You're in the way. We'll pour cold water over her. That will soon bring her round, you'll see.'

The cook, who was standing in the hall, a few yards away, and had been looking on with the air of a complacent prophetess, now began to lose some of her rigidity. The mournful triumph died out of her face. She had no respect for Mrs Dersingham, but for some strange reason she had almost a veneration for Mrs Pearson, who was possibly a far more ladylike and commanding figure in her eyes.

'That's so,' the cook hoarsely declared now. 'A jug of water's what she wants. Accidents will happen and one pair of hands can't be two or three pairs of hands, eight for dinner being out of all reason with them steps and no service lift, but there's no call to be lying there all night, Agnes, having your hysterics and carrying on silly when there's all this mess to be cleared, let alone anything else.'

This treacherous withdrawal of a stout ally, combined with the talk of cold water, soon brought the hysterics to mere choking and sniffing, and in a minute or two Agnes was bending over the ruins. 'I'll clear these away,' she announced between sniffs and chokes, 'but I won't bring anything else and serve it, I won't. I couldn't if I tried, I couldn't. I haven't a nerve in me body, not after what's happened, I haven't.'

'But I shall have to give them *something*,' Mrs Dersingham was saying. Clearly she no longer included Mrs Pearson among the guests. Mrs Pearson had ceased to be one of 'them'.

'Of course you will, my dear,' cried Mrs Pearson, her eyes gleaming with a happy excitement. 'Not that *we'd* mind, of course. It's the men, isn't it? You know what men are! Now, then, what about eggs?'

'Eggs,' the cook repeated, hoarsely and gloomily. 'There's two eggs, an' two eggs only, in that kitchen. Just the two eggs, and them's for the morning.'

'Listen, my dear,' said Mrs Pearson, clutching at her neighbour affectionately and imploringly. '*Do* leave it to me and I promise you I won't be ten minutes. I won't, really. Now not a word! Don't bother about *anything*. Just you leave it to me.' She hurried towards the outer door, pulled herself up before she reached it, and cried over her shoulder: 'But warm some plates, that's all.'

During the subsequent interval, Mrs Dersingham had not the heart to return to the dining-room, though she did just look in, put her face round the door and smile apologetically at everybody and say that it was *too* absurd and annoying and that the two of them, she and Mrs Pearson, would be back again in a few minutes. She spent the rest of the time superintending the salvage work outside the dining-room door and helping cook to find enough fresh plates to warm. She felt hot, dishevelled, and miserable. She could have cried. Indeed, that was why she did not slip upstairs to her bedroom to look at herself and powder her nose, for once there, really alone with herself, she was sure she would have cried. Oh, it was all too hateful for words!

'There!' And Mrs Pearson stood before her, breathless, flushed, and happy, and whipped off the lid of a silver dish.

'Oh!' cried Mrs Dersingham, in the very reek of the omelette, a fine large specimen. 'You angel! It's absolutely perfect.'

'I remembered we had some eggs, and then I remembered we had a bottle of mushrooms tucked away somewhere, and so I rushed upstairs and made this mushroom omelette. It ought to be nice. I used to be good with omelettes.'

'It's marvellous. And I don't know how to begin to thank you, my dear.' And Mrs Dersingham meant it. From that moment, Mrs Pearson ceased to be a merely foolish if kindly neighbour and became a friend, worthy of the most secret confidences. In the steam of the omelette, rich as the smoke of burnt offerings, this friendship began, and Mrs Dersingham never tasted a mushroom afterwards without being reminded of it.

'Don't think of it, my dear,' said Mrs Pearson happily, for her own life, after months of the dull routine of time-killing, had suddenly become crimson, rich and glorious. 'Now, have you got the plates ready? You must have this served at once, mustn't you? Where's that silly girl? Gone to bed? All right, then, make the cook serve the rest of the dinner. She must have everything ready by this time. Call her, my dear. Tell her to bring up the plates.' And they returned at last to the dining-room, two sisters out of burning Troy.

Alas, all was not well in there. Something had happened during the interval of waiting. It was not the women, who were all sympathetic smiles and solicitude: Mrs Trape even dropped the ventriloquial effect, actually disturbed the lower part of her face, in order to explain that she knew, no one better, what it was these days, when anything might be expected of that class; and Miss Verever, though retaining automatically some peculiarities of tone and grimace, contrived to say something reassuring. No, it was the men. Mr Golspie looked like a man who had already said some brutal things and was fully prepared to say some more; Major Trape looked very stiff and uncompromising, as if he had just sentenced a couple of surveyors to be shot; Mr Pearson gave the impression that he had been faintly tee-teeing on both sides of a quarrel and was rather tired of it; and Mr Dersingham looked uneasy, anxious, exasperated. There was no mistaking the atmosphere, in which distant thunder still rolled. The stupid men had had to wait for the more substantial part of dinner; they had felt empty, then they had felt cross; and so they had argued, shouted, quarrelled, not all of them perhaps, but certainly Mr Golspie and Major Trape. Probably at any moment, they would begin arguing, shouting, quarrelling again. Mrs Dersingham, very tired now and with a hundred little nerves screaming to be taken out of all this and put to bed, would have liked to have banged their silly heads together.

Cook came in, breathing heavily and disapprovingly, and gave them their omelette. There was not a single movement she made during the whole time she was in the room that did not announce, quite plainly, that she was the cook, that the kitchen was her place, that she did not pretend to be able to wait at table and that if they did not like it, they could lump it. Her heavy breathing went farther, pointing out that when she did condescend to wait at table, she expected to find a better company than this seated round it. Even Mrs Pearson had apparently lost favour, for she had her plate shoved contemptuously in front of her, like the rest. Real ladies, that plate said, don't rush away and cook omelettes for other people's dinner tables. 'P'raps you'll ring when you want the next,' the cook wheezed, and then slowly, scornfully, took her departure.

'If you don't mind my saying so, Mrs Dersingham,' said Major Trape, 'this omelette's awf'ly good, awf'ly good. And there's nothing I like better than a jolly good omelette.'

A voice from Mrs Trape's direction said that it agreed with him.

'They're right there,' said Mr Golspie to Mrs Dersingham, as if the Trapes were not often right. 'It's as good an omelette as I've had for months and months, and that's saying something, because I've been in places where they can make omelettes. They can't make 'em here in England.' And he said this in such a way as to suggest that it was really a challenge to Trape, who was nothing if not patriotic. Obviously, he and Trape had been quarrelling.

Major Trape stiffened, then smiled laboriously at his hostess. 'Mr Golspie seems to think we can't make anything in England. That's where he and I diffah. Isn't it, Dersingham?'

'Well, yes, in a way, I suppose,' Mr Dersingham mumbled unhappily. He felt divided between Worrell and Angel Pavement, between his old and respected school friend, Trape, with whom he instinctively agreed, and the forceful man who was now saving Twigg and Dersingham and making it prosperous, his guest for the first time, too; and it was a wretched situation. He muttered now that there was a lot to be said on both sides.

'There may be,' said Major Trape. 'But I don't like to hear a man continually runnin' down his own country. Tastes diffah, I suppose. But I feel – well, it isn't done, that's all.'

'Time it was done then,' said Mr Golspie aggressively. 'Most of the people I meet here these days seem to be living in a fool's paradise –'

'Now, Mr Golspie,' cried his hostess, with desperate vivacity, 'you're not to call us all fools. Is he, Mrs Trape? We won't have it.' Then, saving the situation at all costs, she turned to Miss Verever. 'My dear, I forgot to tell you, I've had the absurdest letter from Alice. When I read it, I simply howled.'

'No, did you?' said Miss Verever.

'A-ha!' cried Mr Dersingham, doing his best. 'What's the latest from Alice. We must all hear about this.'

They were all listening now, all at peace for the moment.

'Oh, it was too ridiculous,' cried Mrs Dersingham, despairingly racking her brains to remember something amusing in that letter, or, failing that, something amusing in any letter she had ever had from anybody. 'You know what Alice is – at least, you do, my dear, and so do you. I suppose it isn't really funny unless you know her. You see, the minute I read a letter of hers, of course I can see her in my mind and hear her voice and all that sort of thing, and unless you can do that, well, I dare say it isn't so funny after all. But, you see, Alice – she's my youngest sister, I must explain; and they live down in Devon – oh, miles from anywhere. Will you ring, please, darling? Well, Alice has a dog, the absu-u-urdest creature –'

She struggled through with it somehow, and fortunately cook made such a noise clearing and then serving the sweet that most of the anecdote, presumably the funniest part, was lost in the clatter. The cook had been so noisy, so incredibly heavy in her breathing, and so obviously disapproving, when she was serving the sweet, that Mrs Dersingham dare not have her up again to clear the table for dessert, so as the fruit plates and the finger bowls, the port decanter and glasses, were all on the sideboard, she made a joke of it – showing the last gleam of vivacity she felt she would be able to show for months – and she and Dersingham, assisted by Mr Pearson, who said – tee-tee-tee-tee-tee – that he was used to clearing a table, having been well brought up, did what they could to make the dinner look as if it were coming to a civilized end. Mrs Dersingham felt that Mr Golspie, plainly a porty sort of man, and Major Trape might not want to argue so unpleasantly once they had some port inside them. This was the longest and most ghastly dinner she ever remembered. It was not really very late, but it seemed like two in the morning. As she tried to peel a very soft pear, she felt she wanted to throw it at the opposite wall and then scream at the top of her voice.

Dinner in Soho

HER spirits rose when they actually arrived in Soho, for though she had some mournful memories of its table d'hôte, and had been in London long enough to be sceptical about its romantic bohemianism, she could not resist the place itself, the glimpses of foreign interiors, the windows filled with outlandish foodstuffs, Chianti flasks, and bundles of long cheroots, the happy foolish little decorations, the strange speech, the dark faces, the girls leaning out of the first-floor windows. It was quite a long time since she had last walked along Old Compton Street. It made her sigh for an adventure. Meanwhile, that very evening took on a faint colouring of adventure while they were still searching for old Warwick's restaurant, though, with all the goodwill in the world, she could not transform Norman Birtley, fresh from the Chestervern Agricultural College, into a romantic and adventurous companion.

At last, they found old Warwick's restaurant. It might have been French or Italian or even Spanish or Hungarian; there was no telling; but it was determinedly foreign in a denationalized fashion, rather as if the League of Nations had invented it. No sooner was Norman's hand on the door than a very fierce-looking, moustachioed, square-jawed Latin flung it open very quickly and with a flourish, so that they were almost sucked in. The place was very small, rather warm, and smelt of oil. The lights were shaded with coloured crinkly paper. There were only four other people there, two oldish tired girls masticating rather hopelessly in the far corner, and a queer middle-aged couple sitting almost in the window. The fierce Latin swept them across to a tiny table, thrust menus into their hands, rubbed his hands, changed all the cutlery round and then put it back again, rubbed his hands once more and then suddenly lost all interest in them, as if his business was simply to drag people in and then, having got them seated, to create a momentary illusion of brisk service before they had time to change their minds.

'You can have the whole dinner for three and sixpence,' said Norman, looking up from his menu. 'Wonderful how they do it in these places, isn't it? I mean to say, what would you get in an English restaurant for that? Nothing worth eating, I'll bet. But these foreigners can do it. Of course, it's their job. They know how to cook. Shall we have the dinner?'

Miss Matfield thought they might, and looked about her, not very hopefully, while Norman gave the order to a waitress, a very tall fat girl with a chalky face and no features, who had just appeared. The queer middle-aged couple looked queerer still now, for the man appeared to be dyed and the woman enamelled and it was incredible that they should ever eat food at all. You felt they ought to feed on wood and paint.

Having given the order, Mr Birtley was now looking about him too, and when he had finished doing this and had obviously noted the more picturesque details for the benefit of the other members of the staff of the Chestervern Agricultural College, he beamed at her through his rimless eyeglasses. 'Nothing I enjoy better than studying these queer types,' he whispered. 'A place like this is a treat to me, if only for that reason. Old Warwick told me I'd enjoy that part of it. He's had some very funny experiences in his time. I must try to remember some of the yarns he's told me, once or twice when I've been sitting up with him over a pipe at the Chestervern.'

While Miss Matfield was asking idly what sort of man Mr Warwick was and Norman was telling her, the waitress had brought them the two halves of a grape fruit, the juice of which had apparently been used some time before. They had not finished with old Warwick, who seemed to Miss Matfield a silly old man, when the waitress returned to give them some mysterious thick soup, which looked like gum but had a rather less pronounced flavour.

Miss Matfield tried three spoonfuls and then looked with horror at her plate. Something was there, something small, dark, squashed. There were legs. She pushed the plate away.

'What's the matter, Lilian? Don't you like the soup?'

She pointed with her spoon at the alien body.

Mr Birtley leaned across and peered at it through his glasses. 'No, by George, it isn't, is it? Is it really? Oh, I say, that's not good enough, is it? That's the worst of these foreigners. Do you think I ought to tell them about it?'

'If you don't, I will,' said Miss Matfield indignantly. 'Absolutely revolting!'

But there was nobody to tell. Even the fierce Latin had disappeared. It seemed as if when soup was served, the whole staff hid in the kitchen. Miss Matfield was sure now that her first instinctive disapproval had been right, as usual. This was a foul little place. Unfortunately, she was really hungry, having had a very small lunch.

The next member of the staff they did see obviously could not be blamed for the soup, for he was the wine waiter, an ancient gloomy foreigner. He padded across to Mr Birtley, who was trying not very successfully to explain a very funny thing that had happened last term at the College, held out a wine list decorated with dirty thumb marks, and waited apathetically.

'A-ha!' cried Mr Birtley jovially. 'Let's have something to drink, shall we? Do you think we could manage a whole bottle? I think we could. Yes, let's have a whole bottle. Now then, what is there? Will you have red or white wine, Lilian? It's all the same to me.'

'I'd like red, I think,' she replied. 'Burgundy, perhaps.' It was more sustaining. After all, with bread and butter and some burgundy, it might be possible to stun one's appetite. She had no hopes of the dinner.

'Burgundy it is,' cried Mr Birtley, with an air of a reckless musketeer. 'All right, then. A bottle of Number Eleven. Beaune.'

'You geef me moanay,' murmured the ancient foreigner.

'Righto. Money. There you are.' And then he gave Miss Matfield a wink and smiled at her. She smiled back, softening towards him a little, for he was so obviously enjoying himself and thinking it all so wonderful. Poor Norman!

'You ought to come and see us at the College next time you're home, Lilian,' he said. 'You'd like it. We've got one or two amusing fellows on the staff, and the students aren't a bad crowd. We have little dances sometimes, and tennis in the summer. It's growing too. In a year or two, if I can scrape up some money, I may get a partnership. Not bad, eh! The fact is', and he lowered his voice, as if to keep these confidences away from the waitress, who had just deposited some microscopic pieces of fish in front of them and was still standing near, as if to see if they would have the audacity to eat them, 'the fact is, I get on better with old Warwick than any of the other fellows. He's taken rather a fancy to me, thinks I've got more drive than the others. And as a matter of fact,' he added, looking earnestly at her, 'I have. And I wish you'd come and look me up down there.'

She said she would, if she could manage it, and then explained, while the ancient foreigner poured out the wine, how difficult it was to do all one wanted to do, what with one thing and another, and then, fortified by the burgundy and determined to drive old Warwick out of the conversation for a time, she went on to tell him more about the office and the Club. He listened attentively, though with just the faintest suggestion of patronage. Obviously he thought a good deal more of himself these days, now that he had made such a hit with his old Warwick of the Chestervern Agricultural. But then all men were alike in that: they all thought they were marvellous. However, she could tell from the way he looked at her that he still thought she was marvellous too, which was very pleasant. She could feel herself getting steadily better looking and more attractive.

This could not be said about the dinner. The chicken was not marvellous, was not even pleasant. Like many other places in Soho, this restaurant evidently had a contract that compelled it to accept only those parts of a chicken that could not be called breast, wing, or leg. It specialized in chicken skin. The salad could be eaten, but its green-stuff seemed to have been grown in some London back garden behind a sooty privet hedge. The sweet was composed of a very small ice, the paper in which it had been delivered from the van at the back door, and some coloured water that might have been part of the ice two hours before. That was the dinner, a miserable affair. Even Norman seemed to have a suspicion that it had not been very good, but he did not apologize for it, perhaps out of loyalty to old Warwick. Miss Matfield, in despair, had had two full glasses of the burgundy, a raw and potent concoction, which had produced at once a rather muzzy effect in her mind so that everything seemed a little larger and noisier than usual. Once, just before the coffee, she had found herself wanting to giggle at the thought of Norman taking his sandy moustache back to Chestervern and old Warwick. The coffee, black and bitter, stopped all that nonsense. They smoked a cigarette together over it, and Norman, with tiny beads of perspiration on his ruddy forehead and his glasses slightly misty, talked about old times and smiled sentimentally across the cruet at her.

It was time to be gone. The Latin suddenly decided to notice their existence again, brought the bill, accepted money, proffered change, swept away the tip, and then apparently threw them both into the street, where the air seemed at once remarkably pure and unusually cold.

Cocktails at Lady Catterbird's

LATER that same day, Friday, Charlie went to his first (and last) cocktail party. This was the one that had been mentioned to him the night before by that rich, important, masterful woman with a face like a whitewashed parrot, Lady Catterbird. Charlie had not the least desire to set eyes on her again, but she was determined to get him to her party. *The Tribune* was on her side, too, partly because she was a friend of the proprietor, and partly because an appearance at one of her parties would be good publicity. She was, it seemed, well known for her parties. So Charlie went. He hoped that the beauty-prize girl would be there, but he didn't give much for his hope. This Lady Catterbird didn't seem very enthusiastic about good-looking young women.

Her house was in the corner of a large square, not very far from the hotel. It was about the size of the Utterton Central Free Library, Public Swimming Baths, and Gas and Rates Offices. At the door were two tall young fellows in uniform.

There were two more of them at the foot of the grand staircase and another at the top. After that you came to the waiters, and there seemed to be dozens of them. The party was happening on the first floor. When you got to the top of the stairs you could hear it happening, and when you were nearer, walking along the broad landing, it was deafening. The screaming and screeching were terrible. Charlie asked himself why all the people in the West End of London seemed to scream and screech, men and all. Lady Catterbird was standing at the door of the big room and she recognized Charlie at once, which seemed to him very clever of her.

'Welcome, welcome,' she shouted, keeping hold of his hand. 'So splendid of you. I'm dying, absolutely dying, to have a really long talk with you, only, of course, one can't with all these people. Now will you – promise me – will you just go in and meet people and have a good time and not go, just wait until we're able to have a cosy little talk together? Now promise?'

Charlie, anxious to have his hand back, found himself muttering some sort of promise. Then he was allowed to enter the big room, which was about the size of the Bendworth Museum and Art Gallery. They were all drinking from little glasses, eating sandwiches and bits of things, smoking, and screaming at one another. Charlie pushed his way through, having made up his mind to reach the far corner. On the way he drank a cocktail and didn't much care for it. He realized at once, too, that if he drank many of those things he'd be squiffy. Some of these people were well on already. He landed near a girl with a long white face, like a horse, and she blinked at him and then said in a gruff voice: 'My God! Surely you're Archie Clavordale?'

'No, I'm not,' said Charlie.

'No, you're not, are you? My God! – you're like him. D'you mind?'

'No,' said Charlie, moving on, telling himself that if that girl had only a few more she'd soon be in a terrible state – my God she would. He was now brought up against three men, two of them young and slender and pale, and the other one older and plumper and pink, and all three of them were hissing amiably at one another and smiling and swaying and waving their delicate white paws.

'And sssso I ssssaid to him, "Darling, it'ss perfectly ab-ssssurd – you know it isss,"' one of the young men was saying; and the other two smiled, sweetly, with their heads slightly on one side, and looked as if at any moment they were going to kiss him. Charlie worked his way round this group as soon as he could. This move sent him up against the bulging waistcoat of a very fat man with a very red face. He had a cocktail in each hand and insisted upon giving Charlie one. 'Drink that,' he said, with a hoarse chuckle, 'and take that disgusted look off your face. Where d'you come from?'

'Utterton,' said Charlie.

'Never heard of it. What are you doing here?'

'I don't know.'

'I know what I'm doing,' cried the fat man in despair. 'I'm wrecking my evening. By quarter past seven, at the latest, I'll be three parts tight, reeking of gin, sticky with vermouth, no appetite left, and with the rest of the hellish evening to fill in. I think I shall ride about on buses. Crouch End – Penge – that sort of thing. Gunnersbury. Shooters Hill. Do you know any of these places?'

'No. I've only just come to London.'

'I wish I had,' said the fat man sadly. 'They've built most of the place round me. But not Penge or Gunnersbury. Ah – there you are, Rose.' And he brushed past Charlie, who began to look for some place to put down his half-empty glass. This search brought him to a small table, at which sat two young girls, tall and quite pretty creatures, who were sedately picking over a lot of little things to eat set out on trays. He put his glass down on this table, and in doing so accidentally knocked against one of these damsels. He muttered some sort of apology.

'Not at all,' she said in a very clear, precise voice, looking at him with very clear grey eyes. 'Are you a boxer?'

'No,' Charlie replied, astonished at this question. 'I mean to say – I can box a bit – but I'm not a proper boxer.'

'What a shame! Darling,' she turned to the other girl, 'he's not a boxer. And he looks like one.'

'He talks like one, too. At least, I imagine so,' said the other miss, with the same astonishing air of quiet impudence. 'I'm sorry you lost that point, darling.'

'What are you then – a comedian?' asked the first girl.

'I've seen his face before,' said the second.

'You've not gate-crashed, have you?'

'What's that?' asked Charlie, bewildered.

'Darling, he's just trying to make it hard for us. I'm sure he's a famous comedian. I believe I've seen him in films.'

'Did Lady Catterbird really invite you?'

'Yes, she did,' said Charlie, trying to keep his end up with this pair of impudent chits. 'And I'm not a comedian either.'

'She must have invited him just to make it difficult for us, darling,' the second one sighed. 'And I really do know his face.'

'So do I. He must be a celebrity, or he wouldn't be here. Besides, nobody but a celebrity dare talk with that accent. Isn't he maddening?' She then turned and gave Charlie a sad, sweet smile.

These girls were several years younger than he was, only kids, and he felt he had stood enough from them. It was his turn now. 'If you want to know what I'm doing here,' he told them earnestly, 'I'll just let you into the secret. There's a prize to be given to the one here who's the cheekiest – the one who's messed up the most bits o' food, and talked about strangers to their faces, and so on – the cheekiest. And I'm going round to see who deserves the prize. And so far, I don't mind telling you –'

'Yes, do tell us.'

'It's between you two.'

'Darling, we're shattered.'

'And I hope you stay shattered for a bit,' Charlie muttered to himself as he moved away. He was now within sight of his objective, the far corner. There were not so many people in this part of the room. He would be able to have a quiet smoke in the corner, and possibly sit down to it. In the corner itself, there was a little settee, and the only person on it was a thick-set, gloomy fellow with a large black moustache. He was smoking hard, so Charlie did not hesitate to join him.

'Like this sort of thing?'

Charlie shook his head. 'Right out of my line,' he confessed. 'Never been to one o' these things before and don't suppose I'll ever go to one again.'

The man looked at him curiously. 'You the young chap from the provinces that the *Tribune*'s been running so hard? Thought I recognized you. Well, you've done something, and that's more than most of these creatures have. Rum lot, eh?'

Charlie agreed, and told him about his encounter with the two young girls.

'Ought to have their bottoms spanked and be sent home to bed,' said the gloomy man. 'Boys that talk like girls. Girls that talk like nothing on earth. That's what you get now. No good. No place for a real man. Give me the desert. Know the desert?'

Charlie did not know the desert.

'You can lead a man's life there still.' And he stroked his splendid black moustache. 'Or the pampas. Know the pampas?'

Charlie did not know the pampas.

'That's a man's country. Give me the pampas.'

'They're yours, old chap,' said Charlie to himself.

But the gentleman had not finished his requests yet. 'Give me a good horse, a gun, some biscuits, salt, and tobacco, and some open rolling country with some good game to pot at and a few waterholes, and I ask for nothing better. That's life. This isn't life. It's nothing. Were you ever up in the tall timber country? That's a man's country, too. Up among the tall timbers.'

Charlie did not know what the tall timbers were, but decided not to ask. This fellow seemed to be a famous explorer or some thing of that sort. Perhaps he went to wild places to take films and then show them and lecture about them.

But now he had changed the subject. 'You're not thinking of setting up an establishment in town, are you? No? I wondered. But my name's Dewson – Major Dewson, and just now

I'm in the Interior Decorating and Antique Furniture business. We've done a lot of work for Lady Catterbird here. Here's my card. You might find it useful. Somebody might ask you sometime to recommend a good West End firm of antique dealers and interior decorators. You never know, do you?'

Charlie said that you never did.

'Never up in the Peace River country, were you?' continued the major. 'That's a man's life. Do some of these people good to be up there when it's forty below. Yes, I've known it forty below. Well, I must move on. Got another of these damned cocktail parties to go to yet. Rather be out after moose or bush-whacking down under. Ever out there? Another man's country. Well, here goes.'

Charlie was sorry to see the major go, even though his conversation tended to be both mysterious and monotonous. He settled himself in his corner and watched the crowd, which was thinning now. They were a queer lot, with hardly a pleasant face amongst them. The older ones, men and women, had a hard, greedy, gobbling look about them. The younger ones seemed peevish, discontented. And then there were the young men who were trying to look like girls and the girls who were trying to look like young men. Charlie could not believe that he was examining a fair specimen of a West End party. Lady Catterbird must have a lot of queer friends, that was all. Why was he there? What did she want with him?

A Good Lunch for Sir George

All Tuesday morning it rained hard, and at lunch time they were unusually quiet at the Dog and Bell. Timmy and the Professor, who had decided to keep out of Sir George's sight until after lunch, had posted themselves at a first-floor window to watch for his arrival. Just after one o'clock, when they were beginning to feel rather anxious, a muddy saloon car drew up and there, framed in its window, looking as if it had been moulded out of Cheddar cheese, was the vast dubious face of Sir George Denberry-Baxter. 'And as sober an' sour as the devil,' observed Timmy. They passed the word below.

'Humph! So this is the place, eh?' said Sir George, not yet stirring from the car. 'Hardly my style y'know, Foxfield – brand-new, Americanized, lower-middle-class-on-the-spree sort of thing.'

'It's really quite good, sir,' Sir Reginald told him, 'and it'll be quiet now. You'd hate our lunch at Dunbury Hall.'

'Yes, seem to remember it wasn't very good. Couldn't have a look at the cold sideboard at your club, eh?'

'I haven't one in Dunbury, sir. Really, I promise you won't find this place at all bad.'

'All right. What a place! What a day! What a country!' And grumbling and growling he heaved himself out and made for the entrance. He was sorry now he'd accepted this silly little job, though he'd been glad enough when it was first proposed to him, for it gave him something to do for a day or so and at least a temporary shadow of his old authority. Dunbury was a miserable little town; young Foxfield was a bore; Lady Foxfield was a woman entirely without wit or charm; and there would be a very bad dinner and some dreary local gentry waiting for him tonight at Dunbury Hall. He'd have been just as well off at home, yawning over a book and cursing Ketley.

'Oh! – I say – how d'you do?' cried Sir Reginald, seeing Daisy and Hope, who had suddenly arrived where they could not help being seen and had taken great care to be worth seeing.

'Oh! – how d'you do? Are you lunching here?' cried Daisy, all surprised and lady-like and fluttering.

Sir Reginald had to introduce them to Sir George Denberry-Baxter, who was rather grand and grumpy with them, though he looked sharply several times at Daisy, for he felt he had seen her before somewhere, and regarded the extremely good-looking girl with some satisfaction.

'We feel this is a very great honour to have Sir George Denberry-Baxter calling here,' said Daisy very carefully. 'I must show you our cocktail bar, and perhaps you'll have a drink before lunch. It's such a miserably cold day, isn't it?' And then she bustled them into the bar, which they had to themselves. 'Now we're very proud of Jimmy here, our barman,' Daisy continued, doing her stuff. 'Jimmy, I want Sir George Denberry-Baxter to try one of our Specials. Will you, Sir George?'

'Well, if you insist. Good stiff short drink, is it?'

'We think it's wonderful, don't we, Jimmy?'

Jimmy nodded and smiled, showing his excellent false teeth. He did a little Denga Din work at the back of the bar, and then put before them his pale foaming Specials. A close observer might have noticed that the Specials given to the gentlemen were not only larger but also slightly different in colour from the ladies' cocktails.

'Oh! – I say,' Sir Reginald gasped. 'Got a wollop, hasn't it?'

'Humph – pretty good short drink,' said Sir George, having downed his Special without a quiver of an eyelash. He smacked his lips. 'Vodka in it, among other things – eh?'

'Ah, you need more than one even to start guessing,' Jimmy told him, and at the same time, in true Denga Din style, produced another Special. Sir George swallowed half of it, made a tasting noise, frowned, muttered 'Bacardi perhaps,' swallowed the other half and said: 'No, perhaps not.'

Daisy saw that this was the line to take, at least until Sir George had had a few and became human. The analytical chemist line. Scientific research, not mere boozing. 'Nobody ever guesses even the main things in it,' she said to him, 'though I must say you're doin' better than anybody so far.'

'Oh, I'll get it,' replied Sir George, picking up the third Special. 'Excellent short drink, by the way. Now then!'

Altogether he had six of these depth charges, and both Daisy and her barman regarded him with respect, for here was no ordinary man. Sir Reginald had only had three, but these had left him with a definite tendency towards sweeping gestures and a horrible goggly-squinting look that he directed at Hope. But Sir George was merely becoming amiable. His vast face was pink now instead of yellow. His eye was brightening. And he seemed about half as large again as the disgruntled old fellow who first entered the bar.

'Well, bite of lunch now – eh? Ready, Foxfield? But I say – think we ought to insist on the ladies joining us, eh? What d'you say, ladies? Can't leave us now, eh?'

The ladies, who wanted to giggle when he was not looking but found themselves almost hypnotized by the bright fierce glance when that vast face hung over them like a moon, demurely expressed their pleasure and led the way to the dining-room. There were only two or three nondescript travellers bunched together at one end, and Daisy marched her party up the other end.

'I hope you like oysters, Sir George?'

'Oysters? Madame, I've been waiting for months, stuck there in a ramshackle country house miles from anywhere, just waiting for September and civilization and oysters. You remember the Walrus and the Carpenter? Well, I'm both of 'em. Oysters? Splendid! Oysters by all means.'

'I ordered them specially from Colchester,' said Daisy with some pride.

'You're an extremely sensible woman, and I knew it the moment I set eyes on you. I can lunch like a king on oysters.'

'Oh – but I've ordered a lot of other nice things as well.'

'You have, eh?' roared Sir George. 'Well, you won't find 'em wasted on me. I've been living the most extraordinary existence, in a house miles from anywhere that belongs to a nephew. Servants all walked out – God knows why – and I've nobody to look after me but my man, Ketley, and a deaf old woman, and I've been living for weeks on tinned tongue, boiled eggs and whisky – a barbarous existence. A-ha! These oysters look good. And I'll trouble you for the brown bread, Foxfield.'

'I'm very anxious for you to tell me what you think of some champagne I have here, Sir George,' said Daisy, all very ladylike and artful. 'A lot of people complain it's too dry – and it *is* dry, I'll admit –'

'Can't be too dry for me,' said Sir George promptly. 'But glad to tell you what I think of it. Very sensible of you to suggest it. Excellent idea of yours, Foxfield, coming here. Quite right about it. Didn't trust your judgement, but I was wrong. Always admit when I'm wrong,' he told them all, 'and I've admitted I was wrong all over the place – East Africa, Burma, Borneo and Fiji – I was damnably wrong in Fiji and remind me to tell you about it after lunch if we've time. Is this the champagne you're worried about?'

'Yes, is it all right?' asked Daisy, putting on a sort of helpless-little-woman anxiety. Actually it was the best wine she had in the place. 'Not too dry?'

'Certainly not. Dead right. Mind you,' he continued, after emptying his glass, 'I don't think it's a lady's wine. Or a boy's' – and he looked sternly at Sir Reginald, as if to forbid him touching a drop. 'And no doubt this uncommonly pretty gal here would prefer something sweeter. But for a civilized English adult male taste, it's perfect.' He reached out for his glass again, and found that it had been filled, for the waiter had been carefully instructed that morning by Daisy.

After the oysters, there was an excellent dish of kidneys with a burnt wine sauce, and then a cheese soufflé; and Sir George had two helpings of everything, never stopped talking, never stopped drinking the first-rate champagne; and by the time they were ready for coffee he was in tremendous form.

'I've one or two liqueur brandies I wish you'd try,' said Daisy, still using the same technique, though now, with Sir George all rosy and ripe, it was hardly necessary.

'My palate,' said the great connoisseur, 'is entirely at your disposal. You'd have to go a long way to find a man with a nicer appreciation of good brandy than George Denberry-Baxter. And don't imagine that a good cigar will blunt my palate – though I know some of 'em tell you that – because it won't. Oh – cigars here, eh? Good! Now then, this is brandy number one, is it? Now don't tell me what it is. Let me just give you my impression of it.' He took a prodigious helping, sniffed a bit, then poured in a capacious mouthful, rolled it round and chewed it and slowly swallowed it, closing his eyes. When he opened them again, he stared across the table at Sir Reginald, who had also closed his eyes. 'Foxfield's bottled, isn't he?' Sir George whispered to Daisy. 'Can't hold it, eh? Pity! Wake up, young Foxfield!'

Sir Reginald slowly opened one eye, and said dreamily: 'Did my mother ask you to dinner tonight?'

'She did. Why?'

'Don't go,' said Sir Reginald, wagging his head. 'It'll be ghastly – ab-so-lutely ghastly, ol' boy.'

'Yes, a trifle bottled, I think, though he's quite right about the dinner and I think "ghastly" is *le mot juste*.' He swallowed the rest of the brandy. 'Nothing wrong with this. Capital stuff. Don't let 'em talk you out of it!'

'But is the other better, that's the point,' said Daisy, winking at Hope, who suddenly began giggling.

'What are you laughing at?' demanded Sir George, with mock fierceness. 'Me?'

'Yes,' replied Hope boldly. 'I think you're a wonderful turn.'

'And you're quite right – so I am. Explain why, afterwards. But must settle this brandy question. Least I can do, after the excellent lunch you've given me. Now then.' He tackled an even more prodigious helping of the second brandy. Then he looked up and frowned. 'Turn? Turn?'

'Sorry,' said Hope. 'I wasn't being rude.'

'No, no, no, wasn't thinking of that. Turn, turn?' He wheeled round and pointed an enormous forefinger straight at Daisy's little nose. 'Been trying and trying and trying to remember where I've seen you before. Now I've got it. Turn! You were on the halls, weren't you? Little soubrette with red hair. Saucy little puss. Daisy – Daisy – Daisy –'

'Daisy Barley,' she prompted him delighted with this recognition.

'That's it. Daisy Barley. And you're Daisy Barley, little Daisy Barley. Daisy – for you must allow me the privilege as a very old and fervent admirer – Daisy – your health!'

And that finished his glass of the second brandy. 'Nothing wrong with that brandy. A shade sharper than the first, perhaps, not quite so smooth. I don't know, though. Mustn't do Number Two an injustice by flattering Number One. Better try One again – least I can do.'

Music at the Alingtons'

WHILE Knott was talking to me, the others had settled down in their dim firelit places, and the musicians, beneath a big standard lamp near the piano, were ready to begin. The songs were mostly contemporary work, heard by Oliver in Cambridge, and they were all unfamiliar to me. Only two were English, the rest being Russian, French, and German. They had for me that richly evocative quality which belongs to art when it is as strange as it is beautiful, when it can be enjoyed but not yet understood. As they played and sang I had glimpses of incomprehensible lives ... I wandered through remote forests, dark and melancholy, towards decaying towers ... a little window would open on an orchard bright with unknown blossom ... lovers met at midnight in Prague or Budapest ... the anemones were crimson with the blood of the dying hussar ... poets in black coats trailed along the grey salt-crusted dunes ... under the high blue noon a mysterious procession went past the fields of corn ... girls waited in shuttered rooms, looked in the glass and saw that they were old women ... in search of the Chinese princess with the lute and the emerald birds, we died in the desert ... witches muttered to executioners ... we lived, gathered roses and drank wine, laughed and died, and lived again, waking in woods without a name, staring at the pine-needles and the rusting dagger ...

But all the time too I could see across the room the grave pale face of Joan, darkly mysterious in that shadowy corner, and once or twice I thought she smiled at me, signalling from a hidden land. I could see Bridget, sharply illuminated above her violin, her eyes veiled, her features strongly and nobly sculptured by the light, her face taking on a kind of stern beauty I had never suspected in her. And on the other side of the piano, full in the light, was Eva, sometimes singing in a high clear voice, the golden smiling girl, the sleepy princess of the enchanted trams, still an incredible figure though here so close. And thus seeing them, mistily through the music, I think I fell in love with all three at once. This is possible at eighteen, when love is magic rather than revealed desire, when it rises in us like a tide on which the mind can float, when it can be exquisite and poignant and yet entirely unfocused, arched above a whole company like a rainbow. It seemed to me the most wonderful thing that could ever happen that I should simply be there. The evening ought to go on and on, I felt, for ever.

'Come and see us again soon, Gregory,' said Mr Alington at the front door, as I left with Jock Barniston and the Wilson girl.

'Yes, thank you very much, Mr Alington.' But when can I, when can I? And I could hear the girls laughing inside, half-lost already, with magic briars and thorns growing between them and me. Giving a final glance at Mr Alington's long, dark, dramatic face, smiling now, I made up my mind in a flash that there could be no better life anywhere than his, that here was the perfect example, that I never need leave Bruddersford or Hawes and Company to have everything I wanted.

Boxing Day at Mr Ackworth's

'GOOD lad! Glad to see you,' roared Mr Ackworth in the hall, helping me off with my heavy overcoat. 'Got a bit o' good stuff i' this overcoat an' all. Ah'll bet your Uncle Miles chose that for you, didn't he? Well, you know one or two of 'em 'ere, but not so many. Mostly neighbours. Introduce yourself, lad. Ah can't be bothered. 'Ere's the wife, though. Better be introduced to 'er or there'll be ructions. Annie, this is young Gregory Dawson who 'elps me in t'sample-room.'

'How do you do?' said Mrs Ackworth in a very deep voice. She was a stately, rather handsome woman, who seemed to think that it was her duty to have dignity enough for both of them, with the result that she was not unlike a duchess in a George Edwardes musical comedy. 'Seasonable weather, isn't it?'

'Ay, an' what this lad needs is a drop o' summat to warm 'im up an' get 'im started,' said Mr Ackworth, winking at me.

He took me into a little room full of books, told me to look around it, and then after a minute or two came back with a steaming glass of a very generous size. 'Mulled old ale. Warm you up in a jiffy, lad. Now get it down.'

It was the strongest stuff I had ever tasted up to that time, and it was hot and I drank it quickly. Then I found I had a great desire to giggle. Mr Ackworth, Mrs Ackworth, and their party that I had not yet seen, they all seemed to me exquisitely droll. Mr Ackworth led me across the hall into a drawing-room packed with people, most of them very hot and many of them very fat. The Bruddersford agent of the Canal Company, whom I recognized although at that moment he was blindfolded, was trying to pin a paper tail on to an outline of a donkey. And then I saw that the three Alington girls were there, Joan and Eva and Bridget. They smiled, and I made my way, through a solid but almost steaming ton or so of wool merchants and wives, to join them in their corner. I was one of the magic circle. And this, I realized at once, was a wonderful party.

'You look peculiar to-night,' said Eva, smiling her rich sleepy smile.

'I think it's mulled old ale,' I told her.

'Anyhow,' said Bridget, with emphasis, 'it's a peculiar party.'

'Are the others here?' I asked.

'No, only us,' replied Joan. 'All the rest of the family's gone somewhere else. But won't we do?'

'Yes, it's marvellous,' I said. 'I never expected to see you all here. I'd given you up for this Christmas. I was disappointed.'

Bridget stared at me, widening her green eyes. 'I don't understand you. And I've argued about you a bit. Which one of us is it you're so keen on knowing?'

'It's all three,' I said earnestly. 'No, really it is. I mean – well –' And then I stopped, not knowing how to go on. But I looked from one to the other of them. Bridget still stared; Joan wore a little puzzled frown; and Eva smiled lazily out of her mysterious golden afternoon.

A massive woman, purple-faced and upholstered, had now been blindfolded.

'Nay, steady, Sally,' Mr Ackworth shouted above the din, 'or you'll bust something. Don't turn 'er round, Arthur. She doesn't know where she is now, an' God knows where she'll be pinnin' that tail.'

'I love Mr Ackworth,' said Eva dreamily.

'He's all right,' said Bridget guardedly, 'but I'll bet they'll be playing filthy kissing games soon. You'll see. And – gosh! – isn't it hot?'

'Yes, and I'm very thirsty,' said Joan.

'I'll get you something,' I told her, and scrambled my way to the other end of the room, where I found some claret cup, and returned precariously with three glasses of it.

'Bless you, Gregory!' cried Joan, her fine grey eyes warm and friendly.

'Chuck it, Joan,' said Bridget.

'Chuck what?'

'You know what,' replied Bridget darkly.

Joan looked at me and raised her eyebrows, so I raised mine too. I didn't know what they were talking about, but I was desperately anxious not to be left out of anything. But I didn't please Bridget. 'Don't be a chump, Gregory,' she said.

'I didn't know I was one.'

'I believe you are.' Bridget turned her attention to the party. 'Now what's going to happen?'

Mr Ackworth was shouting that it was time the young ones had a chance. 'An' when Ah say that, Ah include meself.'

'Here it comes,' Bridget muttered.

And it did, the kissing game. For the first few minutes our corner was left alone, but then Mr Ackworth had his chance and chose Joan, and then she chose me, and out I went to her in the hall. I was very shy, for not only was she a few years older than I was but she was also still more than a girl, still a piece of magic, and I was afraid not merely of offending her but also of breaking a spell.

'Not like that,' she whispered. 'Like this, Gregory.'

It was a light kiss but firm and very sweet. And sitting there, a middle-aged man, on that Cornish cliff edge, thirty-odd years afterwards, I remembered it as if it had happened only a few minutes before. So much had gone, and yet the memory of that sudden quick pressure of a girl's lips remained. And then a weight of sadness fell on that fragrant hollow in the cliff, and I felt as if I had been dead for years and years and had not known it until then. With an effort I wrenched myself out of this blue-and-gold afternoon, which no longer had any more life in it for me than a vast painted curtain, and returned to the hall in Joe Ackworth's house.

'Now who is your choice?' asked Joan. 'Mrs Ackworth?'

'Never. I think –' and I remembered Bridget's disgust – 'it had better be Eva.'

'I knew it would be,' said Joan, not without a touch of scorn. 'You're all the same.'

Eva came out smiling. She was, I remembered then, wearing a long pale-blue dress that night, a modest kind of evening dress that girls wore then. She moved smoothly into my arms, and I kissed her several times. It was very pleasant of course, yet curiously unsatisfying, as if there, so close, was that country of golden afternoons, with its meadows and shining rivers, and yet one had not advanced a yard into it.

When I got back to her, Bridget was eating candied fruit, licking her fingers, and looking grumpy. 'I think you're all disgusting,' she announced, 'and it's rather a disgusting party. I don't think I'd play here, even if I was begged to. Eating's the thing to do here, and I'm jolly well going to eat myself sick.'

At that moment a man called Leaton, whom I had seen at the office, where he used to do our insurance business for goods in transit, came up to us. He was a tall, bony fellow with a harsh Bruddersford voice, a sardonic type. 'Aren't you Mr Alington's daughters?' he asked.

After I'd introduced him, he went on: 'Your father told me one of you was studying the violin. Which one is it?'

'It's me,' said Bridget, not regarding him with any interest.

'Well, later on, if you've brought your fiddle, we might 'ave a go,' said Leaton, rubbing his huge bony hands together. 'Joe Ackworth's got a good piano 'ere – Steinway.'

'Can you play?' asked Bridget, still without much interest.

'Ay, a bit. Organ an' piano. 'Obby o' mine, you might say,' said Leaton. 'Got owt with you?'

Bridget replied that, at Mr Ackworth's very special request, she had brought her fiddle and a few odds and ends of music, but that she didn't feel much like playing.

''Appen you will later,' said Leaton, grinning and looking more uncouth than ever. 'If crowd goes in t'other room, we might 'ave a go.' And off he went.

'And happen not,' muttered Bridget. 'You know him – what does he do?'

'Wool insurance,' I told her.

'Pooh! He'll be awful.'

'You don't know,' said Joan. 'And don't be so jolly conceited, Bridget.'

'I don't like you to-night, Joan. Nor you,' she added, turning to me. 'In fact I don't like being here at all, and I wish I hadn't come. It's all too fat and frowsty and wool-merchanty.'

Some game that involved the billiards-table was now proposed, and most of the guests went to play this game, but our little group stayed on in the drawing-room. After a few minutes Mr Ackworth himself, carrying more food and drink, joined us. 'If that lot stays out,' he said, 'Ah'll get 'Erbert Leaton to play a bit for us.'

'Can that man really play?' asked Bridget, rather loftily.

But you couldn't take that line with Mr Ackworth. 'Nah then, young Bridget,' he said, grinning at her. 'That'll do from you. Ah suppose you think 'cos 'Erbert's a slammocky-lookin' sort o' chap an' earns 'is livin' in t'insurance, he amounts to nowt. Well, that's where you're wrong. 'Erbert could 'ave easy earned 'is livin' by music, but bein' an independent sort o' chap he'd rather keep it as a 'obby. An' tak' that grin off your face, young woman,' he added sternly.

'All right, Mr Ackworth.' Bridget was demure now. 'I'd love to hear him play.'

'An' what 'ave you brought with you? Summat good, Ah 'ope. None o' this caffy music. We like solid stuff up 'ere on t'Glen. Go an' fetch it, lass.'

Bridget trotted off obediently.

Eva said: 'That's the way to treat Bridget. Mr Ackworth, you ought to come and live with us.'

'Ah wouldn't be paid to. Ah like peace an' quiet,' he said seriously.

Joan laughed. 'I don't associate you with peace and quiet, Mr Ackworth.'

'Neither do I,' and I grinned at him, 'but I have an idea we all imagine we like peace and quiet. And perhaps we do – in our own way.'

'Ah'll tell you what it is,' said Mr Ackworth to the two girls, 'Gregory 'ere's a bit of a Clever Dick. An' either he'll 'ave to mak' summat special out of 'imself or he'll be one o' them that nobody wants to talk to or listen to.'

I stared at him, for this matched exactly my secret thoughts about myself. He gave me a knowing wink. I glanced at the girls. Eva was looking faintly puzzled, but Joan was nodding wisely. It was a queer moment, and I never forgot it.

Herbert Leaton came up again, still rubbing his huge hands and pulling his long bony fingers and making them crack. He was followed by Bridget, carrying her violin and music-case.

'Nah, sitha, 'Erbert lad,' said Mr Ackworth, in an even

broader accent than his usual one, 'Ah'm goin' to give thee a glass o' right good whisky – special stuff, lad – an' then tha's goin' to play t'piano for us. An' Ah want thee to show these clever bairns just 'ow to do it, 'cos they think they knaw summat an' they knaw nowt yet. Nah, 'ere's thi whisky – an Ah'll fix t'piano up for thee.'

Leaton guffawed, and looked like a lanky North Country comedian in a pantomime. 'Thanks, Joe. An' 'ere's to me an' my wife's 'usband.' And down went the whisky.

Bridget made a face at us. By this time Mr Ackworth had cleared some plates and ash-trays off the top of the grand piano and had opened it. Leaton went shambling across, cracking his fingers harder than ever. 'What's it to be, Joe?' he asked as he sat down.

'Please thysen, lad,' replied Mr Ackworth, lighting a cigar. 'But a bit o' Bach 'ud do me.'

'Me an' all,' said Leaton, hunching himself up over the keyboard and spreading those long bony fingers.

Bridget looked surprised. Then she stopped fidgeting with her own music and settled down to listen.

With one clean stroke, as clean as his opening phrases, Leaton cut straight through the insurance business, the wool trade, Bruddersford, and the twentieth century, straight through to the eighteenth century and Johann Sebastian Bach. These huge hands of his brought out every note, unfaltering and crystal clear. He had too, what many Bach pianists never quite achieve, a singing tone, a warmth and flush, as of sunlight on the marble. Preludes and fugues sang and climbed, and went thundering by. Joe Ackworth's piano became a whole world of changing tone and colour.

'No, no, no, please!' cried Bridget, running over to him when he stopped, and almost embracing him. 'You can't stop now, you can't – you mustn't. Go on. Go on – *please*, Mr Leaton.' There was a break in her voice, and her eyes were very bright.

'Ah told you – didn't Ah – that you knew nowt,' observed Mr Ackworth complacently. ''Ave another drop o' whisky, 'Erbert?'

'Never mind whisky,' cried Bridget. 'And I admit we know *nowt*. But tell him he must keep on playing. He's wonderful. And I couldn't possibly play now.'

Leaton wheeled round on his stool. ''Ow d'yer mean?'

'Not after you I couldn't –'

'Nah stop that.' And Leaton held out one hand for the whisky, and held out the other for Bridget's music. 'What you got there? Let's 'ave a look. Nah 'ere's a bit o' Bach –'

'I couldn't, I couldn't – not after you.' Bridget danced about in her apprehension. 'It would sound frightful. Joan – Gregory – back me up – wouldn't it sound frightful?'

'What about the César Franck?' asked Joan.

'Well – I might try –' said Bridget, hesitating.

'Me an' 'Erbert thinks that's thinnish stuff,' said Mr Ackworth, once again surprising me.

'It'll do, Joe, it'll do,' said Leaton.

'Do you know it?' asked Bridget.

'Ay, Ah've played it –'

'Didn't you play it that time at Gladstone 'All when Thingumbob's accompanist didn't turn up?' began Mr Ackworth.

'Never mind about that, Joe.'

'Yes, all right, Mr Leaton,' said Bridget. 'But who was Thingumbob?'

Herbert Leaton grinned and winked, looking more grotesque than ever. 'Ysaye.'

'Ysaye!' Bridget almost screamed. Then she sat down, her face scarlet. 'Golly! Golly, golly, golly! Look – I'll never understand anything round here – never, never. I'll have to go away and live somewhere else. You go to one place and meet one lot of people, all very nice and natty. And they don't know anything about anything. Hopeless. So you think; "Well, nobody knows anything about anything – and that's that." Then you go to another place – and meet another lot of people – and they jolly well look as if they don't know anything about anything – and then somebody like you' – and she pointed an accusing finger at Leaton – 'turns up who plays Bach like an angel, though you pretend to be in the insurance business or some silliness, and then you say you'll play the César Franck with me and it turns out that you've played it with Ysaÿe. And you're as bad, Mr Ackworth, because I never knew you bothered about music at all –'

'Ah tell you, young Bridget. You know nowt – yet. Give yourself a bit o' time, lass.'

'It's all right saying that,' Bridget grumbled. 'And I know you think I'm very young and silly. I expect I am – really, though I don't feel like that inside. But it *is* puzzling here. Isn't it, Gregory? You must have found that out.'

'Yes, it is. Bridget's quite right. You never know what anybody's going to say and do next. If you think they know something, as Bridget says, then they don't know anything. And if you think they don't know anything, then they know all kinds of things that surprise you. I can't get used to it either.'

'Nah, stop natterin', you kids,' said Mr Ackworth. 'An' if you two are goin' to play, then get on with it.'

So they played the César Franck sonata, and I could see and hear them still, two World Wars away, as I closed my eyes to the Cornish sunlight and shut out of my mind the whole fretting and half-ruined planet of this later year. I could still hear Bridget's brave if rather uncertain tone, with its growing tenderness and grave passion, and Leaton's easy and fluid piano tone; and with an effort I could still catch a glimpse of his ungainly hunched figure and Bridget's frowning little face and her tumbling hair. We had, I remembered, more Bach after that, then food and drink with the rest of the party, and more games and nonsense, with Bridget now in tearing high spirits. I could recall too walking down to the Alingtons' with the three girls, through the thickening snow and the blanket of the night, and after that the trudging and slipping, slipping and trudging, from the Alingtons' to Brigg Terrace, alone but aglow with the immense vague dreams of youth. For wasn't my world, in the snow and the darkness, opening like a flower?

PASTIMES AND PLEASURES

The Football Match

SOMETHING very queer is happening in that narrow thoroughfare to the west of the town. It is called Manchester Road because it actually leads you to that city, though in order to get there you will have to climb to the windy roof of England and spend an hour or two with the curlews. What is so queer about it now is that the road itself cannot be seen at all. A grey-green tide flows sluggishly down its length. It is a tide of cloth caps.

These caps have just left the ground of the Bruddersford United Association Football Club. Thirty-five thousand men and boys have just seen what most of them call 't'United' play Bolton Wanderers. Many of them should never have been there at all. It would not be difficult to prove by statistics and those mournful little budgets (How a Man May Live – or rather, avoid death – on Thirty-five Shillings a Week) that seem to attract some minds, that these fellows could not afford the entrance fee. When some mills are only working half the week and others not at all, a shilling is a respectable sum of money. It would puzzle an economist to discover where all these shillings came from. But if he lived in Bruddersford, though he might still wonder where they came from, he would certainly understand why they were produced. To say that these men paid their shillings to watch twenty-two hirelings kick a ball is merely to say that a violin is wood and catgut, that *Hamlet* is so much paper and ink. For a shilling the Bruddersford United A. F. C. offered you Conflict and Art; it turned you into a critic, happy in your judgement of fine points, ready in a second to estimate the worth of a well-judged pass, a run down the touch line, a lightning shot, a clearance kick by back or goalkeeper; it turned you into a partisan, holding your breath when the ball came sailing into your own goalmouth, ecstatic when your forwards raced away towards the opposite goal, elated, downcast, bitter, triumphant by turns at the fortunes of your side, watching a ball shape Iliads and Odysseys for you; and what is more, it turned you into a member of a new community, all brothers together for an hour and a half, for not only had you escaped from the clanking machinery of this lesser life, from work, wages, rent, doles, sick pay, insurance cards, nagging wives, ailing children, bad bosses, idle workmen, but you had escaped with most of your mates and your neighbours, with half the town, and there you were, cheering together, thumping one another on the shoulders, swopping judgements like lords of the earth, having pushed your way through a turnstile into another and altogether more splendid kind of life, hurtling with Conflict and yet passionate and beautiful in its Art. Moreover, it offered you more than a shilling's worth of material for talk during the rest of the week. A man who had missed the last home match of 't'United' had to enter social life on tiptoe in Bruddersford.

Boxing at the Ring, Blackfriars

NOT Wagner's but the boxing-hall in the Blackfriars Road. It was once the Old Surrey Chapel, and it still suggests a chapel. I remember that when I first saw it, all that remains of my Nonconformist boyhood was wickedly thrilled at the thought of seeing some boxing matches in such a setting. Dick Burge, who was responsible for the transformation, must have been the sort of man I dreamed about when I was a boy, compelled to sit, hot and glowering, under a Children's Address. Its deaconly appearance gave me no thrill last night, however, though it was my first visit for several years. It was not a night for easy thrills. The Blackfriars Road, black and dripping, was being swept by sleet, and I trust that Mrs Burge, now the director of The Ring, will forgive me if I say that, even after the miserable Blackfriars Road, her hall did not seem very snug and lively. The big lights above the ring itself had not been turned up, for it still wanted some minutes to eight; the place was still dim, chill, cheerless; the cries of the youths who offered us apples and bars of chocolate went echoing hollowly, forlornly; and there was nothing to see, to do. I was alone – with a whole row of ringside seats to myself – and I began to wish I had stayed at home. The programme looked dull. Even the 'Important 15 (3-min.) Rounds Contest' did not suggest anything very exciting.

Then the officials made their appearance. The referee climbed into his high chair, and the time-keeper sat down beside his stop-watch and bell. The fat men in white sweaters brought out their pails of water, bottles, and towels, and stumped round to their corners. The announcer climbed into the ring, which was immediately flooded with hard bright light. I like the announcer at the Ring. He looks as if he were taken over from the original chapel. He has an air of mellowed Nonconformity. His trim white hair and white moustache, his black tie, black morning coat, and dark, striped trousers, these things give him dignity; and even when he bellows 'Ley-hay-dees an' Ger-hentle-men, Ser-hix Rer-hound Contest,' you still feel that he is probably the last of the Old Surrey deacons.

Two thin but muscular youths, whose street-corner faces seemed almost an insult to their excellent bodies, climbed into the ring, grinned, touched gloves, and then instantly began pummelling one another. They were poor boxers but good stout-hearted fighters, and they pleased the rapidly growing audience. One of them got a cut early in the contest, with the result that both their faces were quickly crimsoned and there were marks of blood on their bodies. Somebody who knew nothing about the sport might have imagined that they were trying to kill one another, and that the roaring crowd in the cheap seats was filled with blood-lust, but of course actually they were both good-humouredly slogging away, doing little or no harm to one another, and the crowd was merely applauding their lively spirit. It ended in a draw, a great round of applause, and an astonishing shower of coppers in the ring, so many indeed that it took the announcer and an assistant several minutes to pick them up. These two novices had pleased the crowd, and so it had rained pennies on them. The man sitting in front of me – a fellow with huge shoulders, a battered face, and a professional air – had registered the general verdict when he cried: 'A bloody good fight!'

The next two were not so satisfactory. They were dapper dark lads, better boxers than the others but far less pugnacious. One of them was a trifle affected in his footwork and had a funny little trick of his own, a sort of back-kick not unlike that of a stage dancer. This amused the crowd at the back of me. They decided that these antics were effeminate, and immediately, unanimously, christened the author of them 'Cissie'. They indulged in waggish irony. 'Oh, Cissie!' they screamed, as if in girlish terror. 'Don't 'urt Cissie,' they implored. In the last of their six rounds, however, these two improved and hammered one another to such a tune that the crowd was won over, dropped all talk of 'Cissie', and gave them a round of applause as a benediction.

The contest that followed, though it rose to the dignity of twelve rounds, pleased nobody. The two boys appeared to be engaged in a kind of double-shadow boxing. They seemed determined to get through their twelve rounds without giving one another any real trouble at all. 'Oh, 'ave a fight, 'ave a fight!' cried a disgusted sportsman at the back. The referee stopped them at one point and apparently uttered words of reproof. But they did not have a fight. The crowd at the back, tired of giving them ironical congratulations, now began to stamp in unison and to whistle 'All by Yourself in the Moonlight'. The announcer appealed for order, but not very passionately. The timekeeper chatted with his neighbour, smoked cigarettes, and mechanically shouted 'Seconds Out' and sounded his bell. The referee yawned harder than ever. The two boys danced round and round the ring, went back to their corners, were slapped and towelled and massaged, returned to the centre each time looking very ferocious, but did not fight. We were all glad to see the last of them.

Now came the event of the evening. The fat men with cigars and the little hard-bitten men with cigarettes stopped roaming up and down the corridor that led to the dressing-rooms. They all came out, looking knowing and important. The lights above the ring looked harder and brighter than ever. You could not see the other side of the building; everything there was a mysterious blue haze, in which a match occasionally twinkled. 'Cher-hoc-lait' cried the white-coated youth, more hopefully. 'Fine Aipple,' retorted the opposition caterer, sticking his tray of green fruit under our noses. The announcer entered the ring, and there waited, grave, important. There was a cheer. Tom had come out, an old favourite and a Bermondsey lad. A grin lights up his broad flat face; he puts his two gloves together, holds them up to salute friends and patrons. He is attended by several enormous fellows with cauliflower ears, old hands. Another round of applause. The Frenchman is out, with Messieurs Dubois and Dupont in close attendance. 'Ler-hay-dees an' Ger-hentle-men.' Tom has cast aside his beautiful silk dressing-gown, to reveal himself as a brown, stocky little fellow in blue shorts. The Frenchman is performing those mysterious exercises with the elastic ropes that girdle the ring. He is taller and longer in the reach than Tom, but does not look so strong or so fit – a queerly-made, ugly fellow, this 'Froggy', as they quickly decide to call him. He does not look as if he will last more than a round or two.

At first Tom seems to have it all his own way. You hear the thump-pad-thud of his glove on Froggy's lean body. But Froggy does not seem to mind. Now and then that long left of his flashes out and sends Tom staggering. 'Don't take it too easy, Tom,' the crowd tells him. The other Bermondsey lads at the back are full of advice. 'Poke it out, Tom,' they cry; and then 'Turn 'im round, Tom.' And Tom is only too anxious to do all these things, but somehow the ungainly Frenchman never allows himself to be hurt. Now and then, it is true, he blinks and gives a queer little grin, all of which suggests that Tom's blows to the body have made some impression, but he comes back from his corner as fresh as ever. Indeed, somewhere about the tenth round, it stops being Tom's fight, and there is now no talk of his taking it too easy. Froggy is not only very quick with that long left of his, but he is also a crafty fellow. Every time Tom rushes in, he is stopped, and you hear the dull thump of the wet glove. And there are moments when Froggy drives Tom round the ring or bounces him against the ropes. If Tom were softer, he might easily find himself on his back, with the timekeeper's voice measuring out his doom; but Tom is very tough, an old taker of punishment. The last round sees him almost as lively as ever, but now it is Froggy's glove you hear thump-pad-thudding. The final clang – and the referee jerks a thumb towards Froggy's corner. The announcer cannot be heard above the cheers. We do not know Froggy and – to speak candidly – do not like the look of him; but he has proved himself the better man; and so we give him the best cheer of the evening. (Perhaps Froggy's friends in Paris would do the same for Tom – perhaps; it is just possible.) Tom puts his gloves together, shakes them at us, still grinning, and we give him a cheer too. Everybody is good-humoured.

There were more to come, but a great many people were drifting out, now that the great event was over, and I followed them. The Blackfriars Road looked exactly as it had done when I hurried out of it earlier in the evening, a black misery, but the thought of the good-humour I had left behind me kept me warm. When the old Ring is transformed into a gigantic boxing arena, where really big purses are won and lost in a few minutes under glaring film-studio lights, I hope it will keep its good humour. I hope it will, but I have my doubts.

Billiards at Thurston's

BEYOND the voices of Leicester Square there is peace. It is in Thurston's Billiards Hall, which I visited for the first time, the other afternoon, to see the final in the Professional Championship. Let me put it on record that for one hour and a half, that afternoon, I was happy. If Mr Thurston ever wants a testimonial for his Billiards Hall, he can have one from me. The moment I entered the place I felt I was about to enjoy myself. It is small, snug, companionable. Four or five rows of plush chairs look down on the great table, above which is a noble shaded light, the shade itself being russet coloured. Autumn to the cloth's bright Spring. Most of the chairs were filled with comfortable men, smoking pipes. I noticed a couple of women among the spectators, but they looked entirely out of place, just as they would have done among the fat leather chairs of a West End club. I had just time to settle down in my seat, fill and light a pipe myself, before the match began.

It was between Davis and Newman, both of whom have held the championship. They suddenly appeared, in their shirt sleeves and holding cues, and we gave them a friendly round of applause, which they acknowledged with something between a bow and a nod. The marker arrived too. He deserves a word to himself. He was an essential part of the afternoon, not merely because he kept the score and called it out, but because he created an atmosphere. He was a young man, whose profile was rather like that of the Mad Hatter; his face was all nose, teeth, and glittering eye; and he had an ecclesiastical dignity and gravity of manner. He handed over the rest or the half-butt like one serving at an altar. To see him place the red on the spot was to realize at once the greatness of the occasion. Best of all was to watch him removing, with his white-gloved hands, specks of dust or films of moisture from a ball. The voice in which he called out the scores was the most impersonal I have ever heard. It was a voice that belonged to solemn ritual, and it did as much as the four walls and the thickly curtained windows to withdraw us from ordinary life and Leicester Square. And withdrawn we certainly were. After a few minutes the world of daylight and buses and three o'clock winners receded, faded, vanished. I felt as if we were all sitting at ease somewhere at the bottom of the Pacific.

Davis had a broad face and wore a brown suit. Newman had a long narrow face and wore a black waistcoat and striped trousers. Davis was the more stolid and cheerful. Newman suggested temperament. Apart from these details, I could discover no difference between them. They were both demigods. In the great world outside, I can imagine that one might pass them by as fellows of no particular importance, just pleasant, clean, neat men with north-country accents. But in this tiny world of bright-green cloth and white and crimson spheres, they were demi-gods. After the first few minutes I began to regard them with an awe that has no place in my attitude towards any living writer. If one of them had spoken to me (and Newman did speak to the man on my left, who was evidently something of a connoisseur and made all manner of knowing noises), I should have blushed and stammered and nearly choked with pride and pleasure. No modern writer could make me feel like that, simply because no modern writer is great enough. It would have to be Shakespeare; and when you are in this remote little world of billiards, players like Messrs Davis and Newman are Shakespeares: they are as good as that. They have the same trick too: they make it look easy. Watching them, you have to use your imagination like blazes to realize you could not do it all yourself.

I do not know whether I have any right to describe myself as a player, but I have played billiards many a time. If I am staying under the same roof with a billiard table, I nearly always play on it, but on the other hand, I never go out looking for billiard tables on which to play. Public billiard rooms are dreary places, even if you find the game itself fascinating, as I do. Moreover, they are too public for my taste. Once you have a cue in your hand in those places, it appears that everybody who happens to be there has the privilege of advising you. Strangers say, quite angrily: 'Oh, you ought to have gone in off the red there!' Then when you try something else: 'No, no, no! The white's the game. That's it. Only put plenty of side on. Oh no, too hard!' And they make little clucking noises and laugh softly behind your back, until at last you bungle every shot. This does not seem to happen in any other game but billiards. If you play bridge in a public room, strangers do not stand behind you and point authoritatively to your Queen of Spades or King of Diamonds. Nobody makes remonstrative noises at you when you are playing chess. But billiards is anybody's and everybody's game. The adventures of those three shining spheres, as they chase one another over the green cloth, are public property, and the moment you have grasped a cue, you yourself are a public character whose actions can be criticized with freedom. And as I happen to be a very poor performer, I prefer to play in private, almost behind locked doors.

The shortest way of describing the skill of Messrs Davis and Newman is to say that it appeared miraculous when they ever missed anything. Now when my friends and I have played the game, it has always seemed miraculous if anything happened but a miss. The balls always seemed so small, the pockets so narrow, the table so hopelessly long and wide. These professional champions, however, treated every shot as if it were a little sum in simple arithmetic. While they went on calmly potting the red, bringing it back nearer to the white every time, and then collecting cannons by the dozen, we all leaned back and sucked our pipes almost somnolently, secure and happy in a drowsy peace of mechanics and art. It was when they chanced to fail that we were startled into close attention. You could hear a gasp all round you. If the marker had suddenly broken into song, we could hardly have been more astonished. The only persons who never showed any signs of surprise were the two players – and of course the marker. If Davis, after going half way round the table with an amazing number of delicious little cannons, all as good as epigrams, finally missed a shot, Newman quite nonchalantly came forward to make the balls do what he thought they ought to do, for half an hour or so. And the things they did were incredible. He could make them curve round, stop dead, or run backward. But if Newman went on doing this for three-quarters of an hour, quietly piling up an immense score, Davis sitting at ease, nursing his cue, showed no anxiety, no eagerness to return to the table. His turn would come. I tell you, these were demi-gods.

The hall was filled with connoisseurs, men who knew a pretty bit of 'side' or 'top' when they saw it, smacked their lips over a nice follow through, and heard sweet music in the soft click-click of the little cannons, and when a stroke of more than usual wizardry was played, they broke into applause. Did this disturb either of the players? It did not. They never even looked up, never smiled, never blinked an eyelid. Perhaps they had forgotten we were there, having lost all remembrance of us in following the epic adventures of the two whites and the red. Of all games, billiards must be the worst to play when you are feeling nervous. The least tremor and you are done. These two players had every reason to feel nervous, for they were beginning a championship match, but they showed no trace of feeling, not a quiver. And when we clapped them at the end of long breaks, they merely gave us a slight nod. 'Ah, so you're there, are you?' these nods seemed to say. I felt awed before such greatness. These men could do one thing better than anybody else could do it. They were masters. Their world was a small one, bounded by the shaded electric lights and the stretch of green light, but in that world they were supreme conquerors.

To play billiards every afternoon and evening, year in and year out, might seem monotonous, yet I think they must lead satisfying lives. What they can do, they can do, beyond any possible shadow of doubt. They hit the red and it vanishes into a pocket. They have not to convince themselves that they have hit it and that it has probably gone into a pocket, as we have to do in our affairs. What can I do? What can you do? We think this, we imagine that, and we are never sure. These great cuemen are as sure as human beings can be. I envy them, but my envy is not so sharp that it robs me of all pleasure in their skill. When I am actually in their presence, looking down on the table of their triumph, my envy is lost in admiration and delight. When the world is wrong, hardly to be endured, I shall return to Thurston's Hall and there smoke a pipe among the connoisseurs of top and side. It is as near to the Isle of Innisfree as we can get within a hundred leagues of Leicester Square.

Fiction Made Easy

THE Gagnon Company, of Los Angeles, has just produced the Plot Genie. This is – in its own words – 'designed to serve the purpose of giving the writer or author a definite and arbitrary assignment of a number of elements comprising a plot outline which challenges the creative imagination and stimulates it to definite action by charting a course for it to pursue.' I cannot help feeling that the Gagnon boys are a bit turgid there, but there is no doubt that their Plot Genie is going to make a big difference to us writers or authors.

This is how it works. You are given the nine elements that make up 'The Perfect Story Plot Formula'. You are also given a gadget that is called, grandly, 'The Plot Robot', but that is nothing more than three pieces of cardboard glued together. The one in the middle is a revolving round piece on which hundreds of numbers are printed, and one of these numbers can be seen through a little opening in the front piece of cardboard. You are also given an Index, which contains long numbered lists of localities, heroes, heroines, and problems. You revolve the numbers, note the result, then look it up in the Index. When you have done this nine times, you have in your possession all the necessary elements of the Perfect Story Plot Formula, and all you have to do is to make some sense out of them and write your story, play or film.

Let us have a go. We will make it a short story if we can. The first element is *Background or Locale*. I revolve the numbers and am presented with No. 35. No. 35 is, it seems, a Canyon. Good! The background of our story is to be a canyon. We will make it the Grand Canyon and show how we can write rich descriptive prose. And now for a hero. There are two lists: Usual and Unusual; and naturally we prefer Unusual. We get No. 45, and find ourselves landed with a shipwright. This is bad, but it might be worse, for No. 9 is a gondolier, 34 a fugleman, and 147 a galley-slave. Here then we have our shipwright, the only one left in the Grand Canyon, the last of the old breed. Who is to be his lady? And shall we take the Usual or the Unusual list? Better take the usual this time, or we may find ourselves saddled with a Nautch Girl, a Martian, or a Duenna. The Usual then, and the number is 142. Who is 142, and what is she, that all our swains adore her? She is a Ventriloquist's Daughter. I feel that the Usual has played us false.

So far, then, we have a Ventriloquist's Daughter meeting a Shipwright in the Grand Canyon. Already our creative imagination is at work on them, but it need not work very hard yet, for we are to be provided with six more elements for our plot. The next is the Problem, and, for good or ill, the Problem is No. 149. This is not going to be too easy, for 149 is *A religious uprising is threatened by enemies*. Difficult, but not impossible: for example, a fanatical sect has made its headquarters in the Grand Canyon, and its members consider that shipbuilding there is contrary to Biblical instruction. 'Down with the Man of Sin!' I hear them cry, their beards bristling. They could attack him, and then he could be saved at the last minute by the Ventriloquist's Daughter throwing her voice in the beard of the chief prophet. Something like that. Anyhow a beginning. The creative imagination is at work.

But now, whether we like it or not, we must have a Love Obstacle. These two are not only to be faced with a threatened religious uprising, but there must be an obstacle too. It is 128. Hurry up and turn to the list of Obstacles To Love. Well, it might have been worse: *There is an imaginary difference in their ages.* I do not propose to worry much about that. The shipwright is pretending to be his own grandfather ('Clipper' Johnson, late of Cape Cod), and wears a wig and a colossal false white beard. The Ventriloquist's Daughter would not have looked at him twice had there not been *something strange* about the old man's eyes, which reminded her, in their boldness, of one of her father's favourite dummies. The shipwright will not pluck off his wig and beard until after she has rescued him from the religious fanatics. A good scene that, and it almost writes itself. The sun will be setting too, and we shall be able to do the Grand Canyon proud.

This is a story, however, not a mere anecdote, and there must also be a Complication. (Yes, you could do without one, and so could I, but it is in the formula.) We have given ourselves No. 31. Here are the complications, one hundred and eighty of them. I do not consider No. 31 too bad. It is *Deception threatens loss of reward.* You see the possibilities here? A large prize has been offered for the best 150-ton schooner built this year by any man *under seventy.* (The italics, you will be amused to learn, are mine. I have others too.) Undoubtedly the best schooner is 'Clipper' Johnson's, from Grand Canyon, but then 'Clipper' is ninety if he's a day. It ought to be possible, too, to work in a little more ventriloquism into this schooner prize complication. This is going to be a corking short story, absolutely corking.

I do think, however, that having jammed us into a Complication, they might have left out the Predicament. This Story Plot Formula is a shade too perfect for my taste. We do not revolve the numbers with quite our old enthusiasm. We have arrived at 57. (And do not imagine that this is the last one; there are more than fifty-seven varieties of predicaments.) No. 57 is *Threatened with banishment by a tyrant ruler.* This is not going to be helpful. It is the girl's turn, and we shall have to make her an Italian. (This may mean moving the Grand Canyon into Italy.) Or, again, she may be an immigrant who has not come into the United States on the quota. The immigration officers are on her track. Five of them may be seen, even now, slowly descending the winding road into the

Canyon. Good! Let us leave it at that. She can get out of it all, if necessary, by ventriloquism, or by pulling strings, which is a branch of the ventriloquial art.

Even those of you who are now fainting by the wayside can hardly object to a Crisis. A story must have a crisis. This one has No. 115, and a brute it is too. For the first time I feel tempted to cheat and try another number. *About to permit an unrecognized daughter to commit suicide.* This, you must admit, makes it another story. I had seen our heroine as a mere slip of a girl, our hero a stalwart young man beneath his disguise. We shall have to put about fifteen years on one of them. And then the daughter – poor suicidal creature – will have to be brought in. She could, of course, be one of the religious fanatics, or, for that matter, one of the prize schooner judges, or a female immigration officer. I think I prefer the last. And she shall be the shipwright's child, who has been brought up on Ellis Island, a curious melancholy girl.

That brings us to the very last of our elements, the Climax. I notice that the Index calls its list 'Climaxes or Surprise Twists'. I do not like that Surprise Twist. There have been too many already in this narrative. We must hope for a good number. No, this time I propose to cheat. One number is not enough, I shall take three and then choose between them. My first is 33, and that is *wherein it develops that confusion has been caused by the presence of twins or triplets.* Well, we could use it at a pinch. Indeed, we could fill the Grand Canyon with triplets. The next number is 9: *Wherein a witness proves to be mad or deranged.* But why a mere witness? Let them all be mad. I always suspected that shipwright. But we will have one more throw and then we have done. Here is the last of the numbers. It is 164, and the Index says firmly that 164 is *In which an immortal comes to the rescue of the hero.* That will do. We wanted a surprise twist and we have got it. Has anybody written a story in which Poseidon makes his appearance in the Grand Canyon? I doubt it. And in any event, I am sure that there has never been a story in which Poseidon appears in the Grand Canyon to rescue a shipwright, his child, and his beloved daughter of a ventriloquist from the combined menace of religious fanatics, judges of schooner competitions, and immigration officials. That should be a big finish. If the film rights are not worth a lot of money, then Hollywood has lost all enterprise.

Birmingham Whist Drive

THE hall was large, austere in colouring and decoration, and lighted in the most uncompromising fashion by unshaded bulbs of high voltage. It had about as much intimate charm as the average big railway station. I guessed at once that we were in for a formidably business-like evening. Suspended from the ceiling, about a third of the way down the room, was a large indicator, showing the four suits. The remaining two-thirds of the hall, beyond this indicator, were filled with very small chairs ranged round very small tables, most of them not proper card tables but mysterious objects covered with what seemed then, and afterwards, squares of rather dirty blanket material. When you paid your two shillings, you were given a scoring card, either black or red. (Mine was black.) On this card were the rules, the number of your first table, and then spaces for the numbers of your succeeding tables, the tricks you made, and your totals. There were several hundred people there, and most of them seemed to be regular patrons and to know one another. They were mostly middle-aged decent working folk, with only a sprinkling of younger men and women. Nearly all the men smoked, and a fair proportion of the women; but there were no ash-trays. I knocked my pipe out on my heel. What the cigarette smokers did, I do not know. After about ten minutes, a man shouted at us through a megaphone and we all went to our tables. The indicator told us what were trumps by lighting up a gigantic ace of clubs. We started. There followed what seemed to me one of the most strenuous hours I have ever spent. To begin with, the games were played at a tremendous speed, aces being banged on kings without a moment's hesitation. Then there was so much to do. You had to fill in your card and to initial the card on each table. If you were the losing man arriving at a new table – and I nearly always was – you had to shuffle the cards before the cut for deal. And three times out of four it seemed to be my fate to deal, and as the packs at each successive table appeared to be older and older and greasier and greasier, so that they were about four inches thick when they were stacked ready to be cut, dealing was an unpleasant business. Never in my life, not even in the trenches, have I ever seen dirtier and older packs of cards. It was not pleasant to hold them, even when they showed you a smudge of aces and kings; and it was a downright penance to be continually shuffling and dealing them. So what with shuffling, cutting, dealing, playing, gathering tricks up on those bits of blanket, clerkly work with the table card and your own card, changing tables, pushing past enormous fat women, I was kept so busy that after about half an hour of it I was fairly perspiring. And there was never a minute to lose. The whistle blew, as a signal to change tables, the indicator lit up its new suit of trumps, and if you had not finished your game, there were people waiting and looking very cross about it. There was practically no time for conversation, hardly time to smile. What conversation there was about the game, if for once it finished before the whistle blew, I could not understand. Three times my various partners said to me, 'I'd a good back hand,' and I could only assent feebly, for I did not know then and do not know now what a good back hand is. As I have not played whist, which is a very different game from bridge, for twenty years, and as all these games were run off at such a colossal speed, I cannot tell you whether these people played well or badly. I suspect that most of it must have been very perfunctory play, with no nonsense about finessing in it. All my partners were either very big fat women, who bulged over their chairs and the tables, and sweated good-humouredly, or else little witch-like females with sharp noses, tucked-in mouths, and iron spectacles, who held their cards very close to the brooches they wore, hardly ever spoke, and looked very cross, though I do not actually think they were. There were two distinct types among the men: the solid hearty chaps who sat bolt upright, puffing out clouds of smoke and banged each card down, as if sheer force might win the trick; and the little thin cunning fellows who sank down and down and half-closed their eyes as they played, like so many Nibelungs. When the whistle blew after the twelfth game, everybody made a rush for the top end of the hall, and reappeared a few minutes afterwards, eating fruits, tarts, and slabs of cake.

This was the interval, and by this time I had had quite enough whist-driving, but it seemed to me that if one player disappeared the whole elaborate organization would be flung into disorder. So I stayed on and played another twelve games, nearly always losing and so going from table to table and shuffling packs of cards greasier than any I had ever seen before, cards that ought to have been thrown into the dustbin months ago; and I found myself in a far corner where the tables were almost touching one another and enormous women were unable to extricate themselves, and it was sweatier and hotter and smokier than ever. My total score was one hundred and fifty-five, which was some thirty or forty below the best. But there was still a chance that I might win a prize for a 'mystery number', which was drawn by the promoter, after he had given the prizes for the winning scores. There was no excitement at the end, no cheering, no applause. It was all as brisk and business-like as the whole evening had been. When the last prize had been awarded, everybody cleared off, rather as if they were leaving a factory than making an end of a night's pleasure. I suppose they enjoyed it – which was more than I did – otherwise they would not regularly attend these functions, as they undoubtedly do, but anything superficially less like a night's pleasure I never did see.

'Throwing' at Wedgwoods

Now I put on a suit of overalls. So much wet clay had dried on them that they were as stiff and thick as armour. I climbed on to the little high seat, and then tried revolving the 'wheel'. I found the foot pedal hard to regulate and very uncomfortable. They gave me a good lump of clay and I set it whirling and tried to 'centre' it. At first I did not press hard enough, and then I pressed too hard, with the result that the clay shot up into a frightening lop-sided tower and wobbled desperately between my hands. It took me some time to make any kind of reasonable shot at 'centring'. After that I began to try and make things. But my vases had a nasty trick of growing very tall, then very wide at the mouth, and then of releasing most of themselves from the bondage of the wheel altogether. Often, in my excitement, I would forget that my right foot was supposed to be controlling the speed, and, grappling manfully with the clay, I would let my foot press down, with the inevitable result that the speed increased enormously, the clay went round too fast and could not be manipulated, indeed, could not be kept in any kind of order at all and would reach up and try to strangle me or would fling a long strand of itself at a couple of grinning lads five yards away. I decided to experiment with bowls instead of vases, for as soon as the clay was more than about six inches tall it could not be controlled by me. At first the bowls seemed much easier, but time after time something went wrong. The rims would become too thin; or there would be air-bubbles in the clay; or when I tried to shape the outside, towards the bottom, I would press too hard and the whole wretched bowl would begin rising in the air. I was a great success as an entertainer if not as a potter, for all the other folk roared with laughter. I spent almost the whole afternoon wrestling with innumerable lumps of clay. My hands were lost in the greyish wet stuff, and it was all over my face and in my hair. The foot that was more or less on terms with that pedal developed very early a cramp that soon took possession of my entire right leg. But I was determined to make something that afternoon, even if I had long ago abandoned all idea of noble vases and had shrunk to considering, even wistfully, any sort of little ashtray that would stand up at all. I managed it in the end too: a sturdy little bowl that you could use for sugar or sweets or as an ashtray; not one of these inhumanly symmetrical and smoothly finished things, but a bit knobbly and rough, one of your genuine hand-made articles. They promised, almost with tears in their eyes, to be kind to this little chap, to fire him and glaze him and then pack him carefully in straw and wood and send him to me. He has not turned up here yet; though that black basalt fellow I decorated (in my opinion, an inferior production) has been here some time. If Wedgwoods have lost or destroyed it or, in their jealous rage, have locked it away in the safe, I warn them that I shall return to the Potteries and 'throw' again, 'throw' like mad. I have half a mind to install a wheel here – and one more easily controlled than theirs – and have clay sent down by the ton, so that I can tackle this vase-and-bowl problem again at my leisure. One thing is certain, that the guide was right when he said there was life in clay. Set it spinning and there is far too much life in it. You feel it fluttering and straining between your hands like a captured wild thing. Oh – with a little pressure of the palm there, a flick of the thumbs here, to be able to make it flower into every imaginable shape! William de Morgan, after being a potter most of his life, took to writing novels at the end of it. If I had more confidence in my thumbs, I would reverse the process.

Reading Detective Stories in Bed

I FIND this delightful at home, and even more delightful when I am away from home, a lost man. The fuss of the day is done with; you are snugly installed in bed, in a little lighted place of your own; and now to make the mind as cosy as the body! But why detective stories? Why not some good literature? Because, with a few happy exceptions – and there are far too few of them – good literature, which challenges and excites the mind, will not do. In my view, it should be read away from the bedroom. But why not some dull solemn stuff, portentous memoirs, faded works of travel, soporifics bound in calf? Here I can speak only for myself. But if my bed book is too dull then I begin to think about my own work and then sleep is banished for hours. No, the detective story is the thing, and its own peculiar virtues have not been sufficiently appreciated. The worst attempt I ever heard the Brains Trust make was at a question concerning the popularity of detective stories. The wise men woffled on about violence and crime, missing the point by miles. (But then a man who enjoyed his detective stories at night would not bother being on the Brains Trust.) We enthusiasts are not fascinated by violence or the crime element in these narratives. Often, like myself, we deplore the blood-and-bones atmosphere and wish the detective novelists were not so conventional about offering us murder all the time. (A superb detective story could be written – and I have half a mind to write it – about people who were not involved in any form of crime. About disappearance or a double life, for example.) Please remember that most serious fiction now has ceased to appeal to our taste for narrative. The novelist may be a social critic, a philosopher, a poet, or a madman, but he is no longer primarily a story-teller. And there are times when we do not want anybody's social criticism or deep psychological insight or prose poetry or vision of the world: we want a narrative, an artfully contrived tale. But not any kind of tale, no fragrant romances and the like. What we want – or at least what *I* want, late at night; you can please yourself – is a tale that is in its own way a picture of life but yet has an entertaining puzzle element in it. And this the detective story offers me. It is of course highly conventional and stylized – think of all those final meetings in the library, or those little dinners in Soho (with about six pounds worth of wine) paid for out of a Scotland Yard salary

– but its limitations are part of its charm. It opposes to the vast mournful muddle of the real world its own tidy problem and neat solution. As thoughtful citizens we are hemmed in now by gigantic problems that appear as insoluble as they are menacing, so how pleasant it is to take an hour or two off to consider only the problem of the body that locked itself in its study and then used the telephone. (*We know now that Sir Rufus must have died not later than ten o'clock, and yet we know too that he apparently telephoned to Lady Bridget at ten-forty-five – eh, Travers?*) This is easy and sensible compared with the problem of remaining a sane citizen in the middle of the twentieth century. After the newspaper headlines, it is refreshing to enter this well-ordered microcosm, like finding one's way into a garden after wandering for days in a jungle. I like to approach sleep by way of these neat simplifications, most of them as soundly ethical as Socrates himself. It is true that I may burn my bedlight too long, just because I must know how the dead Sir Robert managed to telephone; yet, one problem having been settled for me, I feel I sleep all the sounder for this hour or two's indulgence. And what a delight it is to switch off the day's long chaos, stretch legs that have begun to ache a little, turn on the right side, and then once more find the eccentric private detective moodily playing his violin or tending his orchids, or discover again the grumpy inspector doodling in his office, and know that a still more astonishing puzzle is on its way to him and to me!

Trying New Blends of Tobacco

I HAVE been smoking steadily ever since 1910 (beginning with Cut Cavendish at 3½d. an ounce); and to this day, if my eye is caught by an unfamiliar package on a tobacconist's shelf, I will try a new blend. I may not smoke it with delight, especially nowadays when good new blends are hard to find and many of the old mixtures are not what they once were, but I enjoy the little adventure. There is a certain pious conservatism in this occasional fickleness toward tried favourites. I am preserving the 1910 spirit in smoking; for in those days tobacco was not sold by young women lost in the myths of Hollywood but by solid middle-aged men, pickled in nicotine themselves, who would pull down their canisters of Old Virginia, Perique or Latakia, mix you something new on the spot if necessary, and lived with you in a community of palates. (It was economy that took me first to Cut Cavendish, for these fellows, if you gave them their head, might run you up to 5d. or even 6d. an ounce.) There were tobacconists in those days. Most of them, with much else of value, seemed to disappear during the First World War, their place being taken by bored pushers of packages across counters. There arrived too a vast new horde of unadventurous and ignorant smokers, mere creatures of habit, born to raise the dividends of tobacco combines and cartels. These robots would start with Somebody's Navy Cut and are puffing away at it to this day, hardly knowing that other tobaccos exist. Notice how in pre-1914 literature – for example, in the entrancing fables of W. W. Jacobs (and what delight *he* has given me!) – sensible fellows toss pouches to each other and say 'Try a pipeful of this.' And who talks about tobacco now? The country is crowded with men who pay their four-and-something an ounce and yet could not sustain five minutes talk on tobacco. But I go forward, occasionally pointing a finger at a tin or packet I have never noticed before, in the 1910 tradition. And now I must have smoked everything combustible in a pipe, including coltsfoot and various weird herbal mixtures, belonging to the ritual of nature religions rather than to the honest pleasure of smoking. This means of course that I have set fire and puffed away at a good deal of muck. There have been times when decent pipes of mine appear to have been drenched in cheap scent. I remember occasions when you would have thought I had acquired a packet of gunpowder, there was so much sizzling and sparking, so many sulphurous fumes. I have smoked 'carefully blended' mixtures that tasted like a hayrick on fire. I have opened tins packed by malevolent wizards, whose spells within half an hour conjured what I took to be tobacco into quarter of a pound of dust. But I regret nothing. I have summoned Europe, America, Africa and Asia to fill my pipe. At my age naturally I have my steady favourites – and, without stopping to advertise, let me say that I like to alternate between an honest Virginia and a full rich mixture, heavy with Latakia – but even now I still follow the gleam. 'What's that up there? *Boynton's Benediction.* Well, I'll try it.'

Music at Home

CHAMBER music at home is delightful. Not for everybody of course; mere listeners, passive guest types, may have a hell of a time with it. (Let them go somewhere else and switch on their Third Programme.) No, this kind of music is delightful for actual performers, and for those who are loitering round the edge of performance, waiting to be asked to join in, and for those women – and a few wise men – who enjoy seeing the persons dear to them happy, let the notes fall where they may. There has always been to me a sort of cosy magic about it. (In *Bright Day* I made a musical family a symbol of magical attraction.) You are at home, all safe and snug, and yet are also wandering in spirit, through lost kingdoms, with the music. Even the best string quartets and trios will not always survive the atmosphere, chilly with determined culture, of those horrible little concert halls given up to chamber music. There is too a concert solemnity, as German as liver sausage, that blights many of the sauciest trifles. (We forget that a lot of music has been written *for fun.*) What a difference when you bring in firelight, armchairs, tobacco, and a tray of drinks! The execution – as it often is with us – may be sketchy and even downright murderous, but you can catch the mood of the masters, whether they are looking for the Holy Grail or a pint of wine and a helping of roast goose. (I fancy, though, that the late Beethoven quartets ought to be left out of the home programme.) You wish you could do it better, but you are delighted to be doing it at all. When, for example, Mary (violin) and her friend Joan ('cello) and I (piano more or less) gave up most of a recent week-end to our struggle with the Smetana trio, I doubt if in any but the slowest passages I was hitting more than half the proper notes in the treble or a third of those in the bass; but the girls, aloft on their professional standard, enjoyed it, and as for me, floundering and grunting and sweating, I would not have missed a minute of it for a hundred pounds. Bestriding the hacked corpse of poor Smetana, I drank the milk of paradise. We had no audience, and needed none, but went off, morning and night, into the Bohemian blue together. But I need not perform myself, nor be in my own home, to know this delight. As I write this, many rooms come flickering back, in Bradford and Cambridge, a Lakeland cottage, a studio in Chelsea, half-forgotten mysterious apartments abroad; and firelight and candlelight play tenderly among the instruments; and Mozart and Haydn, Brahms and Debussy, move among us again; and within the ring of friendly faces, ghosts these many years, the little worlds of sound shine and revolve like enchanted moons. Why – bless our bewildered souls! – every time a violin is taken up to the lumber room, a piano is carted away, and in their place is a gadget that turns music on and off like tap water, we move another step away from sanity and take to snarling harder than ever.

My Lawn Tennis

FOOTBALL and cricket were the chief games of my youth, and I never started playing lawn tennis until I was past thirty. The result has been that, having no secure foundation of style, my tennis is erratic. People are always asking me about moods and inspiration in my work. But it is in my tennis that I am a creature of moods and inspiration. Try me one day and I am a rabbit. Try me another day and I am a tiger – not a tiger burning bright but a tiger of sorts. If a public opinion poll were taken on my tennis, the returns would be chaotic. I never know myself whether I shall look like Tilden or tushery. My partners are nearly always surprised, one way or the other. In my time I have slammed across services, smashes, volleys that rocked Wimbledon players, and have been carelessly slaughtered by schoolgirls. Certainly I am not a good tennis player, but on my day I might be fairly described as one of the best bad players in the world. It is on these days, which always come straight out of the blue and cannot be prepared for (so I am no tournament man), that the game yields delight. The ball suddenly becomes twice its usual size, and the opposite side of the court obligingly enlarges itself too. The racket strings hum some faint tune of victory. Time stretches out to allow easy preparation for every shot, but once the balls have crossed the net, by some friendly device of relativity, slow time changes to fast. And – at last – miraculous half-volleys come off. On such afternoons, when the very sunlight has a different quality, all winds fade away, and my trousers keep up, the game takes on a large Homeric air; all thought of the insane world beyond the court hastens out of the mind; and we are at battle and at play, immortal beings, in the Maytime of a favoured planet. 'Sorry, partner!' Yes, I have muttered it ten thousand times, while seeing the green or red ground open into a chasm of disgust and self-contempt. But on my day, when in the mood, when inspiration descends upon me and my racket – what delight!

Quietly Malicious Chairmanship

THERE is no sound excuse for this. It is deeply anti-social, and a sudden excess of it would tear great holes in our communal life. But a man can be asked once too often to act as chairman, and to such a man, despairing of his weakness and feeling a thousand miles from any delight, I can suggest a few devices. In introducing one or two of the chief speakers, grossly overpraise them but put no warmth into your voice, only a metallic flavour of irony. If you know what a speaker's main point is to be, then make it neatly in presenting him to the audience. During some tremendous peroration, which the chap has been working at for days, either begin whispering and passing notes to other speakers or give the appearance of falling asleep in spite of much effort to keep awake. If the funny man takes possession of the meeting and brings out the old jokes, either look melancholy or raise your eyebrows as high as they will go. Announce the fellow with the weak delivery in your loudest and clearest tones. For any timid speaker, officiously clear a space bang in the middle and offer him water, paper, pencil, a watch, anything. With noisy cheeky chaps on their feet, bustle about the platform, and if necessary give a mysterious little note to some member of the audience. If a man insists upon speaking from the floor of the hall, ask him for his name, pretend to be rather deaf, and then finally announce his name with a marked air of surprise. After that you can have some trouble with a cigarette lighter and then take it to pieces. When they all go on and on, make no further pretence of paying any attention and settle down to drawing outrageous caricatures of the others on the platform, and then at last ask some man you particularly dislike to take over the chair, and stalk out, being careful to leave all your papers behind. And if all this fails to bring you any delight, it should at least help to protect you against further bouts of chairmanship.

PEEPSHOWS

The Berkshire Beasts - a Dream

I FOUND myself walking through a large park with an old family friend, let us call her Miss Tweedletop, a somewhat characterless, colourless lady whom I had not even seen for years. Such persons have a habit of popping up in dreams years after we have apparently ceased to give them even a passing thought. They travel, by what devious ways we cannot imagine, into our subconscious minds, look around them bravely and then, shaking the mud off their shoes and taking a deep breath, they somehow contrive to jump up into our dreams. Miss Tweedletop and I, then, were walking through this park, and I knew somehow that we were really one unit of a fairly large party of friends who had all come out for a day's pleasure and sightseeing. How I knew this I do not know, because the dream seemed to begin at the point when we had either lagged behind or out-distanced the main body, which I never saw at all. All my dreams appear to be tiny instalments of an enormous *feuilleton*: I never know the beginning or the end, although I am one of the chief actors, and also, they tell me, the dramatist, producer, and scene-shifter. But I always know a little of what has gone before; I give myself, as it were, a hint of the situation before I set myself on the stage; and on this occasion I knew that we were both members of a sightseeing party.

We were strolling down a sort of carriage drive that swept forward, as such things usually do if there is space for it, in a vast curve. The place was not unlike Richmond Park but rather more trim and well-ordered, perhaps the private park of some duke or other. We had walked slowly forward for some time, slowly because Miss Tweedletop is (or was) an elderly woman; and had been idly talking of this and that, when suddenly I saw, only a little way in front, a most curious group, a herd of the most unlikely creatures. They were of various sizes, but the largest would be easily twice the size of the full-grown elephant. They were not unlike elephants in appearance, except that they tapered more noticeably from head (their heads were enormous) to tail, and though they had the same huge flopping ears, they had no trunks. I am no lion tamer and I confess to being nervous in the presence of all strange animals, but I think that even a lion tamer or an elephant hunter might have felt rather diffident about approaching such creatures, who looked as if they had strayed out of the early chapters of the *Outline of History*. Miss Tweedletop, however, walked on even after she had noticed the astonishing brutes we were gradually approaching.

'Ah,' she exclaimed, but rather slowly, like one who makes small-talk 'there are the Berkshire Beasts.' She said it quite casually, just as people say, 'There is the County Court' or 'There is the Albert Memorial' when they are not excited about the matter themselves nor expect you to be excited about it, but are simply making talk. I could see that Miss Tweedletop thought I knew as much about the Berkshire Beasts as she and every one else did. By this time they were much closer, and I could see that they were a dark green colour and rather wrinkly and shiny, not unlike something between a cheap kind of lady's handbag and one of those foul and unnatural editions of the poets that are bought only as presents; but many thousands of times bigger than the most capacious handbag or the largest edition of Tennyson ever known. They looked bigger than ever. And then I noticed that every one of them, male or female, old or young, was wearing spectacles. Yes, spectacles, rimless spectacles of the kind affected by very intelligent, well-informed persons. They were, of course, much larger than our spectacles; indeed, I noticed that each lens of the spectacles worn by the adult monsters was about the size of an ordinary dinner plate. As the creatures turned their heads, their glasses gleamed and flashed in the sun. I did not see anything very droll in all this; I remember that I thought it a little odd at the time, but nothing more; indeed, unless I am mistaken, it appeared to me that the creatures, peering through or over their glasses at us, looked more sinister than ever.

All this I noticed, of course, during the brief interval of time when Miss Tweedletop made her remark. And then, instead of owning that I knew nothing about the Berkshire Beasts and thus giving myself the opportunity of learning something worth knowing in the natural history of dreamland, like a fool, and a cowardly fool, I allowed a bad social habit to overmaster me, and replied, equally casually, 'Ah, yes. The Berkshire Beasts.' I might have been their keeper for years; I might have spent half my lifetime tracking them down and capturing them in their native haunts (and what haunts they must have had!); I might have been the crazy oculist who had fitted them with their spectacles; so casually did I reply. But meanwhile, I had come to the conclusion that it was high time we turned back. One or two of them were moving in a leisurely but awe-inspiring fashion in our direction, and we were still walking towards them, as if they had been mere cattle or sheep and not monstrosities twenty feet high. True, their spectacles suggested that they were not ordinary monsters, that they knew something of the decencies and courtesies of life, and even hinted, as glasses always do, at a bookish pacifism, a ferocity strictly confined to polemics and debate. Why we should generally associate short sight with good nature is rather a mystery, but we do, and there is always something peculiarly revolting and unnatural about a spectacled murderer, just as there would be about a baby who was caught trying to poison its nurse.

One monster detached itself from the others, perhaps it was the leader as it was certainly one of the largest, and moved gigantically to meet us and then stood, with lowered head, looking at us over the top of its glasses, not ten yards away. I can see it yet with its incredible head, dark green wrinkled skin, its spectacles stretched across a broad flat nose that was at least eighteen inches from side to side. Now or never was the time to turn round and run for it, even though there was no cover, no hiding place, for quite a distance. But the protest died in my throat, for Miss Tweedletop never turned a hair but strolled on with no more concern than she would have had in passing a tobacconist's shop. She did not even seem particularly interested in the creatures; and of course if she knew them and was not afraid, there was no reason for me to fear. But I do not think it was any such piece of reasoning that led me to walk forward by her side without any protest; it was merely the fear of being laughed at by a little old maiden lady. I saw myself being squashed as a boy squashes a black beetle; in a moment or so, those astonishing spectacles would be splashed and reddened by my blood.

But nothing happened. We passed almost under the leading monster's nose and he did nothing but survey us a little sadly and sceptically. It was incredible; the rimless spectacles had won. Perhaps that is why the creatures were made to wear them; before, when they were merely ordinary monsters without glasses, they were probably the most ferocious and dangerous creatures in the world, but now, simply with the addition of these contrivances of glass and wire, they were more gentle than most of our fellow humans. Probably the females were learning to knit monstrously, and the males were cultivating philosophical interests and debated among themselves as to the Knower and the Known. But as to that, I shall never be sure. Something, however, I did learn, for Miss Tweedletop made two more remarks before she tripped back into the lumber-room of my uncared for memories. 'You know,' she said as casually as ever, 'they're only kept now for their singing.'

If she was as casual, I was as foolish as before, for instead of boldly pressing for an explanation after admitting my ignorance, I still concealed it and remarked: 'Really? Only for their singing?' No doubt I thought that, later, perhaps when we had joined the others, by putting a question here and there I could learn all I wanted without confessing my ignorance. If so, I was sadly disappointed, and was rightly served for my foolishness. Miss Tweedletop seemed faintly indignant, as if the tone of my reply cast a shade of doubt upon the ability of the beasts. 'Yes,' she said, rather reproachfully, 'but they sing so beautifully.' And then not a word more, for suddenly she and the monsters and the park and the bright summer day were all huddled away into the playbox of the night and I found my nose sniffing at the cold morning, and myself farther from that park than I am from Sirius. Somewhere in the limbo of dreams, there is a park in which, perhaps, the Berkshire Beasts, like the morning stars, are singing together, singing so beautifully.

Public Dinners

If you go to eat and drink, you are taken in. This is one of the most curious conundrums of the public dinner. Why does the food and drink never taste right? On paper, the dishes, the wines, look well, and in our days of innocence our mouths water over the menu. Even when the food appears on the table, it looks promising. But somehow it never achieves a flavour, except that of warm cardboard or damp wool. Something devilish happens between the kitchen and the table at a public dinner. There are malicious Jinns present. Go to the same hotel with a friend or two, and the identical menu will yield half a dozen delectable courses. It is the same with the wines. An old brown sherry, a Liebfraumilch, some dry champagne, port or liqueur brandy, all these will be reduced at a public dinner to one sweetish liquid of various colours. It is as if they had all come out of a conjurer's trick kettle. And I imagine that the palate promptly informs the stomach that these deceptions are being practised. Hence the resentment inside, that hot reddish feeling that all we public diners know only too well.

It would be charitable to assume that the waiters are aware

of this shameful wizardry. This would explain their gloom at such functions. They are not the men we see at ordinary times. They wear a conscripted look. If their style of serving is mistaken for that of waitresses in popular tea-shops, obviously they do not care. Their tender solicitude for the belly has given place to an air of indifference that only masks a grave misgiving. 'If you do not like zees stuff, sare,' their abrupt gestures are proclaiming, 'don't blame me. You vould come.' The head waiters smile and smile, but no longer with the flawless confidence of their kind. When you see them washing their hands in invisible soap-and-water before the chairman or secretary, you may be sure the action is really symbolic. They, too, know that before the hour-hand has gone round, they will be surrounded by a hundred hot reddish feelings inside, and though a little bicarbonate would cure them of this deed, they dare not insinuate it on to the tables.

Who, I repeat, enjoys these functions? Not the diners; not the chairman, the committee, the guests of honour. The men who have to speak are miserable because now that they are actually here, they are convinced that those little humorous remarks about the Society or whatever it is will not be appreciated, and that the concluding peroration in a nobler strain than most after-dinner speeches will never do for this audience. 'Now I mustn't talk to you too much,' the ladies at their elbows are saying, 'because, of course, you are thinking about your speech. I'm sure it will be awfully good.' These observations, though doubtless well-meant, only deepen their misery. By the time the speakers who come first have pointed out, with what seems the very salt of malice, that everybody present has a right to expect something unusually wise and witty from the speakers who will follow, these wretched gentlemen are really suffering, and ask themselves a hundred times why on earth they ever consented to make a show of themselves in front of such a stupid mob.

Those who have only to listen are in no better situation. Indeed, they are in a worse one. To make a speech is at least to do something, to act, to undertake an adventure. For the speakers the evening has a shape, rising to a peak, as it were, when they themselves rise to their feet. But for the listening guests the evening goes on and on, and they have to drag themselves across deserts of boredom. Somehow there is no escape. You cannot dismiss the speeches altogether, and meditate upon the Brazilian forests, the conquests of Gengis Khan, or the habits of wild-fowl. Your mind is claimed, held, and is then beaten continuously with heavy wooden mallets. Everybody talks too long. 'I will not take your time any longer,' says the speaker, with the simpering mock-modesty of his tribe, and for a moment your heart leaps up, but then, as ever, he goes on: 'There is, however, one – er – thing – that is, one point – I should like to make. Many years ago ...' And for another hundred miles of tractless waste, he rambles on. What makes these fellows so maddening, too, is their trick of explaining that they have been compelled by the secretary or the chairman or some other busybody to speak, and that they do so against their wish. I was at a public dinner the other week, when at least ten speakers spent ten minutes each telling us how they were dragooned into talking, and they all did it with such gusto that it was impossible to believe a word they said. And the fact that I was one of the ten does not make me an apologist for the trick.

Then again, you never know when you have come to the end. There are, we will say, six speakers down on the programme. That is bad enough, but unless you are very lucky it does not stop there. The chairman suddenly goes mad and calls for new torturers. Perhaps Mr Mumble Mumble will say a few words? We should all like to hear the views of Mr Blather Blather. And off they go again, protesting that they had not expected to be called upon, but at the same time – with the utmost effrontery – consulting a sheet of paper black with idiotic notes they have made. The guests yawn and mutter, the waiters droop, the room grows stuffier, and cigars taste hot i' the mouth, but nevertheless Mr Drone Drone has to reply to Messrs Mumble Mumble and Blather Blather, and a vote of thanks must be passed, at incredible length, by old Mr Blah Blah Blah. And outside, wide and beautiful, is the night, and slippers and books and armchairs and dressing-gowns and pipes of tobacco and whisky-and-soda that tastes like whisky-and-soda.

I have narrowed it down to one solitary person. The toast-master enjoys these dinners. He alone is happy. It is astonishing that we who suffer should pay to be there and that he, commanding, red-coated, and at his ease, should be paid for his services. 'My Lords, Ladies and Gentlemen, be pleased to charge your glasses, and pray silence for your chairman.'

How he rolls it out – the ass! Why should we endure such misery for him and his 'Pray silence'? Let him accept an invitation from the Talkies and leave us in peace. He is an anachronism – as his speech plainly shows – and if he is to be encouraged, well, let us take some cross-bow-men into our pay, too, and invite them to use us, in full evening dress, as their targets. If there were no public dinners, there would be no toast-masters, and that, I fancy, explains why we have public dinners. These are our masters and they have us on toast. The time has come when their power must be broken. Let us all attend the last public dinner, taking to it a plan of action. When the toast-master cries 'Pray silence,' let us all throw pieces of bread at him and sing comic songs.

Dissolution in Haymarket

As I was journeying on a bus down Haymarket the other day, about the lunch hour, there suddenly came crashing down upon me a mood such as I have never known before. It was as if a huge black stone had been flung into the pool of my consciousness. It all happened (as we were told it would) in the twinkling of an eye. Everything was changed. The whole cheerful pageant of the street immediately crumpled and collapsed, with all its wavering pattern of light and shade, its heartening sights and sounds, its warm humanity, its suggestion of permanence, and I was left shivering in the middle of a tragedy. Not something magnificent, you understand, with funereal guns roaring out over the battlements of Elsinore or queens with bright hair dying for love, nothing after the high Roman fashion; but a dreary tragedy of cheated fools and illusions blown to the winds, of withering and decay, dust and worms. I saw this world for a moment or so through the hollow eyes of the prophets and the great pessimists, and what I saw left me shivering with cold and sick at heart. Nor did there remain with me that cosy painted chamber of the mind into which I might retire, there to forget in comfort, for it, too, was desolated, heaped about with cold ashes and with its tattered curtains flapping in the wind. All the stir and noise and glitter seemed nothing but fast-shredding pigment on a dead face.

I might have been old Donne himself, brooding over corruption and putrefaction and the gnawing worm; and it was his words that returned to me: ' ... all our life is but a going out to the place of execution, to death.' What was the bus I was in but a greasy tumbril, and what were all of us, jogging there empty-eyed, littered with our foolish paraphernalia of newspapers, umbrellas, parcels, but a company of the doomed? There we were, so many grinning skeletons masquerading in this brief and bitter carnival as fat citizens, charwomen, bus conductors, chorus girls; idly juggling with thoughts of our destinations, the offices, restaurants, clubs, theatres that claimed us; when, in truth, we had all but one sure destination – perhaps round the next corner – the narrow grave. 'The sun is setting to thee, and that for ever.' And on the face of every one there, hurrying with me to the place of execution, I read the marks of weakness and decay, and seemed to see that untiring hand at work furrowing the brow and dimming the eyes. Everywhere was dissolution. The whole street was mouldering and rotting, hastening with all that was in it to its inevitable end. The crowds I saw through the windows seemed made up of creatures that were either gross or wasted, shuffling, bent, twisted in limb, already bleached and mangled by disease; and here and there among the crowd, in bright contrast and yet infinitely more pitiful, were the few who had youth and strength and beauty, who moved as if they thought they could live for ever – who had not yet heard, from afar, the hammering, the slow tread, the pattering of earth upon the coffin.

There was something more than the old thought, death is certain, festering in the heart of that mood. That, indeed, is a thought we are always quite willing to salute, with a mere wave of the hand, but are really very unready to entertain, except when we make its first acquaintance in childhood, when it has a trick of bringing a whole host of grimacing shadows about our bedsides. But there was something more behind that sudden tragic vision I had. There was a sense of universal dissolution, of this life as a pitiful piece of cheating, of bright promise all ruthlessly scattered. Nothing remained but the certainty of decay and death. The more you loved life, delighting in whatever it had of beauty and goodness to offer you, the more openly you bared your breast for the stroke of its dagger. I saw all of us there – my fellow passengers in the bus, the driver and the conductor, the policeman and the hawkers, the playgoers waiting at the pit door, the crowds shopping or loafing – as the victims of this great treachery, lured into worshipping a loveliness that must fade and pass, trapped into setting our hearts upon things we can never keep with us, upon beings who smile for an hour and then miserably perish. It is well, I thought, for the grandest of our old preachers to say: 'We long for perishing meat, and fill our stomachs with corruption; we look after white and red, and the weaker beauties of the night; we are passionate after rings and seals, and enraged at the breaking of a crystal,' and then to make it plain that these things will not avail us. But other and nobler things, it seemed to me, would avail us even less, for the more we opened our hearts, making ourselves eager and loving, the more certain amid this universal dissolution was our ultimate misery. We are the poor playthings of Time, dandled for an hour and then flung to rot in a corner; and yet we are all born, as was said of Coleridge, hungering for Eternity.

So brimmed with such thoughts, feelings, old quotations,

strange images, clustering together like pieces in a kaleidoscope to form one tragic vision of things, I was carried down the desolated length of Haymarket, where man spendeth his vain life as a shadow. As those last words will suggest, my mood had by that time crystallized into the utter hopelessness of that other and greater Preacher. Vanity of vanities! Had I been a natural man instead of the smooth mountebank demanded by decency and encouraged by my natural timidity, I should have descended from the bus, put ashes on my head, and cried 'Woe!' to the assembled hawkers and playgoers and policemen, stunning them with gigantic metaphors. That is what, in my heart, I wanted to do, so surely was I possessed by this sudden hopeless vision and by a mixed feeling of contempt and pity for my fellow mortals. Yet I sat there, quietly enough, and still well aware of the fact that I was on my way to lunch with two friends at a club not very far away. I was, as it were, purely automatically aware of this fact, for in those last moments, so rapt had I been in my vision, I had no sense even of personal identity. But I moved forward, as a man might over a darkening field of battle, towards the club and my friends, and arrived there and greeted them in a kind of dream; and then, suddenly, out of my dream, I looked at them sharply and curiously, these friends of mine, whose grim sentence and that of all they held dear still seemed to be ringing in my ears. How strangely childish, touchingly naïve, their smiling confidence, their little preoccupations, their chatter. I saw them seating themselves opposite me at the lunch table, and it was as if they were people acting on a distant stage; yet I did not feel completely detached from them, but, on the contrary, felt a kind of tenderness for them and all their little toys and antics. Then I heard one of these doomed creatures propose that we should drink Burgundy. I stood out for something lighter, for though I like a glass of Burgundy as well as the next man, I maintain it is far too heavy for lunch.

The Brown Lounge

THERE is a room here asking for a murder. It is one of the three lounges. The first lounge is to the right of the entrance hall, and is always full of middle-aged Scotswomen playing bridge. (Why are these hotels always full of middle-aged Scotswomen?) The second lounge is to the left of the entrance hall, and is a leathery, railway-guide and illustrated-paper sort of place. One end of it is always occupied by young wives sitting up very stiffly and waiting for their husbands, who are at the telephones asking if Mr Murchison will be in or telling somebody that they can offer 2,500 at 3¾. The other end appears to have been annexed by a man with a vaguely military appearance, who yawns a great deal but contrives to look as if he has only to have two more to be tipsy. It is the third lounge, at the far end of the entrance hall, that is ripe for a murder. It is much bigger than the others but hardly used at all.

Yesterday, I happened to be in the hotel about half-past four, and so ordered tea. After waiting about ten minutes, I asked the waiter where it was. 'I've put it in the Brown Lounge for you, sir,' he said, and then it was that I discovered this mysterious room at the end of the hall. It was closely shuttered and very dimly lit, full of enormous chairs and settees, and there were dim acres of engravings and photogravures on the walls. I groped my way to a very large chair and a very little table with a tray on it. The only other people there were two old women who talked in whispers; and if one of them had turned out to be Dickens' Miss Havisham I should not have been surprised. All the noises of the hotel and the streets outside were banished with the closing of the door, and there was no sound at all but the vague whispering of these two old women. Usually I linger over tea, but yesterday there was no lingering. It seemed like eating bread-and-butter in a mausoleum. If ever I want to murder a man, I shall take him in there.

I can see the whole thing. I shall pretend that I want to have a quiet chat with my victim and shall suggest coming to this hotel for tea. As soon as we arrive, I shall seek out the head waiter, that sinister figure. 'I want tea for two,' I shall tell him, softly but with the right emphasis. 'Ah, tea for two,' he will say, looking at me with those colourless eyes. 'The Brown Lounge?' There will be a kind of cold flicker in those eyes. 'Yes,' I shall reply, very softly. 'The Brown Lounge. Tea for two. And a sharp knife.' Then I shall rejoin my man, and, talking very loudly and cheerfully, with many a clap on the back, I shall march him down the hall and into that shuttered room. 'Rather a dreary sort of hole this, isn't it?' he will say, staring about him. 'Not a bit of it,' I shall reply. 'Just a quiet hotel for gentlefolk, that's all.' The head waiter himself, I trust, will bring the tea and the knife, and as he goes will nod casually towards a gigantic sideboard not far away, and I shall understand. The rest will be easy. It is possible, indeed highly probable, that the two old women will be sitting there, but I do not imagine for a moment that they will interfere or pay any attention to my business with the knife and the sideboard. They will, I fancy, just go on whispering together, like true gentlefolk staying at a quiet hotel.

Bruddersford Funeral

THIS being a funeral in the grand tradition, it was a very lengthy affair. The assembly of the carriages and the mourners took some time. Then there was the long slow drive out to Dum Wood Cemetery, where serious Bruddersfordians go walking on fine Sunday afternoons, many a year before they are taken there to await the last trump. Then followed a service in the cemetery chapel, where the Rev J. Hamilton Morris, B.A., of Woolgate Congregational Chapel, tried to dwell upon the virtues of the deceased and found it very difficult because he knew very little about her. He did what he could, however, looked manfully at the tear-stained or grim faces, and finally asked the grave where its victory was. And when all was done, there was the long drive back, not to 51 Ogden Street, but to Caddy's in Shuttle Street, where a funeral tea had been ordered. Caddy's, being old-fashioned, still made a speciality of these repasts, and on their business cards might be seen, sandwiched between *Catering* and *Wedding Cakes* the announcement: *Funeral Teas*. Mourners, mostly relations, still come considerable distances, and not only must they be refreshed but they must also be provided with an opportunity to exchange news, for many scattered families only meet at a funeral. It is not perhaps true to say that these teas are the most jovial functions known to elderly Bruddersfordians, but it must be admitted that they are generally a success, going with a swing that many social events in Bruddersford never know. Everybody has that pleasant feeling of having carried through a painful duty; after a sight of the open grave, it is good to return to life, to eat and drink and swop news with uncles and cousins; and, moreover, what with long rides, services, and standing about in cemeteries, to say nothing of the havoc wrought by the emotions, a mourner develops a real appetite and funeral teas are good solid meat teas. That is the reason why the comedian who plays the Dame in the Bruddersford pantomime never fails – has not failed these last thirty years – to bring down the house with the remark: 'I buried 'im with 'am.' On this occasion, Mrs Bairstow had ordered Caddy's to provide a sound specimen of their knife-and-fork tea, and they had disappointed neither her nor any of her hopeful guests.

Among those who did full justice to both the ham and the tongue was Mr Oakroyd's old friend and our old acquaintance, that independent craftsman and keeper of hens, Mr Sam Oglethorpe. Here was one person Mr Oakroyd could talk to, and though actually he did not do much talking, he kept close to Sam from the moment they all tramped up Caddy's stairs.

'Well, Jess,' said Mr Oglethorpe, 'I'll ha' to be off. I've getten t'hens to see to, tha knaws. Farls can't wait if fowk can.'

'Ay,' said Mr Oakroyd disconsolately. Then he brightened up. 'Here, Sam, I'm coming wi' yer.'

'Won't they want yer?' said Mr Oglethorpe. They had wandered away from the tables now.

'If they do, they mun want on. Ther's nowt I can do here nar.'

'Right, owd lad,' said Mr Oglethorpe cheerfully. 'We'll get t'tram.'

Women's Hostel

THE Burpenfield Club, called after Lady Burpenfield, who had given five thousand pounds to the original fund, was one of the residential clubs or hostels provided for girls who came from good middle-class homes in the country but were compelled, by economic conditions still artfully adjusted to suit the male, to live in London as cheaply as possible. Two fairly large houses had been thrown together and their upper floors converted into a host of tiny bedrooms, and there was accommodation for about sixty girls. For twenty-five to thirty shillings a week, the Club gave them a bedroom, breakfast and dinner throughout the week, and all meals on Saturday and Sunday. It was light and well ventilated and very clean, offered an astonishing amount of really hot water, and had a large lounge, a drawing-room (No Smoking), a small reading-room and library (Quiet Please), and a garden stocked with the hardiest annuals. The food was not brilliant – and no doubt it returned to the table too often in the shape of fish-cakes, rissoles, and shepherd's pie – but it was reasonably wholesome and could be eaten with safety if not with positive pleasure. The staff was very efficient and was controlled, as everybody and everything else in the Club was controlled, by the Secretary, Miss Tattersby, daughter of the late Dean of Welborough, and perhaps the most respectable woman in all

Europe. The rules were not too strict. There were no compulsory religious services. Male visitors could not be entertained in bedrooms but could be brought to dinner and were allowed in the lounge, where they occasionally might be seen, sitting in abject misery. Intoxicants were not supplied by the Club but could be introduced, in reasonable quantities, into the dining-room when guests were present. Smoking was permitted, except in the dining- and drawing-rooms. There were a good many regulations about beds and baths and washing and so forth, but they were not oppressive. In the evenings, throughout the winter months, fires, quite large cheerful fires, brightened all the public rooms. The lighting was good. The beds and chairs were fairly comfortable. Dramatic entertainments and dances were given two or three times a year. All this for less than it would cost to live in some dingy and dismal boarding-house or the pokiest of poky flats.

What more could a girl want? Parents and friends of the family who visited the Burpenfield found themselves compelled to ask this question. The answer was that there was only one thing that most girls at the Burpenfield did want, and that was to get away. It was very odd. You were congratulated on getting into the Burpenfield when you first went there, and you were congratulated even more heartily when you finally left it. During the time you were there, you grumbled, having completely lost sight of the solid advantages of the place. The girls who stayed there year after year until at last they were girls no longer but women growing grey did stop grumbling and even pointed out to one another these solid advantages, but their faces always wore a resigned look.

There was, to begin with, this institution atmosphere, which was rather depressing. The sight of those long tiled corridors did not cheer you when you returned, tired, rather cross, headachy, from work in the evening. Then, if you were not going out, you had to choose between your little box of a bedroom, the lounge (usually dominated by a clique of young insufferable rowdies), or the silent and inhuman drawing-room. Moreover, Miss Tattersby, known as 'Tatters', was terrifying. Very early, Miss Tattersby had arrived at the sound conclusion that a brisk rough sarcasm was her best weapon, and she made full use of it. You felt the weight and force of it even in the notices she was so fond of pinning up: 'Need residents who have First Dinner take up *so* much time ...'; 'Some residents seem to have forgotten that the Staff has other duties besides ...'; 'Is it necessary *again* to remind residents that washing stockings in the bathrooms ...'; that is how they went. But this, after all, was only a pale reflection of her method in direct talk, and some girls, finding themselves involved in an intricate affair concerning a pair of stockings or something of that kind, preferred to conduct their side of the case by correspondence, in the shape of little notes to Miss Tattersby hastily left in her office when she was known to be out. Many a girl, after a little brush with 'Tatters', who was immensely tall and bony and staring, and looked like a soured Victorian celebrity, had faced the most infuriated director at her office with a mere shrug. The confident Burpenfield manner in commercial life, of which we have seen something in Miss Matfield in *Angel Pavement*, was probably the result of various encounters with Miss Tattersby.

But what Miss Matfield, who was cursing the place all over again as she left Miss Morrison and went upstairs to her room, disliked most about the Burpenfield was the presence of all the other members, whose life she had to share. There were too many of them, and their mode of life was like an awful parody of her own. The thought that her own existence would seem to an outsider just like theirs infuriated or saddened her, for she felt that really she was quite different from these others, much superior, a more vital, splendid being. Those whose situation was not at all like her own only annoyed her still more. There were the young girls, all rosy and confident, many of whom were either engaged (to the most hopelessly idiotic young man) or merely filling in a few months of larking about, trying one absurd thing after another, while their doting fathers forwarded generous monthly cheques. Then there were the women older than herself, downright spinsters in their thirties and early forties, who had grown grey and withered at the typewriter and the telephone, who knitted, droned on interminably about dull holidays they had had, took to fancy religions, quietly went mad, whose lives narrowed down to a point at which washing stockings became the supreme interest. Some of them were frankly depressing. You met them drooping about the corridors, kettle in hand, and they seemed to think about nothing but hot water. Others were mechanically and terribly brisk and bright, all nervy jauntiness, laborious slang, and secret orgies of aspirin, and these creatures – poor old things – were if anything more depressing, the very limit. Sometimes, when she was tired and nothing much was happening, Miss Matfield saw in one of these women an awful glimpse of her own future, and then she rushed into her bedroom and made the most fantastic and desperate plans, not one of which she ever attempted to carry out. Meanwhile, time was slipping away and nothing was happening. Soon she would be thirty. Thirty! People could say what they liked – but life was foul.

The Giant Teashop

A BUS took him to the West End, where, among the crazy coloured fountains of illumination, shattering the blue dusk with green and crimson fire, he found the café of his choice, a teashop that had gone mad and turned Babylonian, a white palace with ten thousand lights. It towered above the older buildings like a citadel, which indeed it was, the outpost of a new age, perhaps a new civilization, perhaps a new barbarism; and behind the thin marble front were concrete and steel, just as behind the careless profusion of luxury were millions of pence, balanced to the last halfpenny. Somewhere in the background, hidden away, behind the ten thousand lights and acres of white napery and bewildering glittering rows of teapots, behind the thousand waitresses and cash-box girls and black-coated floor managers and temperamental long-haired violinists, behind the mounds of shimmering bonbons and multi-coloured Viennese pastries, the cauldrons of stewed steak, the vanloads of harlequin ices, were a few men who went to work juggling with fractions of a farthing, who knew how many units of electricity it took to finish a steak-and-kidney pudding and how many minutes and seconds a waitress (five feet four in height and in average health) would need to carry a tray of given weight from the kitchen lift to the table in the far corner. In short, there was a warm, sensuous, vulgar life flowering in the upper stories, and a cold science working in the basement. Such was the gigantic teashop into which Turgis marched, in search not of mere refreshment but of all the enchantment of unfamiliar luxury. Perhaps he knew in his heart that men have conquered half the known world, looted whole kingdoms, and never arrived in such luxury. The place was built for him.

It was built for a great many other people too, and, as usual, they were all there. It steamed with humanity. The marble entrance hall, piled dizzily with bonbons and cakes, was as crowded and bustling as a railway station. The gloom and grime of the streets, the raw air, all November, were at once left behind, forgotten: the atmosphere inside was golden, tropical, belonging to some high mid-summer of confectionery. Disdaining the lifts, Turgis, once more excited by the sight, sound, and smell of it all, climbed the wide staircase until he reached his favourite floor, where an orchestra, led by a young Jewish violinist with wandering lustrous eyes and a passion for tremolo effects, acted as a magnet to a thousand girls. The door was swung open for him by a page; there burst, like a sugary bomb, the clatter of cups, the shrill chatter of white-and-vermilion girls, and, cleaving the golden, scented air, the sensuous clamour of the strings; and, as he stood hesitating a moment, half dazed, there came, bowing, a sleek grave man, older than he was and far more distinguished than he could ever hope to be, who murmured deferentially: 'For one, sir? This way, please.' Shyly, yet proudly, Turgis followed him.

That was the snag really, though. This place was so crowded

that you had to take the seat they offered you; there was no picking and choosing your company at the table. And, as usual, Turgis was not lucky. The vacant seat he was shown, and which he dare not refuse, was at a table already occupied by three people, and not one of them remotely resembled a nice-looking girl. There were two stout middle-aged women, voluble, perspiring, and happy over cream buns, and a middle-aged man, who no doubt had been of no great size even before this expedition started but was now very small and huddled, and gave the impression that if the party stayed there much longer, he would shrink to nothing but spectacles, a nose, a collar, and a pair of boots. For the first few minutes, Turgis was so disappointed that he was quite angry with these people, hated them. And of course it was impossible to get hold of a waitress. After five minutes or so of glaring and waiting, he began to wish he had gone somewhere else. There was a pretty girl at the next table, but she was obviously with her young man, and so fond of him that every now and then she clutched his arm and held it tight, just as if the young man might be thinking of running away. At another table, not far away, were three girls together, two of whom looked very interesting, with saucy eyes and wide smiling mouths, but they were too busy whispering and giggling to take any notice of him. So Turgis suddenly stopped being a bright youth, shooting amorous glances, and became a stern youth who wanted some tea, who had gone there for no other purpose than to obtain some tea, who was surprised and indignant because no tea was forthcoming.

Mr Smeeth at the Queen's Hall

His seat was not very comfortable, high up too, but he liked the look of the place, with its bluey-green walls and gilded organ-pipes and lights shining through holes in the roof like fierce sunlight, its rows of little chairs and music stands, all ready for business. It was fine. He did not buy a programme – they were asking a shilling each for them, and a man must draw a line somewhere – but spent his time looking at the other people and listening to snatches of their talk. They were a queer mixture, quite different from anybody you were likely to see either in Stoke Newington or Angel Pavement; a good many foreigners (the kind with brown baggy stains under their eyes), Jewy people, a few wild-looking young fellows with dark khaki shirts and longish hair, a sprinkling of quiet middle-aged men like himself, and any number of pleasant young girls and refined ladies; and he studied them all with interest. On one side of him were several dark foreigners in a little party, a brown wrinkled oldish woman who never stopped talking Spanish or Italian or Greek or some such language, a thin young man who was carefully reading the programme, which seemed to be full of music itself, and, on the far side, two yellow girls. On the other side, his neighbour was a large man whose wiry grey hair stood straight up above a broad red face, obviously an Englishman but a chap rather out of the common, a bit cranky perhaps and fierce in his opinions.

This man, moving restlessly in the cramped space, bumped against Mr Smeeth and muttered an apology.

'Not much room, is there?' said Mr Smeeth amiably.

'Never is here, sir,' the man replied fiercely.

'Is that so?' said Mr Smeeth. 'I don't often come here.' He felt it would not do to admit that this was the very first time.

'Always crowded at these concerts, full up, packed out, not an inch of spare room anywhere. And always the same. What the devil do they mean when they say they can't make these concerts pay? Whose fault is it?' he demanded fiercely, just as if Mr Smeeth were partly responsible. 'We pay what they ask us to pay. We fill the place, don't we? What do they want? Do they want people to hang down from the roof or sit on the organ pipes? They should build a bigger hall or stop talking nonsense.'

Mr Smeeth agreed, feeling glad there was no necessity for him to do anything else.

'Say that to some people,' continued the fierce man, who needed no encouragement, 'and they say, "Well, what about the Albert Hall? That's big enough, isn't it?" The Albert Hall! The place is ridiculous. I was silly enough to go and hear Kreisler there, a few weeks ago. Monstrous! They might as well have used a racecourse and sent him up to play in a captive balloon. If it had been a gramophone in the next house but one, it couldn't have been worse. Here you do get the music, I will say that. But it's damnably cramped up here.'

The orchestral players were now swarming in like black beetles, and Mr Smeeth amused himself trying to decide what all the various instruments were. Violins, cellos, double-basses, flutes, clarinets, bassoons, trumpets or cornets, trombones, he knew them, but he was not sure about some of the others – were those curly brass things the horns? – and it was hard to see them at all from where he was. When they had all settled down, he solemnly counted them, and there were nearly a hundred. Something like a band, that! This was going to be good, he told himself. At that moment, everybody began clapping. The conductor, a tall foreign-looking chap with a shock of grey hair that stood out all round his head, had arrived at his little railed-in platform, and was giving the audience a series of short jerky bows. He gave two little taps. All the players brought their instruments up and looked at him. He slowly raised his arms, then brought them down sharply and the concert began.

First, all the violins made a shivery sort of noise that you could feel travelling up and down your spine. Some of the clarinets and bassoons squeaked and gibbered a little, and the brass instruments made a few unpleasant remarks. Then all the violins went rushing up and up, and when they got to the top, the stout man at the back hit a gong, the two men near him attacked their drums, and the next moment every man jack of them, all the hundred, went at it for all they were worth, and the conductor was so energetic that it looked as if his cuffs were about to fly up to the organ. The noise was terrible, shattering: hundreds of tin buckets were being kicked down flights of stone steps; walls of houses were falling in; ships were going down; ten thousand people were screaming with toothache; steam hammers were breaking loose; whole warehouses of oilcloth were being stormed and the oilcloth all torn into shreds; and there were railway accidents innumerable. Then suddenly the noise stopped; one of the clarinets, all by itself, went slithering and gurgling; the violins began their shivery sound again and at last shivered into silence. The conductor dropped his arms to his side. Nearly everybody clapped.

Neither Mr Smeeth nor his neighbour joined in the applause. Indeed, the fierce man snorted a good deal, obviously to show his disapproval.

'I didn't care for that much, did you?' said Mr Smeeth, who felt he could risk it after those snorts.

'That? Muck. Absolute muck,' the fierce man bellowed into Mr Smeeth's left ear. 'If they'll swallow that they'll swallow anything, any mortal thing. Downright sheer muck. Listen to 'em.' And as the applause continued, the fierce man, in despair, buried his huge head in his hands and groaned.

The next item seemed to Mr Smeeth to be a member of the same unpleasant family as the first, only instead of being the rowdy one, it was the thin sneering one. He had never heard a piece of music before that gave such an impression of thinness, bonyness, scraggyness, and scratchyness. It was like having thin wires pushed into your ears. You felt as if you were trying to chew ice-cream. The violins hated the sight of you and of one another; the reedy instruments were reedier than they had ever been before but expressed nothing but a general loathing; the brass only came in to blow strange hollow sounds; and the stout man and his friends at the top hit things that had all gone flat, dead, as if their drums were burst. Very tall thin people sat about drinking quinine and sneering at one another, and in the middle of them, on the cold floor, was an idiot child that ran its finger-nail up and down a slate. One last scratch from the slate, and the horror was over. Once more, the conductor, after wiping his brow, was acknowledging the applause.

This time, Mr Smeeth did not hesitate. 'And I don't like that either,' he said to his neighbour.

'You don't?' The fierce man was almost staggered. 'You don't like it? You surprise me, sir, you do, indeed. If you don't like that, what in the name of thunder *are* you going to like – in modern music? Come, come, you've got to give the moderns a chance. You can't refuse them a hearing altogether, can you?'

Mr Smeeth admitted that you couldn't, but said it in such a way as to suggest that he was doing his best to keep them quiet.

'Very well, then,' the fierce man continued, 'you've got to confess that you've just listened to one of the two or three things written during these last ten years or so that is going to *live*. Come now, you must admit that.'

'Well, I dare say,' said Mr Smeeth, knitting his brows.

Here the fierce man began tapping him on the arm. 'Form? Well, of course, the thing hasn't got it, and it's no good pretending it has, and that's where you and I' – Mr Smeeth was given a heavier tap, almost a bang, to emphasize this – 'find ourselves being cheated. But we're asking for something that isn't there. But the tone values, the pure orchestral colouring – superb! Damn it, it's got poetry in it. Romantic, of course. Romantic as you like – ultra-romantic. All these fellows now are beginning to tell us they're classical, but they're all romantic really, the whole boiling of 'em, and Berlioz is their man only they don't know it, or won't admit it. What do *you* say?'

Mr Smeeth observed very cautiously that he had no doubt there was a lot to be said for that point of view. When the interval came and he went out to smoke a pipe, he took care to keep moving so that the fierce man, who appeared to be on the prowl, did not find him.

The concert was much better after the interval. It began

with a longish thing in which a piano played about one-half, and most of the orchestra, for some of them never touched their instruments, played the other half. A little dark chap played the piano and there could be no doubt about it, he *could* play the piano. Terrum, ter-*rum*, terrum, terrum, trum, trum, trrrrr, the orchestra would go, and the little chap would lean back, looking idly at the conductor. But the second the orchestra stopped he would hurl himself at the piano, and crash out his own terrum, ter-*rum*, terrum, terrum, trum trum trrr. Sometimes the violins would play very softly and sadly, and the piano would join in, scattering silver showers of notes or perhaps wandering up and down a ladder of quiet chords, and then Mr Smeeth would feel himself very quiet and happy and sad all at the same time. In the end, they had a pell-mell race, and the piano shouted to the orchestra and then went scampering away, and the orchestra thundered at the piano and went charging after it, and they went up hill and down dale, shouting and thundering, scampering and charging, until one big bang, during which the little chap seemed to be almost sitting on the piano and the conductor appeared to be holding the whole orchestra up in his two arms, brought it to an end. This time Mr Smeeth clapped furiously, and so did the fierce man, and so did everybody else, even the violin players in the orchestra; and the little chap, now purple in the face, ran in and out a dozen times, bowing all the way. But he would not play again, no matter how long and loud they clapped, and Mr Smeeth, for his part, could not blame him. The little chap had done his share. My word, there was talent for you!

'Our old friend now,' said the fierce man, turning abruptly.

'Where?' cried Mr Smeeth, startled.

'On the programme,' the other replied. 'It's the Brahms Number One next.'

'Is it really,' said Mr Smeeth. 'That ought to be good.' He had heard of Brahms, knew him as a chap who had written some Hungarian dances. But, unless he was mistaken, these dances were only a bit of fun for Brahms, who was one of your very classical men. The Number One part of it he did not understand, and did not like to ask about it, but as the elderly foreign woman on his right happened to be examining the programme, he had a peep at it and had just time to discover that it was a symphony. Brahms's First Symphony in fact, they were about to hear. It would probably be clean above his head, but it could not possibly be so horrible to listen to as that modern stuff in the first half of the programme.

It was some time before he made much out of it. The Brahms of this symphony seemed a very gloomy, ponderous, rumbling sort of chap, who might now and then show a flash of temper or go in a corner and feel sorry for himself, but for the most part simply went on gloomily rumbling and grumbling. There were moments, however, when there came a sudden gush of melody, something infinitely tender swelling out of the strings or a ripple of laughter from the flutes and clarinets or a fine flare up by the whole orchestra, and for these moments Mr Smeeth waited, puzzled but excited, like a man catching glimpses of some delectable strange valley through the swirling mists of a mountainside. As the symphony went on, he began to get the hang of it more and more, and these moments returned more frequently, until at last, in the final section, the great moment arrived and justified everything, the whole symphony concert.

It began, this last part, with some muffled and doleful sounds from the brass instruments. He had heard some of those grim snatches of tune earlier on in the symphony, and now when they were repeated in this fashion they had a very queer effect on him, almost frightened him. It was as if all the workhouses and hospitals and cemeteries of North London had been flashed past his eyes. Those brass instruments didn't think Smeeth had much of a chance. All the violins were sorry about it; they protested, they shook, they wept; but the horns and trumpets and trombones came back and blew them away. Then the whole orchestra became tumultuous, and one voice after another raised itself above the menacing din, cried in anger, cried in sorrow, and was lost again. There were queer little intervals, during one of which only the strings played, and they twanged and plucked instead of using their bows, and the twanging and plucking, quite soft and slow at first, got louder and faster until it seemed as if there was danger everywhere. Then, just when it seemed as if something was going to burst, the twanging and plucking was over, and the great mournful sounds came reeling out again, like doomed giants. After that the whole thing seemed to be slithering into hopelessness, as if Brahms had got stuck in a bog and the light was going. But then the great moment arrived, Brahms jumped clean out of his bog, set his foot on the hard road, and swept the orchestra and the fierce man and the three foreigners and Mr Smeeth and the whole Queen's Hall along with him, in a noble stride. This was a great tune. Ta *tum* ta ta *tum*, ta *tum* ta-ta *tum* ta *tum*. He could have shouted at the splendour of it. The strings in a rich deep unison sweeping on, and you were ten feet high and had a thousand glorious years to live. But in a minute or two it had gone, this glory of sound, and there was muddle and gloom, a sudden sweetness of violins, then harsh voices from the brass. Mr Smeeth had given it up, when back it came again, swelling his heart until it nearly choked him, and then it was lost once more and everything began to be put in its place and settled, abruptly, fiercely, as if old Brahms had made up his mind to stand no nonsense from anybody or anything under the sun. There, there, there, there, *there*. It was done. They were all clapping and clapping and the conductor was mopping his forehead and bowing and then signalling to the band to stand up, and old Brahms had slipped away, into the blue.

There was a cold drizzle of rain outside in Langham Place, where the big cars of the rich were nosing one another like shiny monsters, and it was a long and dreary way to Chaucer Road, Stoke Newington, but odd bits of the magic kept floating back into his mind, and he felt more excited and happy than he had done when he had heard about the rise that morning. Undoubtedly a lot of this symphony concert stuff was either right above his head or just simply didn't mean anything to anybody. But what was good *was* good. Ta *tum* ta ta – now how did that go? All the way from the High Street to Chaucer Road, as he hurried down the darkening streets and tried to make his overcoat collar reach the back of his hat, he was also trying to capture that tune. He could feel it still beating and glowing somewhere inside him.

Southampton-San Francisco

On the morning of December 30th, somewhere in Southampton, perhaps at the top of the long gangway leading into R.M.S. *Gargantua*, reality broke down for William. He walked through an invisible crack into another world. No sooner had he been conducted into the interior of the *Gargantua* than he said good-bye to sense; and the safe little world, with its fixed boundaries, fell away from him. The interior of the *Gargantua* was crazy; as if a monstrous hotel had been cut in half, one of the halves compressed and then wildly mixed with parts of a seaside promenade, a fancy fair, and a factory. After visiting his cabin, that iron box in the Louis XIV style, and unpacking some astonished clothing there, William set out on a tour of exploration, and stepped, bewildered, from a gymnasium into a half-timbered Tudor smoking-room and from there straight into a barber's shop, and, moreover, a barber's shop that appeared to be filled with large dolls and false noses. Then everything that happened had an incalculable and lunatic aspect. Uniformed personages made a fuss; there were huge vague noises; much waving of handkerchiefs by tiny figures far below at the dock side; and then Southampton gently disengaged itself from the *Gargantua* and went sliding away into the cold mistiness, taking with it the world that could reasonably contain Buntingham and its malting business, Greenlaw of the Grammar School, water-colours and chess. The *Gargantua* was glad to be rid of such last vestiges of sanity, and immediately abandoned all pretence. It sounded bugles, played waltzes, and conjured forth cocktails and salted almonds and toasted cheese in the smoking-room, and whisky and bottles of beer and Scotch broth and Lancashire hot-pot below in the dining-saloon. After that, everybody but William seemed to disappear, and he went for long lonely walks along glass-enclosed promenades and through empty drawing-rooms in red and gold and writing-rooms in blue and silver. The outside world grew dark and sleety; it took to whistling hard; and finally the *Gargantua* halted near some noises and a few flickering lights that called themselves Cherbourg. Some cold wet people came aboard, stared about them for a moment with great disdain, then disappeared for days.

The year expired in a vast heaving idiocy. All night the *Gargantua* laboured and protested and groaned, with much dragging and clanking of chains, like an industrious spectre. William's bath water retreated from him and tried to form a wall; his dressing-gown stretched itself and stood out stiff; something in the pit of his stomach turned over from time to time; and he treated the huge menu card, which broke into Old Year–New Year gaieties, with a certain ascetic scorn. Only a few red-faced hearty men kept him company during those first days, though on one of the decks, securely swaddled in chairs, were four young American Jewesses, whose faces, painted with bright orange cheeks and purple lips, suggested the most glowing health, but whose anxious eyes seemed to be staring out of another life. With enormous lengths of heaving promenades and rooms in five different styles practically to himself, William felt very lonely and not quite right in his head. Suddenly, however, on a morning when a little pale sunshine could be seen and the *Gargantua* did not protest and groan quite so much, the place swarmed with people, and people apparently on the easiest, friendliest terms with one another. They ate and drank down in the dining-saloon and up in the restaurant and the smoke-room; they played games, went in for competitions, flirted, danced, wore funny hats and threw paper about; they stayed up half the night having rounds and rounds of drinks and sandwiches and shouting the most intimate confidences to one another. William was nearly one of these people, but not quite: he felt rather like a neglected older inhabitant. But he found that he had a companion, almost an old friend, in the man who sat next to him at table. This was Mr Julius Thedalberg, of the Gard Burrastein Products Inc. of New York; a pale and sad-faced man of indeterminate middle age, who spoke in the slowest and most despairing tones that William ever remembered hearing, but who yet contrived to enjoy himself enormously and to eat and drink and smoke more cigars than anybody else there. Within half an hour of his first appearance at table, Mr Thedalberg had adopted William, who really began to feel that somehow he must be one of Mr Thedalberg's old friends. Mr Thedalberg marched him round and round the decks and in and out of the smoke-room, and talked firmly to him about business conditions and the Gard Burrastein Products Inc. (of which he was a proud executive) and prohibition and home life and divorce and ward politicians and Paris and his daughter in college and his son at school. The sunshine was blotted out by alternating visitations of fog and sleet, but nobody cared any more about that, for they were all busy eating more and more caviare and sardines and olives and salted almonds and drinking more and more dry Martinis and double Side-cars and staying up later and later every night to reveal their last secrets. William sometimes felt he had been pitchforked, with baggage and bed, into an endless birthday party given by a stranger. By this time, there was nothing about Mr Thedalberg that William did not know; but, on the other hand, Mr Thedalberg knew nothing about Faraway Island, the pitchblende and P. T. Riley, for when William discovered a certain golden haze in the smoke-room, a haze through which Mr Thedalberg loomed as his oldest and dearest friend, and found himself wanting to talk about such matters, something always told him it was time to go to bed.

Then one morning the *Gargantua* suddenly stopped groaning, and the mists outside were wiped away to reveal an incredible place of grey gleaming towers. Mr Thedalberg took William by the arm, pointed to this and that, and was proud and sentimental. He was also surprisingly helpful. In his ignorance of America and the Americans, that land and race of born hosts, William had imagined that once they were within sight of New York, Mr Thedalberg's ancient friendship would suddenly melt away; but there he was wrong, for Mr Thedalberg was on hand both before and after they passed through the customs, gave William the address of a good hotel, and insisted that they should spend the evening together. William was only too glad to accept these kind offices. So far as it is possible to like a person who is not quite real, William liked Mr Thedalberg; and Mr Thedalberg at least was more real than anybody or anything else, for now the unreality of the *Gargantua* was replaced by the still wilder unreality of this city, into which William plunged as if he had suddenly jumped up from his seat in the Buntingham picture theatre and had dived into the life shown on the screen there. He spent the day being whirled up and down elevator shafts, walking along streets that were roaring canyons, and staring up at cliffs and mountain sides of reinforced concrete and shining brick façades. Prompt to time Mr Thedalberg arrived in the evening, complete with a programme of hospitality, all of which was carefully announced in that sad and despairing voice, and so began William's first and last night in New York City.

They went first to a speak-easy that was nothing but a dim back room, and there they swallowed two fiery cocktails each. Then they moved on to an Italian restaurant speak-easy that appeared to have been constructed out of a hastily covered backyard, and there they dined, heatedly, heavily, and indigestibly. The next item on the programme was a cheap burlesque show down town, at which they finally arrived, to William's astonishment, in an elevator; and this show consisted of three battered Hebrew comedians who exchanged grim and smutty jests, and of a chorus of tired and bored girls, who proceeded, time after time, to remove what scanty clothes they wore and to reveal their rather chalky pulpy charms for the benefit of rows of glassy-eyed and teeth-sucking clerks and warehousemen. Struggling with the wild weather inside him, in which indigestion provided the thunder and raw alcohol the lightning, William sat dazed before this powerfully anaphrodisiac spectacle, which Mr Thedalberg, for his part, regarded with neither approval nor disapproval, but with a sort of vague scientific interest. After an hour or so of it, they left for a German speak-easy, a place of Gothic gloom, sham armour and imitation carved wood, where a roaring crowd of patrons sweated over seidels of synthetic beer, waltz choruses, and vast limp sausages. Here, flushed girls would suddenly jump up, wriggle violently to the music, then scream with laughter, and to one of the noisiest of these, William, to his embarrassment, was introduced by the solemnly waggish Mr Thedalberg as a fellow citizen of Knoxville, Iowa. It was late when they left this underground bedlamite Nuremberg for the keen air and hard glitter of the street, but Mr Thedalberg had not yet completed his schedule, and so William, who by this time was desperately tired and rather depressed, could not suggest that he would like to go to bed. Thus they arrived, sometime between one and two in the morning, at the colossal arena of the Madison Square Garden, in time for the beginning of the fifth day of the Six-Day Cycle Race. A few thousand spectators, a mere handful in that vast interior, were staring and blinking and yawning and chewing, their faces cruelly etched in the glare of the arc lights. A band blared brassily from some distant aerie. Ghosts in white jackets hawked peanuts and hot dogs and ice cream. Loud speakers made announcements, but they did it in such tones that it seemed as if metallic giants were roaring in agony and proclaiming the eve of Doomsday. Stringy little cyclists were busy coming on or going off duty, some sleeping beside the track, others stretching their legs towards the masseurs, and the rest of them silently and gravely circling round the course. William felt he was looking on at some fantastic ritual. There was something hypnotizing about these circling figures. Time perished: it was neither late last night nor early this morning; it was no hour that could ordinarily be found among the twenty-four. William stared as a drowned man might stare at the antics of the deep-sea creatures in some green gulf. His head was too large, too heavy; his eyeballs were bound in brass; his legs ached; his mouth was a desert of cactus and old bones; but he knew these discomforts only vaguely. He was not happy; he was not unhappy; he was fathoms deep in some ugly trance. How long the wheeling figures went round and round without any sort of break he could not have told, but at last, after many years, the band and the voices broke into a note of new urgency, the spectators sat up, the ghosts turned to stare, and suddenly all the cyclists shot forward and went racing like mad, as if one last effort would enable them to escape from the circling hell of the track. Instantly, Mr Thedalberg, like the other spectators, was insanely resurrected: 'Attababy!' he yelled, springing to his feet and waving his hat. 'Come on, come on. Attababy!' A wild fear swept through William's bewilderment. At any moment, now, it seemed, this city might go mad. Reason was rocking beneath these lunatic towers. But the pot of wheels and legs and pedals, which had threatened to boil over, now simmered down again, and Mr Thedalberg, as quiet and sad as ever, said that they might as well go. In the entrance was one of those dwarfs who occasionally find their way on to the stage, a manikin with a large unhappy face, the body of a small child, and the legs of a baby. William nearly fell over him, for he suddenly came reeling out of the shadow, to wave a doll's hand at one of the attendants there and to greet him in a high cracked voice. For once the melancholy face of this dwarf wore a smile, or rather a wide idiotic grin: he was very drunk. William stared at him for a moment, then turned to Mr Thedalberg, thanked him for the evening, and said that he felt tired. Mr Thedalberg, announcing the fact that it was now three-thirty, said that he thought they could call it a day, shook William's hand, and made a short solemn speech proclaiming the solidity and worth of their friendship. William felt that if Mr Thedalberg had been slightly more real, he could have grasped Mr Thedalberg's hand and wept over it. Never had he felt more lost and homeless.

Twelve hours later, he was in the train to Chicago, still tired, and rather hot and short of breath. A large and untidy landscape, powdered with snow, went jolting past; he sat and stared and tried to read jumping print among a strange people, mostly with loud confident voices, dried cheeks, and anxious eyes; black men, easy and jovial fellows who seemed to have retained some secret of a rich luscious life that their masters had lost, set before him unfamiliar dishes, admirable to the eye but queerly disappointing to the palate and digestive system; he undressed and slept behind green curtains, and brushed his teeth and shaved himself in a lavatory-cum-smoke-room in which too many travellers had been sweating and smoking cheap cigars for far too long a time; and Chicago came, roared and rattled at him, showed him a bright glimpse of an icy lake, darkened above him, then finally sped away, before the windows of another train, into the double shadow of night and fading illusion. It was not long before the landscape became larger and untidier than ever, and gradually men began to disappear from it. Dusty plains followed the cultivated fields, only to be followed in their turn by sheer desert, leagues of fantastic rock, and hills as uncompromisingly barren and as wrinkled in the sun as an old man's brown gums. The train stopped at stations with names that seemed the very syllables of outlandish romance, but the places themselves were rarely more than a dull huddle of boxes along the track. Somehow, little or nothing came to light up his sense of wonder. The landscape, the look of the skies, and the very climate, these changed as the miles, hundreds and hundreds and hundreds of them, were run off; but there was something alternately maddening and depressing about the way in which the lives of these people refused to change, as if God had ordained that they should carry with them into these wildernesses an Ark of the Covenant containing specimens of Chesterfield and Lucky Strike cigarettes, the universal Life-savers, chewing gum, and Coca Cola, and a model of a Ford car. But William was only maddened or depressed in a sort of huge dim dream. He found it all more and more difficult to believe. His mind, removed from its base of custom and accepted fact, drifted like the tumbleweeds he stared at through the window, the tumbleweeds that blew across the desert plains. What wonder there was sprang from the simple act of constant journeying. It was incredible that this now familiar interior of hot dry air, magazines and dollar novels, ice water and steak and apple pie, had just shaken him out of Cheyenne, Wyoming, and was even now climbing towards Ogden, Utah. On a Sunday morning of crisp sunshine, he stood among a group of his fellow travellers, all busy photographing, in the observation car at the back of the train, and gaped at the Great Salt Lake, a vast sheet of blue glass, across which the train went rattling for more than an hour. He told himself firmly that now he was actually crossing, on a cut-off that retreated into a knife edge, the famous Great Salt Lake, round whose incrusted shores, where the salt seemed to sparkle ready for the cruet, were spread those legendary and sinister creatures, the Mormons. But nothing happened inside him. It was all too unreal. Utah went, and Nevada arrived, a place of extraordinary desolation, merely so much geology. Among mountains as bare and remote from life as a relief map, he retired yet once more behind his green curtains, performed the familiar acrobatic trick with his pyjamas, listened to the train hooting through these chasms of the moon, and fell into a vague melancholy reverie. The Commander and Ramsbottom – where were these shadows now? Faraway Island, with its black treasure of pitchblende – was it a dream? He thought of his life in Buntingham, the familiar round of the malting house and of his water-colours and books and chess and bridge, friends like Greenlaw, and the few women he knew well and the other women he always thought he would like to know better and yet could never really trouble himself about; and all this life and these people retreated into something very small, dull, faded. Yet that was all that was really his, that small, dull, faded patch of life. Beyond it was nothing but changing shadows. Reality was not here for him. At the moment it was nowhere for him, and he felt curiously sick at heart. It was as if for years and years he had been the victim of a spell that prevented him from breaking through into some infinitely richer life, a glamorous world of colour and passion and careless laughter. He knew that world existed: sometimes the wizard veils were cruelly twitched aside for a second, and there was a sudden flame of colour, a glimpse of a profile, or the sound of voices raised round some enchanted supper table. The spell had been lifted for a moment when Uncle Baldwin had first spoken to him of Faraway; and it had been lifted again when he had stared into the bubble of sea and sky at Lugmouth; but now that he had actually begun the quest, had let himself be carried half the globe away from his old life, the sinister magic had descended upon him again, spreading a grey film over this whole continent. Very tired, nervously exhausted by the long rattling journey, he stretched and turned in his berth, as if some new posture might release him from his depression. There was nothing heroic about William that night: he was a miserable little man.

Yet in the morning it was all different. It ought not to have been, but it was. He had had a poor night's sleep, and was compelled to cut it short, for everybody had to be up early. They were due into Oakland, the railway terminus for San Francisco, at about eight that morning. William and his fellow green-curtainers had to leave their berths at a much earlier hour than usual, and there was the usual unpleasant congested bustle of washing and dressing and packing in a small space. Nevertheless, William felt that it was all different. The train seemed to be descending rapidly now, as if anxious to plunge them all into the waiting Pacific. This place had no likeness to the barren world he had quitted last night; there was dew in it, and sap, and blossom; it was green and luscious, beginning to sparkle already with the clear sunlight; a man could be happy among these vestiges of noble forests, these orchards hanging on the hills; and William found himself with another and sweeter taste in his mouth. He was tired no longer, and all depression fled. He was eager again, and he noticed a similar eagerness in most of his fellow travellers. They might have all come to this California looking for gold. Perhaps they had, and were already finding it. Here, on these rich hillsides and in these fragrant gulfs, was gold enough, the last witness, it might be, to that golden world where lovers and philosophers fleeted the time carelessly, as they were reported to do in Arden. William stared out in a mounting excitement, and when the train arrived at Oakland, he was among the first to leave it for the San Francisco ferry. It seemed to him, as he walked down the long platform, that the air was like a fine dry sherry, and he found it whetting his appetite for life.

Little Fishes in Tahiti

THE Commander and Ramsbottom shared the largest bungalow, nearest the road and about fifty yards away. The bungalows allotted to Terry and William were quite pleasant, and very tropical and romantic. Each consisted of a wide verandah, used as a sitting-room, a bedroom painted green and white, very cool, shaded, and a shower-bath. They were set in a garden, through which there wandered a stream that made a constant happy music among the stones. There were ponds filled with great lilies, many strange flowering shrubs, and here and there, at a fantastic angle, a coconut palm. In this garden, a Chinaman, wearing a hat as big as a cartwheel, worked methodically, never making a sound, never looking up, like a man in some old Oriental drawing. It was all very charming, and from their neighbouring verandahs Terry and William would interrupt their unpacking to tell one another how much they liked it. Beyond the dark stems and leaves, the lagoon was like a great blue diamond.

'You all right, Dursley?' asked the Commander, suddenly popping up.

'Yes, thanks. I like this place.'

'It's not bad. Pretty good quarters. Price is a bit stiff, of course. Much more than you pay in Papeete.'

'Oh! Do you know, I never asked. What do we pay here?'

'Ninety francs a day. Everything in, of course.'

William worked this out. 'No, it's not cheap, is it? I always thought you could live for next to nothing in these places.'

'You could at one time,' said the Commander ruefully. 'But not now. Unless you live with the natives, of course.

Lot of sailors desert here still and go and live up in the hills, with a native woman. It doesn't cost them anything to live. And if you wanted to pig it here, I suppose you could easily live on a few francs a day. But if you want to live decently, it costs you just as much to live here as it does to live anywhere else. That's how things are, y'know, these days.' And the Commander wandered into the bedroom, from which he returned to advise William to let down the mosquito-netting round his bed. There were, it seemed, plenty of mosquitoes in Tahiti, and this was the rainy season, when they began to breed. William regarded the mosquito-netting with disfavour.

'We might have a bathe before lunch,' said the Commander. 'I can hardly ever get Ramsbottom in, but you and Miss Riley ought to like it. Bathing's pretty good here. You ought to wear shoes, though.'

William had some canvas shoes. They arranged to bathe in a quarter of an hour, and Terry said she would come, too. A little before noon, they filed solemnly along the little jetty that ran out near the big central bungalow: a very stringy brown Commander; a small, compact, and somewhat self-conscious William; and a shapely, gorgeous, and entirely unself-conscious Terry. The water at the very edge of the lagoon looked uninviting, for the sand there was black; but farther out, near the end of the little jetty, the lagoon had a wonderful sparkle and green clarity. And it was quite warm and very buoyant.

'Bill, look, look!' screamed Terry, in high excitement.

And William looked. The water was radiant with magical little fishes, hundreds and hundreds of them; fishes brighter than emeralds, turquoises, sapphires; fishes fantastically shaped and striped, like football teams or platoons of extravagant soldiery; and they all went swimming in companies, the black-and-white stripes with the black-and-white stripes, the flashing blue ones with all the other flashing blue ones. There were even tiny shoals of ghostly fishes, hardly opaque at all, like creatures cut out of thin celluloid. The Commander had a pair of diving goggles, and Terry and William took turns at wearing these and keeping their heads below water as long as possible to stare at the magical little fishes. It seemed incredible that one could ever be unhappy in a world that contained those fishes. If that was what Nature could do, William reflected, then somewhere in or behind Nature was an exuberant artist, shouting with laughter as he plunged his brush into his pots of coloured fire. Gay and grateful, William would have liked to have thanked somebody for the little fishes. He would have liked to have thanked and congratulated the little fishes themselves. Why could one do nothing but stare in this green silent world? Why couldn't a man talk for a minute or two to these little fishes, just exchange a brief message? Wasn't it in the *Arabian Nights* that the coloured fishes began talking in the pan? That was life in a fairy-tale. But then these fishes seemed to be in a fairy-tale, too. Yet William knew that he himself was not in a fairy-tale, even though Terry was swimming beside him and he was splashing South Sea water and Faraway Island was waiting for them all. There were probably good scientific reasons, he reminded himself, why the fishes were so enchantingly coloured and shaped. Was it possible for life to be magical, a fairy-tale, if looked at from one side, and at the same time to have good scientific reasons for itself, if looked at from another? He puzzled over this, as he lazily floated above the pageant of the fishes, a monstrous shadow in its sky. And for years afterwards, at odd moments, there would come a sudden sheen of unearthly blue, brighter than the flash of a kingfisher, and then the little fishes would go swimming through his mind, and he would be back in the lagoon ... puzzling over their magic.

Magic in Tahiti for Mr Ramsbottom

'WHAT'S this?' said the Commander, suddenly brisk and alert. 'Can't you find Ramsbottom? Why, we left him with you, Hockaday.'

'He wasn't with me more than ten minutes,' said the major. 'Then he went off on his own somewhere. Thought he'd gone for a siesta. Looked sleepy, I thought.'

'He looked pickled to me,' Mrs Pullen drawled, making a statement, and not criticizing the absent one.

'He was a bit lit,' said Terry. 'Well, we've just got to find him, that's all. Come on, you two sleeping beauties, you've got to find him.'

'Make enquiries,' said the major. 'One of the girls or boys round the place probably saw him. Don't miss much, so long as it isn't work.' And he put his bandy little legs into action.

The others trailed in the same direction. It was still very hot, and everybody was feeling the effect of that enormous lunch. Nobody was actually snappy, but at any moment somebody might be. Hockaday returned to say that Ramsbottom had been seen going inland, walking by the stream up the narrow steep little glen. It was decided that Terry, Mrs Jackson, the Commander, and William should explore this glen in search of him. They found a narrow track, wandering between pandanus trees and enormous bamboos, then climbing among great ferns, wild banana trees, and the strongly smelling lantana, and up they went, finding the shade and the cool air above the rushing stream very welcome. After about twenty minutes' easy walking, they came to a little waterfall, and above the fall, a charming pool, dappled in sunlight and green shade, and hung about with dripping roots and maidenhair.

'Well,' cried little Mrs Jackson, 'just look at his lordship.'

And there his lordship was, like one of the more disreputable antique gods. He was wearing nothing but his trousers, but the upper half of him was richly garlanded with crimson-and-white flowers. A little native boy, naked except for a loincloth, was sitting at one side of him, and a little native girl, who might have been shaped out of brown satin, was sitting on the other side, and both of them were watching his face, with the solemnest black eyes, and carefully fanning it with enormous leaves. And the wreathed and fragrant deity himself was leaning against a mossy bank, his spectacles almost at the end of his nose, his mouth wide open, snoring with majestic rhythm and sonority.

The four of them went up quietly and formed a semi-circle. The two native children jumped to their feet, flashed looks of enquiry at the newcomers, then grinned and did not attempt to run away.

'Isn't he a picture?' said Mrs Jackson softly.

'I'll say he is,' said Terry.

'Ah, Ramsbottom!' William whispered. 'If Manchester could only see you now!'

'Eh!' said Ramsbottom, without, however, opening his eyes.

'Ramsbottom,' called the Commander quietly, 'it's time you were up.'

Ramsbottom slowly opened his eyes, and blinked at them; he carefully adjusted his spectacles, and stared at them; a large fat smile gradually spread over his face; then it gradually disappeared, and he looked puzzled. The two native children now claimed his attention, and there must have been something in his eye that alarmed them, for suddenly they bolted and a moment later it was as if they had never been there. This fact added to Ramsbottom's bewilderment. He pushed the flowers away from his forehead.

'Now wait a minute,' he began slowly, 'wait a minute. Let's get this straight. Was there two kids here or not? There was, eh? That's good. And what about that girl? Was she here?'

'Mr Ramsbottom,' cried Terry reproachfully, 'you don't mean to say there's been a girl here too.'

'Well, that's what Ah want to know. Now wait a minute. Ah'm that mixed up, Ah don't know fairly if Ah've been dreaming or not, but if them kids was here, then Ah didn't dream them. And Ah don't think Ah can have dreamt rest of it.'

'Where are the rest of your clothes?' asked the Commander.

'Rest of my – Here, wait a minute.' He felt his bare garlanded chest in dismay. 'Ah started with a shirt and white coat on, Ah'll swear to that. And now Ah've lost them, and sitting here like a young flower show. Excuse me, ladies. But Ah must get up.' It was then that he discovered his shirt and coat, for he had been partly sitting on them. Asking the ladies to excuse him again, he vanished round the corner, returning a minute later clothed and ungarlanded.

'I think I liked you better just wearing the flowers, Mr Ramsbottom,' said Terry.

'So did I,' cried Mrs Jackson, who, rather to William's surprise, was enjoying all this immensely and getting quite giggly.

'Ah'll tell you what it is,' said Ramsbottom solemnly. 'Ah'm in a maze, as you might say. Ah'm trying to sort it out how Ah got here.'

'That's what we're wondering,' William told him. 'We heard you were lost and so came to look for you.'

'Mrs Jackson here and Mrs Pullen are anxious to get back,' the Commander added.

'Oh, well, if that's it, Ah'm sorry. Let's be getting on, and Ah'll tell you about it afterwards, when Ah get it sorted out.'

It was when they had got back to the hotel and were waiting for the car that he told his story. 'You see, Ah'd had a right good tuck-in at lunch and more than a toothful o' wine and liqueur, and what with that and the 'eat, Ah was feeling a bit muzzy and heavy and sleepy. But Ah thought Ah'd walk out a bit, 'cos it doesn't suit me to lie down and sleep straight after a heavy meal, Ah've got to move about a bit first, d'you see? So Ah thought to myself – when the major had done telling his tale, which was all something and nothing – Ah thought to myself Ah'd go and sit by that stream, for coolness' sake. Well, Ah started walking up that path where we've just been – taking my time, and, as Ah said, a bit muzzy – and Ah went up and up, till suddenly Ah bumps into as queer a looking chap as ever Ah set eyes on. To begin with, he'd long hair, and a beard that reached half-way down to his middle; and all the clothes he was wearing wouldn't have made two decent pocket handkerchiefs. And he wasn't a native – not he! He was as white as we are, was this chap, or he had been, for now he was all over a brick-red colour, and his hair and beard must have been quite yellow once, and now they were just turning grey. He was a big chap too, thin as a lath – you could count his ribs as easy as ninepence – and he had a great nose on him, jutting out like Flamborough Head. It takes a bit to surprise me, especially down here, but Ah'll tell you, that chap did. It was like bumping into Elijah in the wilderness.'

'He must be a nature man,' observed Mrs Jackson. 'There are a lot of them, and they live by themselves, in little huts, just on fruit and stuff – no money at all. And they don't wear clothes. It's an easy way of living, though I must say it wouldn't suit me. You just might as well be a sheep in a field and have done with it.'

'Well, wait a minute. This chap was no sheep. So Ah says hello to him, and he says hello to me. And we starts talking. He could speak a sort o' queer English, but as a matter o' fact, he was a Russian, and Ah fancy he said he'd been a count or a prince. Anyway, Ah asked him some questions, and he answered 'em, telling me how he lived, much as you said, Mrs Jackson. And he asked me if Ah could give him a pencil, for he was wanting one badly, and as it happens Ah always keep a pencil or two on me, so Ah gave him one, and he was right pleased with it. He told me he only lived a step or two away, so Ah said Ah'd go up with him and have a look. So we went a bit farther up, just above that pool where you found me, and he took me to a bit of a hut he had, a place nearly as bare as a bone. Now Ah may have been muzzy, but you see, Ah'm remembering it all right. Nay, Ah think it must have happened, all right. It sounds daft, but Ah can't have dreamt it.' Here Mr Ramsbottom paused, and looked at his listeners.

'What did happen?' asked the Commander, rather impatiently.

'It's all right saying that, but Ah'm taking my time 'cos when Ah've done you'll call me a liar. So we squats down in this hut of his, and he talked and Ah listened, half asleep, and then he told me he'd spent years and years studying something or other – Ah know there was a lot o' meditation and concentration in it – a sort o' magic stuff – and he could do this, that and the other. Well, Ah'd heard these tales before, and

Ah laughed in his face, sleepy as I was. That nettled him a bit, and he brought that great nose of his close to me, stared and stared with eyes like a cat, and said if Ah'd think of somebody Ah'd known well and tell him, he'd make 'em appear. Ah thought to myself this chap's gone dotty with living up here alone so long. However, Ah thought Ah'd humour him. You've got to humour 'em, haven't you?'

His audience agreed that you had to humour them.

'All right then. So, being a bit muzzy and sleepy and daft, Ah said to him, silly as you like, "Ah'll have another word with Maggie Armitage." Now this Maggie Armitage Ah hadn't set eyes on for nearly twenty year. She were an old sweetheart o' mine, and just about twenty year since Maggie and me had had one o' the grandest holidays any man ever had, at Blackpool. So, silly as you like, Ah said to him "Produce Maggie Armitage." He told me to think about her for a minute or two, and Ah did and he stared and stared. Then he told me to wait there a minute, and he went out. And Ah hadn't to wait long neither. Somebody came in.'

'It wasn't Maggie Armitage?' shrieked Terry.

'It was,' cried Ramsbottom. 'It was Maggie Armitage all right, and she might have just come off Central Pier, Blackpool, with me, twenty year since. No different at all. She walked straight in, said "Hello, Johnny lad," and came and put her two arms round my neck and her cheek against mine, just as she'd done many a time, and Ah can remember telling myself that if this was dreaming, Ah'd dream on a bit, 'cos Ah never liked anybody better than Ah did Maggie. Then she said, "Let's go and sit by that pool, Johnny," and she took me by the hand, and we went down and sat where you saw me – yes, we did, Maggie and me. She sat down close to me and put her head against my shoulder and Ah held her tight, and she asked me how things were with me and Ah told her and Ah asked how things were with her, and it was all so quiet and peaceful – nay, bless my soul! – Ah don't remember when it was so quiet and peaceful. Then all of a sudden – and Ah remember it as plain as plain can be – Ah gave a sort o' shiver. No waking up or anything like that, just a sort o' little shiver. But then Ah found it wasn't Maggie who was there at all.'

'Wasn't there anybody there?' Terry demanded, looking at him wide-eyed.

'Yes, Ah was holding somebody all right. But it wasn't Maggie, it was one of these native lasses, all black eyes and hair and brown skin. Not Maggie at all. Well, that made me jump, and this girl – a nice enough lass, Ah dare say – gives a giggle and a wriggle and rubs my cheek with her hand – and then Ah felt that sleepy all of a sudden, Ah couldn't keep my eyes open. Just dropped straight off. But Ah woke up once, and there wasn't a girl there, but them two kids you saw, fanning me. And Ah thought to myself, "Nay, lad, you're going daft," so Ah went to sleep again, and next time Ah wakened up, all you lot were there. And that's as true as Ah'm here.'

'I think you dreamt most of it, Ramsbottom,' said the Commander.

'Well, happen Ah did,' replied Ramsbottom, puzzling it out. 'But when did Ah start dreaming? Answer me that. That Russian nature chap, did Ah dream him?'

'You didn't dream all those flowers you had hung round you,' said Mrs Jackson briskly, 'because we saw them ourselves. I expect you dreamt all the Maggie Armitage part, though.'

'You must have been very much in love with her, Mr Ramsbottom,' said Terry.

'That's what I think, Miss Riley,' said Mrs Jackson.

'Well, Ah might have been one time,' said Ramsbottom meditatively, 'and Ah must say Ah was right glad to see her, this afternoon. She never told me how she got there, y'know.'

'I think you really met the Russian nature man,' said William, 'and that he was a magician. He conjured that native girl into Maggie Armitage for you for a time. And then it didn't work any longer, and you found out.'

The Story of Hatch

THE crowd, which by this time had seated itself round two tables put together, was almost entirely composed of film people. Ennis, Jubb, a Mr Finberg, a Mr Forman, a Miss Garraty, a Mrs Jarvis, a fat man called Pete, and a synthetic blonde referred to as Georgie. The rum punches and Rainbow cocktails were in brisk circulation. Ennis, now comfortably filled with liquor and looking at once more droll and sinister than ever, dominated the company. They were talking about pictures and Hollywood. All these people, as William soon discovered, made it plain to you that they were sick of pictures and Hollywood, but for all that, they never seemed to talk about anything else. They themselves were such stuff as films are made of, and their lives were rounded with a little celluloid.

'That was the time that poor little guy, Hatch, thought he was playing the Emperor Nero,' Mr Forman remarked reminiscently, 'and he came on the lot all dressed up for it.'

'Yeh – the poor little ham,' said Jubb.

Georgie found her voice. 'Wasn't he the feller that committed sooicide in the studio?'

'He was.'

'I was with the old R.O.V. at the time,' said Ennis, swivelling his one bright eye and instantly commanding their attention. 'Poor little Hatch blew his top in just outside the old-time saloon in the Western set – you remember it, Jubb? You too, Forman. He was through. He'd had too many kicks in the pants. Yes, he was a ham all right – and too much even for the old R.O.V. studio – but he thought he was a great actor. It wasn't just losing the dollars he cared about – it was his art – yes, sir. When you found yourself in a corner with little Hatch, you had to listen to him on his art, and he'd tell you with tears in his eyes.'

'That's so,' said Jubb. 'He came crying to me many a time, right at the end. Griffith ought to have signed him up just for his tear apparatus.'

'The last few weeks there wasn't a God-awful trick that those rough-necks in the R.O.V. didn't play on him, and old Lastein – he was head then – knew all about it and never interfered. They gave that little ham a bad break. But he had his revenge all right. And he had it after he'd committed suicide. That's the queer thing. There aren't many people in Hollywood know this story, because the heads of the R.O.V. had it hushed up. Believe me or believe me not, but Hatch haunted that studio.'

There were shrill cries of interest and excitement from the women. The men made more sceptical noises, indicating that either they didn't believe in ghosts or didn't believe in Pat Ennis.

'He haunted that studio all right,' Ennis continued solemnly, though that drooping eyelid of his seemed to droop harder than ever now. 'And he haunted it in a new way, the way a film studio ought to be haunted. It cost the R.O.V. a packet before they could rid of him too. Oh – it was very neat. You never heard of a ghost having a better idea.'

'What was it?' asked somebody.

'Pat Ennis,' cried Miss Garraty, 'I'm just not going to believe a single word of this.'

'Suit yourself,' said Ennis. 'But Jubb here will bear me out. It started this way. About two or three weeks after little Hatch had shot himself, Jimmy Morgan came rushing up to me and said, "Who put Hatch into *The Diamond Trail*, d'you know, Pat?" I told him I didn't know, and I didn't know Hatch had been in it. "Neither did I," said Jimmy, "but he's there all right. I've been going through the rushes with Lastein and Hatch is there all right, and Lastein's raving mad." So I went along to see those rushes – I'd done most of the scenario – and there was Hatch, not doing anything big, and not helping on the picture at all, but pretty prominent, for all that. Well, Lastein tried to get to the bottom of it, but everybody swore that he'd never put Hatch in. Nobody could remember him being there when they were shooting. The result was, they had to cut that picture to hell, and two of the sequences had to be shot all over again. The next picture we finished was *His Frozen Bride*, and this time I went with Lastein and Morgan and one or two of the others to see it run through. Hatch was in it again. I thought Lastein would go mad. You couldn't get rid of Hatch. He popped up every two or three minutes, and did his ham stuff. Lastein cursed the whole God-damned lot of us, said he'd fire us all, and had a conference on the Hatch question. Every man there who'd had anything to do with *His Frozen Bride* – and I was one of 'em – swore to God that little Hatch had never been near the lot. Lastein said it was a conspiracy. We were all in it together, he told us. The veins were sticking out of his forehead like blue ropes. I was sorry for him, though I was a damn sight sorrier for the rest of us. He said he'd get to the bottom of it if it cost him every dollar he had and he had to wreck the whole organization. We weren't going to make a fool of him. And all the rest of it. Then one of the chief camera-men – I forget his name, but he was a queer devil – got up, pointed a long yellow finger at Lastein, and said: "Mr Lastein, you can't get to the bottom of this. There is no conspiracy. It is not natural but supernatural. This little actor went and destroyed himself because he was not given his chance here. Now he is haunting us – not the studio, that would be too easy for us – but the films themselves." Lastein told him to go and see a doctor. Somebody said: "Let's go and see some more rushes." Lastein agreed, after a bit of persuading, and we all went over and saw about half a picture we were shooting then, called *The Bull on Broadway.* Was Hatch in it? I'll say he was. Got a better part this time, too. Lastein jumped up and screamed with fury. "Mr Lastein," said this camera-man – and I can hear his voice now, very quietly coming out of the dark – "Mr Lastein, you forget. All these scenes have been taken since this man died." It was true. We all knew it. I tell you, folks, there wasn't a sound in that room for the next sixty seconds.'

'Mr Ennis,' said Terry earnestly, fixing her beautiful eyes upon his long melancholy face, 'this isn't true, is it?'

'Miss Riley,' he replied solemnly, taking out his corn cob pipe and pointing the stem at her, 'this is a ve-ery curious world, as you'll learn later. Queerer things than that might be happening on this balcony to-night. I could tell you of other things quite as queer.'

'I'll say you could, Pat,' said Mr Finberg, grinning.

'Tell 'em the rest, boy,' Jubb commanded.

'Well, that settled it. We went into conference again, and Lastein said; "Vell, boys, I guess I've been blaming you for nothing. Now that fellow Hatch is dead, he seems to have found some vay of giving himself parts in all our pictures." Wogenberg, head of the publicity, spoke up then. "Yeh," he said, "and – oh boy! – what a story he's given us. I can make this story break into every front page from here to Rhode Island." Lastein, who knew his stuff, wasn't having that. "You can," he said: "but take it from me, Vogenberg, you're not going to. You're going to keep it under your hat – and that goes vith all of you. This has got to be kept quiet, or it'll be all up vith the R.O.V. And vy. I'll tell you. Either the public vill believe it or not. If they believe it, they vill feel there's something queer and nasty about R.O.V. pictures. If they don't believe it, then they vill laugh at us for trying to pull something too raw. Ain't that right?" We agreed it was. Then old Lastein appealed to me. "The question now is, vat is to be done? Ennis, you're a writer, you ought to know about ghosts and such things, and you knew Hatch ven he vas alive, vat you think ought to be done?" I thought a bit, then told 'em. I argued this way. Hatch – or his ghost, anyhow – had the drop on us. We couldn't fight him, or we'd be cutting every picture we made to hell. We'd got to give him what he wanted – *once*, and then there was a chance he'd be satisfied and turn his ghostly attention to something else. Therefore, I said, the only thing to do is to let him stay in this picture and put his name among the featured players. I admitted that was taking a chance, because little Hatch's ghost might see that as a sign of encouragement and want to star in the next picture. But if he was just doing it out of cussedness, well then, it might stop at that. It took some time to make Lastein see it, but we all worked hard on him, and in the end he agreed. Hatch stayed in the picture, and if you dig up *The Old Bull on Broadway*, you'll find Roderick F. Hatch among the featured players in it. And the trick worked. Believe me, folks, Hatch never popped up in another picture.'

'*That* is the only part I do believe,' said Mr Finberg, speaking for the company.

William on Easter Island

THEY said good-bye to the Commander in a little burying ground, high on a grassy slope, where the great sea winds were for ever blowing and the thunder and spray of the Pacific never left the air. But it was impossible to believe that there were only two of them now and not three. They were always expecting the Commander to come round the corner. After the first few days of sharp grief, during which they eased their hearts by talking to one another about their dead friend, this puzzling loss did not bring William and Ramsbottom closer together, but tended more and more to separate them. They usually spent the evenings together, but then Purvis would be with them, and the three of them would play cards, leaning forward in the narrow yellow circle of lamplight and idly throwing greasy kings and queens on to the red-chequered tablecloth. But the days found them going their separate ways. Ramsbottom seemed to have aged a good deal and to have lost a lot of his gusto. His great body sagged; his face was pouchy; and he spent much of his time dozing in the bungalow. It was fortunate for him that there was not much liquor to be had on the island; otherwise he might have soaked himself in it. As it was, he drank far more than his share. Once or twice William remembered, with a shock of dismay, the shining, bustling, beaming figure that he had first met in the hotel at Lugmouth, so far removed from this frowzy Ramsbottom who lolled about the bungalow. It was as if the Commander had kept him in check and braced him, and now that the Commander had gone, he did not care, simply let himself go.

William was energetic and enterprising enough. Purvis found a quiet horse for him, and after a few cautious and fairly successful experiments with it, using the unfamiliar high Mexican saddle, William turned horseman and thus was able to explore the island. Day after day, if the weather was reasonably fine, he went out, sometimes with Purvis on his rounds, but more frequently, especially during the later weeks, by himself. But though he saw everything there was to see, ate well and slept well, was pestered by flies during the day and bitten by mosquitoes at night, yet through all these seven weeks William seemed to be living in a vague dream. Of all the chapters of his Pacific adventure, the one that afterwards appeared the strangest, the most unreal, was this period of waiting on Easter Island for the schooner for Tahiti. He might have spent the whole time slightly drugged. Long afterwards, when the remotest and most fantastic of the low islands or the Marquesas still shone brightly, clearly, in his memory, there would be times when he could hardly believe that he had ever passed those weeks on Easter Island; he would hesitate to talk about them, as if he might be successfully accused of inventing the experience. It was very odd, of course, this roaming about on horseback on this unvisited and mysterious island; but that was not the reason that he found it all so dream-like; it was something in himself; he was not fully alive, was half-numbed inside, a man for ever moving through mists of his own creation.

Day after day, sometimes in clear sunlight, sometimes under a lowering sky, with the wind blustering all round him, he would ride out towards the ring of burial platforms on the South and East coasts or the sculptors' workshop on Rano Raraku, with its queer avenue of fallen statues. The statues themselves, which turned up all over the island, but were most plentiful on the slope of Rano Raraku, became familiar companions, though they never lost their air of remote mystery. They all had the same flat-backed heads, the same bold noses, short upper lips and long chins, but differed from one another as members of a family differ. He spent hours dreamily answering their defiant dark stare. Sometimes they would fade into merely so much weathered stone, would hardly seem more significant than so many rocks above the trembling grass. But at other times they would come gigantically to life, and then it was like staring at giants buried up to their necks in the hillside, and it seemed as if at any moment they might shake their vast shoulders, scatter the earth about them, and arise in their dark majesty and wrath. The whole island changed like that. One day it would appear to him as it always appeared to Ramsbottom, as a windy, desolate, high place of bunch grass and volcanic rock, almost treeless and waterless, a region without a single grace of landscape or seascape, two thousand weary miles from anywhere. Another day it would take on gigantic airs of mystery and austere beauty. Generations of forgotten men, tens and tens of thousands of them, architects and sculptors and labourers, had planned and sweated on these heights, turning them into one colossal memorial of the dead. And now nobody knew who they were, where they had come from, how they had lived. There was to have been ring after ring of burial platforms, great paved dancing-grounds, and long avenues of images up which the funeral processions would pass to the higher platforms. The plan was there, and half the work was done. It had been stopped, quite suddenly, as if with one stroke of the sword. There had been a catastrophe like the end of a world, and sometimes it seemed as if sinister rumours of it still hung in the wind, and then the island was a terrifying place, in which the mind of man shrank to a pin-point of quivering consciousness.

Most of the time, however, he moved about in a cloudy dream of sea and wind, grass and rocky hillsides. He had adventures. There was the bad fall he had on one of the crumbling burial platforms above La Pérouse Bay. There was the unpleasant scrambling he let himself in for on the afternoon when he went to explore the crater lake of Rano Kao, at the southern extremity of the island. A melancholy sheet of water it was, too, this crater lake, matted with reeds, thick, slimy, of a lunar remoteness, and the mere possibility of falling into it horrified him. But these adventures only broke the spell for an hour or two. One part of him seemed to have hibernated. He neither accepted this period of waiting nor protested against it. He merely kept on living through it. He did not count the days nor try to hurry them away, but simply let them trickle past him. Only during the last few days he was there – though he did not know for certain that they would be his last few days, for the schooner had no exact date fixed for her arrival – did he find this curious spiritual lethargy breaking down, to give way to an intense desire, a sudden hunger and thirst of the soul, to be away from all this, to be back home again, pulling his business together, settling into the life of Buntingham again, perhaps marrying and having children. At these moments he felt that all this journeying up and down the Pacific had been a miserable waste of time, with something corrupt at the heart of it.

The Blue Bell at Utterton

SOME people imagine that the industrial population of this country has at its command an unlimited supply of amusements on which it wastes its time and money. There is talk of decadent Rome, of games and circuses. Such people should spend a week working on the night shift at Utterton and trying to amuse themselves there in the afternoon, the night-worker's leisure period. Utterton is one of those small gloomy towns in the North Midlands, and its chief concerns are coal and various chemical products of the more unpleasant kind, such as acids and explosives. Its ten thousand inhabitants are housed monotonously behind blackened bricks. A tram or bus will soon take you out of the town, but the neighbouring countryside is depressing, having paid a stiff price for its coal and chemicals, and it implores you to forget about it and lose yourself in the town. But an ordinary afternoon in Utterton, even if the weather should happen to be fine, does not offer many attractions. Even the largest of the shops, the Utterton Co-operative Society's store, does not invite the passer-by to linger at its windows. There is a Free Library, but its reading-room is always filled with unemployed men, staring glumly at photographs of society beauties or polo teams until they are able to grab hold of a periodical that means something to them. There are no less than three picture-theatres in the town, but unfortunately they do not open until six o'clock on ordinary weekdays. There are football matches in winter and cricket matches in summer, but only on Saturdays or an occasional Thursday, when the shops are closed. You can, of course, go and stare at the canal, mostly oil and coal-dust; or at the little railway station, where ironical poster artists implore you to winter in Cairo; or at the fronts of the closed picture-theatres; or at your idle fellow-citizens, who stand about at every corner, but are in their thickest clusters in the Market Square, where they can watch the trams and buses arrive and depart, and catch the flying rumours of three o'clock winners. To these varied delights, on this Tuesday afternoon, there hurried that new decadent Roman, that pampered child of games and circuses, Charlie Habble. He took one look at the familiar Market Square, into which a little spring sunlight was faintly filtering, and then disappeared into the Smoke Room entrance of the largest public-house there, the 'Blue Bell'.

It would be easy to show the 'Blue Bell' crowded with poor sodden wretches who, urged and goaded by a merciless publican and his staff, were eagerly soaking in alcohol in order to forget their responsibilities and to give themselves courage to go back home, smash the furniture, beat their wives, and starve their children to death. It would be equally easy to show the 'Blue Bell' as a place of roaring good fellowship, with a Christmas-card atmosphere, the 'Boar's Head', Eastcheap, and the 'White Hart' out of Pickwick; good old ale, ripe characters, story and song; Merrie England and down-a-down-derry. Unfortunately neither of these fine and satisfying pictures would be anything but false. Behind the bar were two bored girls and a young man who loudly sucked at a hollow tooth; and in front of it were a few men who did not seem to be busy either drinking themselves to death or achieving any miracles of good fellowship. There were neither drunken curses nor shouts of laughter. The general atmosphere was like that of the Market Square itself, one of apathetic waiting: the barmaids were waiting for closing time; their customers were waiting for somebody they knew to arrive or for some moment to strike, a quarter-past or half-past; the place itself, like the whole town outside, seemed to be waiting for something to happen that it could hardly believe now would happen. Once inside, Charlie Habble knew immediately that the 'Blue Bell' would not cheer him up, but then he had not entertained great hopes of it.

The taller barmaid, who knew him by sight, brightened a little when she saw him, and as she set his glass of bitter on the counter she condescended to observe that his friend had not been in lately. As this 'friend' – for barmaids, whose work and outlook give them a rather too roseate view of masculine life and its relationships, are fond of this talk of 'friends' – was simply a man he had picked up one night there, a man he had never seen before or since, Charlie did not care whether the chap had been in or not, but he felt flattered by the barmaid's interest in him. It did not flatter his male vanity, for the young woman did not attract him at all; but it increased his self-respect and dignity as a citizen. He was noticed in the 'Blue Bell', and that was something. It gave him some sort of standing in the place.

Arrival at the New Cecil Hotel

CHARLIE had never seen anything like this place except in films, and not often in films. The carpet, which was a deep purple and went on for hundreds of yards, was inches thick. Somewhere a band was playing. There were a dozen men in purple and silver uniforms, and waiters in evening dress, page-boys, and saucy-looking girls in a fancy costume, who carried trays of papers and cigarettes. The chairs were so deep and soft that the people who sat down in them almost disappeared. The lighting was the cleverest he had ever seen, with not a lamp visible. Just having a look inside this place was as good as seeing a musical show at the theatre. Its one great drawback was that it was very stuffy, much too warm. Charlie felt he could hardly breathe. The only air to be had in there was so warmed up and scented and fourth-hand that your lungs found it useless. He had never been in so large and so high a room that seemed so suffocating. The very carpet threatened any minute to let you sink so far that you would be choked. There did not seem to be any windows, and once you were well inside the place, you could not tell by looking about you what time of day or night it might be. And all the men in uniform and the waiters looked as if they had forgotten long ago how to tell day from night.

Hughson marched him up to a sort of large desk that was all glass and shining metal. Behind it sat a very glossy young man, who might have been made out of silk hats and American cloth.

'The manager,' said Hughson grandly.

'I am very sorry, sir, but the manager is not in the building. He will not be back until six-thirty.'

'The assistant manager, then.'

'Certainly, sir. But may I ask – what name?'

'This is Mr Charles Habble, the man who saved Utterton and half the Midlands – and the nicer half. I am Mr Hughson of the *Daily Tribune*. The assistant manager at once, please.'

They waited while the glossy young man telephoned. 'Well, what do you think about this home from home?' Hughson asked. 'Is it or is it not fit for heroes to live in?'

'It's no place for me,' Charlie told him. 'Why, it's ridiculous. I shan't know what to do with myself in a place like this.

You might as well settle me into Buckingham Palace and have done with it.'

'Buckingham Palace! My dear chap, there's no comparison. Staying in Buckingham Palace would be roughing it after this place. This is wonder super de luxe. Even the very air, you notice, is predigested. But don't stand any nonsense from it, remember that. Treat it like a mere dog. Here's the assistant manager, on the run. He's keen, you can see that – oh – keen. I was just saying,' he added unblushingly, as the assistant manager came up, 'that you were obviously keen.'

'I am keen, very keen.' And, smiling, looking at them very hard, making vague sounds of welcome, he gave them a keen hand-shake. He was a tall fellow with a very wide mouth and prematurely bald in front, so that he appeared to have a colossal forehead. He was dressed in various natty arrangements of black-and-white, and Charlie never remembered seeing anybody who looked quite so neat. Having shaken hands with them, he brought his own hands together with a sharp slap. 'All arrangements have been made. We have a little suite on the second floor – one of our rose and grey Antoinette suites – for Mr Habble, whom we are proud to have as one of our guests. I will show it to you myself. This way, gentlemen, please.'

He led them to one of the lifts. 'Notice our system of indicators. I tell you instantly where your lift is, and I never fail.'

Charlie was a trifle puzzled by his last remark, for the man did not tell them where their lift was, but pointed to the indicator. It was only later that he realized that this was the assistant manager's way of talking, when he was at his keenest. He did not talk about the thing, he became the thing. Once they were in the lift, he became the lift. 'Notice, please, I'm free from air pressure. I don't give you that sinking feeling. And I stop exactly at the floor you want, can't stop anywhere else.' In the corridor on the second floor, he turned himself immediately into a system of light signals. 'You don't hear me ringing and ringing all the time,' he told them proudly. 'You don't hear a sound from me. I do my work quietly, entirely with lights.' But he was at his best as a rose and grey Antoinette suite, as bedroom, sitting-room, and bathroom. Charlie particularly admired him as a needle-spray bath. His final and grandest transformation was into the telephoning service system. 'You notice,' he cried, pointing to his other self, 'I'm a dial arrangement. You want the valet; all right, put me in there, take up my receiver, and merely ask. You want the shop – some studs, some flowers, a cigar, gloves, dress ties, or socks – slip me round there, speak into my receiver, and there you are – at the shop. I don't take a second and I'm foolproof.'

'What do I do to you if I want the Exchange?' Hughson enquired.

'Twist me round there and I'm through to our switchboard. When you've finished, put me back – like that. Simple, isn't it? Well, Mr Habble, we're delighted to see you here, and I hope we shall make you comfortable. Our motto is "Luxury and Service".'

'A very good motto, too,' said Hughson solemnly. 'I've never had enough of either.'

'All you've got to do is to ask,' he told Charlie. Then turning to Hughson, he said in a lower and more businesslike tone: 'Our publicity man, Mr Brooks, will be coming up soon. Good afternoon.' And he left them at ease in the rose and grey Antoinette sitting room, which was warm and airless and not unlike the inside of a chocolate-box.

'Wonder Hero' and 'Miss England'

It was quite late in the afternoon when he found Stanleydale Road, a street of tall, gloomy houses. The door of Number 25 hadn't been painted for a long time. The basement window was cracked, and through an opening in it there came the sound of an old gramophone and a smell of fried onions. The door was opened by a girl, so small and untidy that she looked like a ragamuffin child pretending to be a servant.

'Can I speak to Miss Ida Chatwick?' asked Charlie, his heart going bump-bump.

'Top floor. On the right,' the infant snapped, holding the door open. 'She's in.'

He did not walk up those stairs; for some strange reason, he crept up them. When he reached the top landing, he had to stop, not simply because he was out of breath, but because a swelling excitement inside threatened to suffocate him. There was her door, on the right. He kept quiet, did not move, for just then he heard something. Not mere crying, but sobbing; and it came from behind that door. An odd sort of sudden sweat seemed to break out all over him. He knocked on the door, and then at once the sound of sobbing ceased. He knocked again, and now there was movement inside the room. The door was opened just a few inches. 'What do you want?'

'It's me. Charlie Habble. Do you remember?'

And then he was inside the room, looking at her. He saw quite clearly how untidy and miserable she looked, her face all swollen; but she was the girl he had been thinking about all the time, the girl he was looking for. 'Nay,' he said gently, 'don't cry.' Involuntarily he opened his arms, and now, there she was, inside them pressing her face against his shoulder, crying like anything, while all he could do was to hold her tighter and make daft little noises at her. As he held her there the light of certain knowledge broke in upon his bewildered mind: he knew that all her great plans for herself had come to nothing; he knew that he would beg her to marry him and that he had only to persist and she would agree; he knew that she was weak and rather vain and would always be quickly dissatisfied, and was not at all the solid sensible girl that would make a good wife for a man like himself; he knew it all, and did not care: he was content with her there, heavy on his heart. The way they would take now together might not lead to easy content, might bring trouble down on them like rain:

but it was his road and hers, and they had to take it or refuse to live. In this moment, he was not the blind happy lover, but a wise man, one for whom, for a tick or two of time, there is a pattern in the shifting muddle.

'I've thought about you such a lot ...'

'I've thought about you all the time ...'

'I wondered where you'd got to ...'

'I've been looking for you for days and days, just to see you once before I went ...'

'But do you really ...?'

'All the time I have, only I never thought ...'

'I can't believe it, can you?'

'Think I can't! Are you sure ...'

'You're – well – you're you – that's it.'

'Is it? Tell me again. I haven't been me – not since I saw you last ...'

A lot of that, of course. At first the emotions drowned the words. Their hands, for ever coming together and then gripping hard, were more eloquent. They might have been – as indeed they felt they were – the only two real flesh-and-blood beings in a huge city of ghosts.

But after a cup of tea, how they talked then! Explaining themselves, reassuring one another, comparing this moment of his with that moment of hers, they talked the last glimmer of daylight out of the decaying chasm of Stanleydale Road; talked the fierce lights of commerce into the lower half of the sky and the mild non-commercial stars into the upper half, at which they stared together between Mrs Malligan's dirty lace curtains; while Mrs Malligan herself, over a bottle of stout in the basement, made up her mind to double the rent of the top floor right because the young lady up there had evidently decided to go in for the old game. Both lovers had a battle to describe, but it was Ida who could show the deeper wounds.

'I'll tell you now, Charlie,' she began. 'I couldn't before, when I didn't know how you felt about me. I was crying because I didn't know what to do. I'd thought of killing myself – turning the gas on or something. You can say it's all been so quick, I can't have had a bad time, but I have,

Charlie – it's been awful. I didn't know what to do, I didn't know what to do. You see, Charlie, I expected such a lot when I got that prize. You can't blame me, can you? Anybody would, wouldn't they? – after all that fuss. And I was no good for pictures – they told me so. I cried a lot then. But I tried other places, and it was no good. I went from one place to another until I could have dropped. Nobody offered me a decent job of any sort. I never met anybody all the time who was really friendly. The decent men told me straight out I wasn't any good and told me to go back home. The other sort – and there's plenty of them about – just wanted what they could get, and I could see they didn't even want that in a really friendly way. You see what I mean, Charlie? They didn't care about me – not one of them. You could tell that by the way they looked. I seem to have had hundreds looking like that at me – and it got worse and worse. And I was a little fool about that money they gave me as part of the prize. I was sure I was going to be all right, and I spent a lot of it, nearly all of it on clothes and things, and it just went. And I couldn't go home, Charlie. I just couldn't. Perhaps I would have done, I don't know – perhaps I would, instead of killing myself – because when it comes to the point, I know, I'm an awful coward. But I couldn't. I'd been so grand with them all after I'd got the prize and thought everything was going to be wonderful, and they'd have never let me forget it, never. If I'd just come to London as an ordinary girl looking for a job, I bet I could have stuck it all right, but I didn't, you see, Charlie. They brought me up here and made such a fuss about me, as if I was somebody wonderful, and then it all just went. And nobody cared at all – that was the really awful thing – nobody cared. Do you see what I mean, Charlie?'

'Yes, I see what you mean,' said Charlie slowly. 'It's the let-down that did it.'

'You see, it's like you going to a party or something and thinking everybody there so nice and friendly and all of them making such a fuss of you, and then suddenly it isn't a party at all and they're all strangers and nobody cares about you. Oh – Charlie!' And she clung to him.

'And don't forget,' he told her, 'that I've come a bigger cropper than you.'

'Charlie, don't say that – "cropper". That's what they always say in Pondersley. I could hear them saying, "Oh – she's come a cropper" – and that's why I was afraid to go home.'

'All right then, Ida. No croppers. But what I'm trying to say is that I'm only an ordinary working chap who hasn't even got a job at all just now. That hero business is all done with. Don't forget that.'

'I don't care, Charlie. Besides you're not an ordinary working chap at all – you've got a lot more about you. And now,' she added proudly, confidently, 'you're going to have a lot more still. Aren't you?'

'Am I?' But he felt himself growing a bit already. He realized, perhaps obscurely, that Ida might be weak on her own and yet strong when attached to him.

They crept closer, mumbled a little, and then were quiet. London, no concern of theirs now, went roaring by, as if over some Niagara. It did not matter any more; they had done with it, and were their own real selves again, only of course bigger and wiser than those two gaping fools who had been brought in triumph from the Midlands.

Fantasy in the Cotswolds

THE house itself had a Gothic craziness. There was no sense, though an infinite antique charm, in its assembled oddity of roofs, gables, windows, doorways. It might have been plucked straight out of one of Hoffmann's tales. You caught glimpses of such houses in the old silent films of the *Ufa* company, when it allowed its producers to be as romantic and symbolical as they pleased. There was a tiny courtyard between the house proper and a large outhouse, which had on its wall a painted wooden knight whose hand was waiting to strike a big bell.

In this courtyard were a score or so of white pigeons that rose and fluttered at our approach, so that for a second there seemed to be a blizzard raging. When the last pigeon had gone creaking to the roof, the courtyard and the manor house, the whole valley, sank again into deep quiet. Not a mouse stirred. Round the walls were coats-of-arms and painted inscriptions. Beyond the outhouse were descending squares of gardens, where a stream wandered from one clear carp pond to another, slipping past clumps of miniature box, marjoram and rue and thyme, and the shadow of the yews. Olivia and Malvolio would have been at home anywhere in this garden. We could not find its contemporary owner, of whom the gardener at the gate had only the vaguest news. I began to fancy that there was no such person or that at the best he would turn out to be a ghost. And when at last we did meet him, though he spoke and behaved like a very courteous and charming English gentleman of leisure, I could not rid myself of this fancy, which was sustained by the fact that his clothes and general appearance were not the clothes and general appearance of a contemporary person. He was, in fact, one of the last of a famous company, the eccentric English country gentry, the odd and delightful fellows who have lived just as they pleased, who have built Follies, held fantastic beliefs, and laid mad wagers. But why English? Was there not Don Quixote? You could have settled *him* into this house in a jiffy. I half expected to meet him.

The owner then, in the most charming fashion, conducted us over his house. He did not live there, but in the outhouse. The manor itself he now used as a sort of museum. The inside was as crazy as the outside, and as beautiful in its own way. We looked into ancient dim panelled rooms, in which were collections of spinning wheels, sedan chairs, model waggons, weapons, old musical instruments (you ought to have seen the black wooden Serpents), and blazing lacquer from Peking. One room was filled with old costumes, cupboard after cupboard of gowns, crinolines, uniform coats, bonnets, beaver hats, cockades. You could have dressed whole opera companies out of that room. I have never seen such a collection outside a public museum. He then took us over the outhouse, where he had his bachelor living-room and workshop. They looked at a first glance like the early illustrations to *The Old Curiosity Shop*. It is only those Dickens illustrations that can give you any idea of the amazing litter of things in these queer ramshackle rooms. There were tools and implements of every kind, coats-of-arms, skulls, black letter folios, painted saints, colossal tomes of plainsong, swords and daggers, wooden platters, and I know not what else. Neither in one house nor the other did I catch the smallest glimpse of a modern book or a newspaper or anything else that belongs to our own age. The twentieth century was nowhere in evidence and the nineteenth had only just dawned there. But the owner no longer spent his time collecting these relics of the past; his hobby now was the construction of a whole miniature old-fashioned seaport; boys' play on a smashing adult scale, defying all common sense but glorious in its absorption in the exquisitely useless. This miniature seaport, which must be on a scale of about an inch to a foot, for most of its houses were about two feet high, has a proper harbour in one of the ponds in the garden. It has its quay, its fleet of ships, its lighthouse, its railway system, with station, sidings and all, its inn, main street and side streets, thatched cottages, and actual living woods, made up of the dwarf trees in the garden. The owner, who has had some architectural training, has designed, built, and painted the whole village himself. It is portable, except for the harbour works, and is brought out and erected in the garden in summer and then taken into the house in winter. Its creator has now decided that it should have a castle, and he showed us an excellent preliminary drawing of this imposing building, which will be several feet long and will easily dominate the place. I hope there will be no trouble in the village with the two-inch lord of this castle, for by this time the place may have settled down to an easy democratic existence and it may resent this sudden descent into the feudal system. This Lilliputian seaport, which has a name, is still so real in my mind that I could easily write a novel about it. I know that, if I have a chance, I shall have to go there again and see what is happening to it, in the shadow of that castle, above which I shall be able to tower gigantically, like Gulliver himself. And if I have no opportunity of seeing it again, I am glad to have seen it once. It crowned the day for me. Most excursions of this kind, which begin with such promise, offering you some remote valley, some village or house drowned in lost time, so many signposts to what will be supremely odd and romantic, have a bad trick of fizzling out; but not this one, which became curiouser and curiouser until at last, at the other side of the moon, we landed at the seaport that was two feet high, in a harbour where the goldfish, fat fellows of nine inches or so, came glittering in like whales of red gold.

Liverpool Docks

We made for the docks. I had seen these docks before, but oddly enough, although I have sailed to or from Hull, Goole, Harwich, Tilbury, the Pool of London, Dover, Folkestone, Newhaven, Southampton, Plymouth, and Avonmouth, I have never either arrived at or departed from this port of Liverpool. Nor am I sorry, for they have always seemed to me most gloomy docks. That romance of the sea, about which we have always heard and read so much, has to set its opening chapter in some very dismal quarters of this country. Trams going whining down long sad roads; a few stinking little shops; pubs with their red blinds down and an accumulation of greasy papers under their windows; black pools and mud and slippery cobblestones; high blank walls; a suspicious policeman or two; that is usually the opening scene. You see it in London. You see it in Liverpool, miles of it. Docks and slums, docks and slums. We are an island people; even yet we owe nearly everything to the sea; our foodstuffs are brought in ships and our manufactures are taken away in ships; but when you visit most of our larger ports you see nothing but slums.

'Welcome!' we cry to the sailor, and immediately make him free of Wapping, London, and Wapping, Liverpool. If there is anything to choose between these two Wappings, the London one has it. I caught a glimpse of the other that afternoon. We reached the docks, put out our pipes and entered their precincts, where a vast amount of gloom and emptiness and decay was being carefully guarded. It was deep dusk. There were some last feeble gleams of sunset in the shadowy sky before us. Everything was shadowy now. The warehouses we passed seemed empty of everything but shadows. A few men – far too few – came straggling along, their day's work over. We arrived at the edge of the Mersey, and below us was a long mudbank. The water was a grey mystery, a mere vague thickening of space. Something hooted, to break a silence that immediately closed up afterwards to muffle the whole spectral scene. We walked slowly along the water-front, from nothing, it seemed, into nothing; and darkness rose rather than fell; and with it came a twinkle of lights from Birkenhead that reached us not across the river but over a gulf that could not be measured. I have rarely seen anything more spectral and melancholy. It was hard to believe that by taking ship here you might eventually reach a place of sharp outlines, a place where colour burned and vibrated in the sunlight, that here was the gateway to the bronze ramparts of Arabia, to the temples and elephants of Ceylon, to flying fish and humming birds and hibiscus.

Rehearsal in Newcastle

WE rode in trams again, among a smell of wet clothes. In the shadow of an enormous ebony bridge, which looked as if it stretched into the outer spaces of the universe, we found a large but almost deserted pub. But vague noises came from upstairs, and I was steered in their direction. That was the rehearsal. It was being directed by a middle-aged man in a blue suit, who peered at his players through the smoke of his cigarette. When we crept in, a spectacled young man in a raincoat was declaiming with passion some lines about Greek gods and Trojan heroes. 'Now then,' said the producer, when the spectacled youth had retired, gasping, 'now then, chorus.' Then, to my surprise, about a dozen women, mostly rather short women in coloured mackintoshes, who had been standing about in a slightly shamefaced fashion, like the mothers of children at a dancing class, suddenly grouped themselves, slowly moved forward, as if sowing imaginary seed or strewing invisible flowers, and in far-away voices began chanting verses that prophesied woe. A very tall girl, as if maddened by the sight of so many coloured mackintoshes, rushed out of a corner, flung up an arm, made her eyes flash away as if she were a human lighthouse, and angrily addressed the chorus, giving them three woes to their one. This roused another young man in a raincoat, who appeared to be in a towering rage and apparently did not care if he gave himself a sore throat. But the raincoats were not to have it all their own way. The mackintoshes grouped themselves again and returned to their chanting, conducted enthusiastically by the producer, who encouraged me to hope that he was about to throw away his cigarette and dance for us. Perhaps he might have done, but just then a rather shy and pretty tweed winter coat swam forward and told us softly that she was Argive Helen, and then delivered quite a long speech about herself, with coloured mackintoshes rustling all round her. Those who know the *Trojan Women* may search in vain for a scene in it resembling this, and possibly my memory may have failed me; but it was certainly the *Trojan Women* they were rehearsing. If you had been standing in the saloon bar downstairs and had heard them moving about on the floor above, how many guesses would you have had to make before you reached the right conclusion? You would have said they were playing snooker, or dancing, or having a whist drive, and might have gone on guessing for days before you had suggested that they might be rehearsing the *Trojan Women*. If you were writing a story about a large pub in Newcastle, you would never have the impudence to fill its first-floor front with people rehearsing Greek drama. But there is no end to the impudent surprises and odd twists of reality. My companion had now quietly delivered his message, and at the conclusion of Helen's speech and before the mackintoshes could get going again, we sneaked out, and down the stairs I muttered: 'What's Hecuba to them, or they to Hecuba?'

The Copper Kettle Café

IN Greater London, a stone and brick forest nearly thirty miles long, thirty miles broad, eight million people eat and drink and sleep, wander among seven thousand miles of streets, pay their insurance money, send for the doctor, and die. Through the centre of this vast area of asphalt hills and paved valleys, these orchards of lamp-posts and traffic lights, the River Thames goes winding, looking from above no more than a silvered thread lying across an arterial road. Yet the river made all this. The river brought the old Roman galleys (one of them could be floated on the weekly milk supply of the modern city) from Ostia to the port of Londinium, for those cargoes of wheat and lead that might be taken as symbolic of the later national character of these island people. The river carefully laid along its terraces a nice mixture of clay and sand, that brick-earth out of which this forest grew. The inhabitants drink the river, run it through their wash basins and bath tubs, two hundred million gallons a day. Do they think about the river? Some do, even apart from those who still work on its greasy dimpled flood. Everything that man has thought about is considered here by somebody, from the diameter of Betelgeuse to the smaller parasites of the flea. Not since the City of the Golden Gates sank with all Atlantis has there been, in any one area of the world, so much thinking about everything, as well as so much stupidity about everything, as there is here. Eight million human creatures. The commercial capital of the globe. But there is commerce here unknown to the Port of London Authority, the Stock Exchange, the Board of Trade. The thoughts, the dreams, the old shuddering fears of these eight millions depart along fantastic wave-lengths, leaving our own familiar space-time continuum, to build little heavens and hells in new time and strange dimensions of space. In exchange, radiations from distant stars penetrate the haze and perhaps bring to the pavements below obscure news that cannot be found in the evening papers. As we know, there are eight million private dramas being acted in this jungle of brickwork and cement, where steel-clawed ravenous monsters like bankruptcy and unemployment and angina pectoris and starvation and cancer come crashing through the thickets, where a favourable bank balance and a good digestion and an easy mind and love-found-and-fulfilled occasionally light the jungle ways with a flash of blue wings. But there are also eight million parts being acted here in a gigantic Mystery, with green globes and moons and suns and black space as scenic sets, a few tattered pages as a prompt book, and two famous illusionists, Here and Now, as stage managers. And what this is all about, nobody knows. The youngest of six half-starved children, listening to the rats in the darkness of a back room in Hoxton, does not know. The expensively educated and comfortably maintained elderly clerical gentleman who writes for the papers telling us all is well (or as well as is deserved) with this youngest of six in Hoxton, does not know. The gaunt young man hard at it in the Reading Room of the British Museum, preparing to denounce the elderly cleric and all his kind, does not know. Eight million, with all their houses, furniture, knick-knacks, mortgages, insurance policies, bills of sale, prescriptions, and love letters, rolling on in one gigantic Mystery. And eight million busy with their own private dramas, making the whole stone forest steam and hum. And there among them, toiling away with a thousand other organizations to victual them, is the Copper Kettle Café Company, Ltd.

Strange as it may seem, this company owed its success to the fact that most of the eight million are still poetically and not scientifically minded. Sometimes in happy ignorance, sometimes perhaps not, it fed its customers with increasing quantities of citric and tartaric acid and cotton-seed oil, sulphur dioxide and sodium sulphate and potassium bromate, manganese and copper, lead and arsenic. But these chemicals and metallic poisons were consumed in an atmosphere, specially created by the company, that lured the vague poetical mind of the customer away from all consideration of scientific matters. It reminded the customer of the time when meat and fish were not taken out of a tin, when there was real yeast and honest flour in bread, when fruit came straight from the tree and not from sulphur dioxide gas chambers. It belonged to some Arcadian ideal of English life, in which buxom, apple-cheeked landladies and sweet demure serving maids waited behind chintz curtains upon the traveller with all that was fresh, pure, delicious in food and drink. Once inside a Copper Kettle café, which had a large imitation copper kettle hanging above its entrance, you forgot the roaring and stinking petrol engines outside, the smoke and the fog and the mud, the miles and miles of brick and stone and steel concrete, the whole metropolitan madness. You were back where actually you never belonged. You were a child again with a picture book.

Bloomsbury Hotel Bedroom

It was high and narrow, and both the longer walls bulged inwards, to suggest that at any time now it might be narrower still. It was furnished with a single brass bedstead, a wash-hand basin and jug, a squat brownish chest of drawers and a mirror, a brownish bedside cabinet with a cracked marble top, and two yellow cane-bottomed chairs. The uncompromising rules and regulations of the Lomond Hotel, which seemed to regard its guests as potential criminals, were tacked on the door. There were no pictures on the walls, only an endless pattern of pickled cabbages and decayed grapes. Young and hopeful and excited though he was, Edward was immediately cast down, instantly defeated, by this bedroom. Compared with this, the third-class railway carriage in which he had spent the last five hours had been a cosy home. There was a chill mustiness about the atmosphere of this bedroom, a cold contempt for its occupants, a vault-like air of being entirely removed from the real warm life of humanity, that took the heart out of him. He felt at once that he was only the latest of a long line of people, arriving here in high hopes, who had been desolated by this room. And he was right. The only flavour these inhuman boxes have is that of their occupants' accumulated misery. They smell of disappointment, loneliness, despair. They are not hotel bedrooms in the greatest city in the world, they are the narrow way, the dangerous gate, the ordeal, through which all newcomers must pass before they can reach the gold-paved streets. Mrs Parkinson, that little maid, that gummy old man, with their sinister appearances and disappearances, are not real people waiting on travellers; they are infernal sentries, devilkins of the gate, goblin inspectors and examiners.

The Hospital

'You won't like it, you know.' Beatrice's eyes, like two dark birds of prey, were fixed on Rose's. 'That hospital – it's hellish. If they were miserable, it wouldn't be so bad. But – but –' and her voice lifted and shook and took on a terrible intensity – 'they're all so bloody bright.'

No sooner had they entered the hospital, early the following evening, than Rose knew exactly what Beatrice had meant. It was not an ordinary hospital. You did not go in there to have a finger taken off or a broken bone mended. It was a hospital for those who were dying by inches. We are all dying by inches, we are all slowly rotting above our graves, but unlike the patients in that hospital, we are not constantly aware of the fact. But they knew all about their inches. They stared out of decaying bodies. Yet the whole institution, with its long corridors, its polished floors, its shining wards, its starched white uniforms, its little wagons of dressings and drugs, its trays and flowers and screens and framed notices, was determinedly bright. From floor to floor, ward to ward, with the doctors and attendant matrons, went thousands of little jokes, some of them the tiniest jokes known to man. The nurses wore a fixed smile, had loud cheerful voices, and told one another, over the beds they were straightening, what a ridiculously spoilt lot their patients were. And the patients themselves, while the mind kept watch at all in the crumbling tower of the body, chaffed the nurses, and exchanged among themselves, while the nurses could overhear them, merry little anecdotes about missing floor brushes, belated sleeping draughts, cups of tea that had gone cold. Within these walls was a little world, and a world from which many things, such as sex, economics, politics, had been banished. Once inside there, it did not matter if democracy or autocracy should win, capitalism was as good as socialism, easy divorce as moral as divorce made difficult, and all systems of education were alike. Newspapers ceased to be important. A perpetual gentle birthday party seemed to be going on in there. When a guest was ready to leave it, screens were placed round his bed, and doctors and nurses, their set smiles fading for once, disappeared behind them, and very soon the male orderlies brought the stretcher from the mortuary. Next day, probably, there was a bewildered new face, a new guest, and the party went on, with a few new jokes in circulation. Even at parties in the best society some guests will be tactless, and it happened here now and then, often in the middle of the night, when the world might easily seem one vast torture chamber, with Pain lording it over the universe, for then somebody might suddenly scream and scream. But these little slips were never referred to, always carefully ignored. And on the third floor of this hospital, in a small ward with three other men, was Lawrence Vintnor, in the twenty-sixth and last year of his life.

'Lawrence,' said Beatrice, and even she was brighter in here than she was outside, 'this is Rose.'

'Hello,' said Lawrence, putting out a bloodless hand. It clung to Rose's as if it were feeding upon her vitality.

He was like Beatrice, with the same eyes, the same nose. He was so much like Beatrice that Rose never saw her again without being reminded of him, a fact of some importance, for her subsequent adventures would have been quite different if it had not been for this resemblance. But Lawrence was not merely thin, he was a shadow of a young man. All the life that was left to him was burning away in his great eyes. He was a staring, faintly smiling skeleton. Rose had had no experience at all of death, and very little of sickness, but she knew at once that Beatrice had been right: this brother of hers was dying. Even now he seemed to belong to Death rather than to Life. He was smiling at her out of the grave. At the first moment of their encounter, Rose had been startled and repelled, all the more so because there seemed to come from this wasted figure a faint but sickly sweet odour of decay and corruption. But no sooner had he smiled, had his hand clung to hers, had she looked into the great hollow eyes, than her feelings changed, and from some depths, unknown to her before, there came rushing a deep spring of emotion, almost sweeping her away. She felt ready to cradle him in her warm arms, to give him her own rich blood, to stay there and care for him day and night until he was cold for ever. This feeling was quite impersonal. To her he was not a person, but at once more and less than a person. She was so strongly moved that she could not speak, she could only look at him and try to smile at him.

The Lovers in the British Museum

THEY looked about them, wonderingly. Those half-animal, half-human gods and goddesses, ready to frighten your life out, but understandable in a queer way! These kings! What chaps! The huge heads, like those of stone giants buried up to the neck, staring out, waiting to be released, to stump straight out into Great Russell Street, with half the gallery hanging round their shoulders!

'You know, Edward,' said Rose, shyly and earnestly, 'I think you can tell about these emperors and kings or whatever they were, just by looking at these heads of them. You know that some were nice and kind, and some were terrible and cruel. There's something about them that tells you. Look at that one.'

'He's a fierce one.'

'I'll bet he was a human devil. And still is, if you give him half a chance. I wouldn't come here at night by myself and stand looking at him – not for anything. He'd come alive again, and start ordering the others to do all kinds of devilish things. Honestly, he would, Edward.'

She took his arm and squeezed it. He looked to see if anybody was coming, and then drew her behind the gigantic head and arm of *Thothmes III*. When he tried to kiss her, she made a little face at him and escaped by turning away, but when she saw his look of disappointment, she turned back, rested in his arms, and sweetly raised her lips to his. And for several moments they stayed there, pygmies in the shadow of that head and arm, but so rapt and oblivious in the trembling primrose ecstasy of first love that it is a wonder that all those gigantic heads did not turn towards them and open despairing eyes, that the granite and black marble fists did not clash together, that all the vast litter and ruin of dead-and-gone life there did not quiver in ghostly reawakening and cry: 'We too, we too! We remember. At Thebes and Memphis, Babylon and Nineveh, Xanthus and Halicarnassus, in temples that are dust, and gardens that are desert, long ago, long ago. But we too, we remember.'

Hand in hand, these children of our day, which has a streaked red sky that might mean sunrise or sunset, stared at Sennacherib and Ashur-nasir-pal and Shalmaneser and Ashur-bani-pal, and made little or nothing of them and their victories and their conquests and their tributary kings and their palaces and horsemen and footmen. The long bearded faces spoke never a word. The kings of kings were silent for ever. Yet the happiness Rose and Edward knew might never have flowered, the two of them might never have met, never even have existed, if one of these kings had not boasted in his cups, if one of these horsemen had not fallen wounded far from Assyria, and who shall trace that path and write that chronicle? And though we know who Sennacherib was and what came of him, who knows who we are and where we are going? Those winged lions from Ashur-nasir-pal's doorway have survived nearly three thousand years. Where will they be in another thousand years, and who will be looking at them then?

The Aircraft Factory

ONCE inside the factory we shall have to stay there, so we had better take a quick look at it first from the outside. It is the main factory of the Elmdown Aircraft Company Limited, which is known to be doing quite a good job. It is tucked away into a misty hollow in the South Midlands, with a long flat space behind for the airfield. It's all okay. Rather out of the way, of course, ten miles from the nearest town, but that was what was wanted. From high above, as the test pilots frequently report, the factory can hardly be seen at all. The roofs are nicely camouflaged, and the stiff coloured netting, breaking the hard angles, is a wizard show. Even from the ground, on some days, the giant sheds are not easy to make out. Staring through the mist at those painted walls, you might think you were looking at a queer toy village.

One of our grandfathers, suddenly arriving here, would have thought somebody had gone mad. From the old-fashioned standpoint, there's a kind of lunacy about the place. The very road outside the factory does not seem to belong to that country at all, and might have been hastily unrolled there like a vast gritty carpet. The factory itself, when it stops being a toy village with painted trees and meadows, looks as if it had not been built there but brought from some distant city and dropped by the roadside, as if a giant child, using the whole country as its sand-pit, had picked the thing up and then idly poked it into position with an immense forefinger. Half a dozen liners, jammed together between those low green hills, would hardly look more out of place. And just after dawn and then again at dusk, the population of a small town swarms in or out of that front entrance. They come and go in cars, on bicycles, and packed into buses. It looks like a conjuring trick. In fact, it is a conjuring trick. Where do they all come from? Where do they go to? Who are they? They emerge in a dim thick stream of humanity – for daylight has either not quite arrived or just gone – and then instantly thin out, disperse, and vanish. A grinding of gears, a hooting of horns, some tinkling of bicycle bells, a shout or two, and they are gone. Except on Saturday. Then, daylight sees them, and they see daylight. That's their life – and perhaps now it is all our lives – daylight on Saturday. And not before.

But what happens when you have passed the notices about unauthorized persons, the guarded gate and the barbed wire, the sergeants with brick-red faces and indigo uniforms, when you have shown your pass and punched the time-clock? Won't daylight find you, sooner or later, inside the factory? No, there is no daylight inside the factory. There are no windows. The roofs are darkened. The factory inside is like a colossal low bright cave, lit with innumerable mercury-vapour lamps that produce a queer greenish-white mistiness of light. In there three in the morning and three in the afternoon just look the same. Nothing tells you except the rhythm of work whether it is noon or midnight. You might be deep in a mountain or at the bottom of the sea. The pageant of the hours, sunrise to high noon, sunset to glittering night, and the old procession of the seasons, all the budding, flowering and withering of the world, all have vanished. For this is a cave life. It is a magic cave, with money – perhaps more than you have ever seen before – adding itself for you, with hot-pot and ginger pudding simmering and steaming in electric ovens, and unending streams of thick dark tea, with music, hot or sweet, screaming above the machine tools, with ultra-violet rays and radiant heat and M. & B. 693 to be had for the asking, and, not least, with urgent work to be done. It is perhaps the same cave in which Aladdin found himself imprisoned by the magician, the cave of the wonderful lamp. If you can find the lamp and use it properly, you can ask for palaces and gardens, and they will be yours. It may turn out yet to be that very cave.

It is a greenish-white hive in which the combs are stored with shaped non-ferrous metals. It is a termitary out of which come rolling great winged creatures. It is a power-house. Take away these drawing offices, these toolmakers' sheds, these long rows of machines, these workers on assembly, and within ten days the whip is at your back. All the brave drilled men, willing to rush towards death, all the flags and national anthems, all the patriotic speeches, cannot rescue a people now. Without such factories as this, they are lost or dependent. Where these factories are, there is power. Without them we could not survive in wartime, and it is unlikely that we shall be able to survive without them – with different jigs turning out different jobs, and the rhythm easier, but otherwise with not many great changes – in the world after the war. They will remain power-houses. What we don't know yet is for whose sake their power will be operated. We can only hope. Daylight on Saturday.

And now we are inside the Elmdown Aircraft Company's factory, and must stay there. Sun, moon, and stars are gone, and there is only the unearthly, lunar glare of the mercury-vapour lamps. There are faces everywhere, thousands of faces, vivid, sometimes startling, in this dramatic top-lighting. Even above the screeching and hammering and rasping of metal on metal, voices can be heard. Behind the eyes that stare at the lathes and presses, at tiny gears and tangles of insulated wire, at great curved flanks of aircraft, thoughts are busy, dreams glow and fade. Here are people.

End of the Day Shift

It was nearly the end of the day shift. The rhythm of work, which had slackened during the tea period and just afterwards, had suddenly speeded up again, as if everybody were making a last, blinding effort, as if both men and machines were desperately trying to carry the day by a final assault. The sounds seemed both harsher and higher, with a hint of the hysterical in them. The planing, milling, drilling, hammering noises reached a deafening unison. The metal screamed a last protest. The white sparks flew in crazy showers. The lighted caves, with their twinkling greenish mist, seemed endless, as if whole new vast sheds had been suddenly added. The thousands of faces under that remorseless top-lighting now looked like caricatures of those that had arrived this morning: eyes that had been merely deep-set were now startlingly sunken; small noses dwindled to mere buttons of flesh, while large noses became terrifying beaks across which the tightly-drawn skin might snap at any moment; thin elderly mouths disappeared altogether; and generous young ones, with what remained of the crimson lipstick on them turning dark and purple, pouted and gaped in a mysterious sensuality; there were faces like those of corpses, and faces that might have belonged to galvanized dolls. The energy of the place seemed now a little out of control, as if at any moment, if that time signal did not ring, metal would bite and tear into metal without respect for any gauge or micrometer, as if soon whole machines would vanish in blazing fountains of sparks, as if the very mercury-vapour lamps would begin to spout green liquid fire and the quivering air itself would crackle and explode.

Mr Cheviot stood again on his balcony, brooding over the wide scene. He might have been a stage director and this the dress rehearsal of his greatest spectacle. He too had had a long day, not unlike an eleven-hour obstacle race. He was worried about his production figures, which were down again. There were various good reasons for it – and he had them all ready in his mind – but he knew that they were not good enough. In the last resort it was the human factor that counted. You could make things easier and quicker for the workers; you could drive them a bit; you could do still more by encouraging them; but when all was said and done, their individual efforts, which when added together gave the factory its production, depended upon what they were thinking and feeling about the war. If they were indifferent, bored or depressed, as so many of them were now, then they just couldn't stay on their toes. It was only natural. Mr Cheviot, a fair man and not without wisdom, did not blame them, not even to himself. But they would have to be gingered up somehow or other.

A figure wearing an overcoat untidily and a hat at the back of its head, an arrangement that suggested that here was a man who did not care whether he went or stayed, joined him on the balcony, lit a cigarette, and stared gloomily down at the crowded roaring floor.

Mr Cheviot turned. 'Well, Bob? Taking a last look, eh?'

Elrick continued to stare down. 'Y'know, you'd think, to look at 'em now, they were all sweating their guts out. Now wouldn't you, Mr Cheviot, eh?'

The other nodded. 'I've been thinking about those figures too. They won't do, will they, Bob? No, they won't do.'

'God save us! You needn't tell me,' cried Elrick bitterly.

'I know I needn't,' said Mr Cheviot easily, turning now completely to look hard at his works superintendent, who had an explosive reckless air about him.

'Take it easy, Bob. Just take it easy,' he said, giving the other a companionable touch on the shoulder.

'That's their trouble – they're taking it so damned easy,' cried Elrick, drawing at his cigarette in a bitter contemptuous manner, as if it were a thing he despised.

'I know, but it's never been your trouble, either inside or outside the works.' Mr Cheviot hesitated a moment, then brought his formidable eyebrows down hard. 'What are you doing tonight, Bob?'

'Doing? Me?' Elrick seemed to hurl the enquiry right away from him. 'Going home, I expect. I'm not off on a blind, if that's what you're worrying about.'

'No, no, that's not it at all. But I was wondering. If they're not expecting you particularly –'

'They expect me when they see me,' said Elrick sharply. 'And it doesn't matter a damn either way.'

'Then come and have a bite of dinner with us, Bob,' said Mr Cheviot. 'I can give my wife a ring, and I know she'll be pleased to see you, and there are one or two things we might talk over, eh?'

Elrick's hard and rather swollen face suddenly dropped whole years, as if a mask had been ripped off it, and now there was almost a boy's shyness lurking in it. He nodded. 'Thanks very much, Mr Cheviot. If it's no trouble. A bit of company tonight –' But his voice died away.

The hard clamour of the time signal rang throughout the enormous shed, and immediately the roaring and screaming of the machines sank to a hum, above which the sound of relieved voices could soon be heard. Thousands of little figures in white, green or purple overalls began swarming towards each end of the shop. Several rows of lights vanished, and here and there were sudden invasions of dimness and quiet. Another day shift was done. And two men, feeling tired and somewhat dispirited but conscious of a little warmth of understanding and companionship between them, turned abruptly and left the balcony.

Music While You Work

A LITTLE later, as if to provide the necessary rich accompaniment to Nelly's confused but glorious speculations, the Scottish Variety Orchestra of the B.B.C. came crashing into its 'Music While You Work'. One of the loud speakers was not very far from Nelly, and to her all the familiar noises of the factory paled and faded before this new, highly-coloured, and glittering pageant of sound. As she listened, entranced, little pictures, like fragmentary bright dreams, went zig-zagging across her mind with the music. A military march, brassy and triumphant, brought a glimpse of soldiers on parade, not the grim, steel-helmeted soldiers of wartime, but the other and somehow more real soldiers of peacetime and picture books, gay and harmless in their scarlet and shining black, like life-sized busy toys. A lilting, whistling tune, heard years ago, recovered some memory of a seaside holiday, and suddenly the worn planks of the pier were there, the white dresses, the canvas shoes, the ice cream and peppermint rock, the salty wind and the vast blue twinkle of the sea. A waltz, perhaps from some musical comedy film she had once seen, conjured into the misty greeny-white light of the factory some richer and more golden lights, coming from great chandeliers, under which there twirled mysterious hussars and lovely blonde girls in glimmering silk gowns. And then the inevitable spurs went *jingle-jangle-jingle* again, and Nelly, who liked a good Western, went trotting across strange cactus-haunted deserts with tall horsemen, heroes every one of them with deep thrilling voices, pretending to ride away but only waiting to worship the ground some girl, not unlike Nelly, trod on, heroes with small dark moustaches, strong arms, and great black horses ...

And there, by her side, smiling down at her, *was* a hero. This was Wing-Commander Reeves, R.F.C., late of Fighter Command and now seconded for duty to the Ministry of Aircraft Production. Nelly had seen him several times before, for he came round the factory regularly, and had once given them all a talk in the canteen, and another time had introduced two other airmen to them there. Mr Cheviot had told them once how Wing-Commander Reeves had fought in the Battle of Britain, how he had won his decoration, and how he had been shot down with his Spitfire blazing. And now Wing-Commander Reeves had two quite different faces. The one you saw on the right side was smooth, brown, handsome, and smiling, the face of a good-looking young man who had curly fair hair, attractive blue eyes, and a small fair moustache, really an adorable young man. The one you saw on the left side was hardly a face at all, for it was very rough, purplish, fixed and glaring, and didn't look young or old but altogether queer and different, like a face from the moon or somewhere. And Nelly knew that he had spent months and months in hospital just having that doubtful sketch of a face put together for him. And from whichever side you looked at him, Wing-Commander Reeves, so to speak, got you, for the right side attracted you at once, just because it was so manly, handsome, and merry, and the left side made you so sorry for him that you felt ready to do anything he asked; although all that he did ask was that you should work as hard as you could to give the boys more planes. And now here he was, by her side, smiling at her, and it looked as if for the first time he was going to speak to her personally.

'Hello!' he said.

'Good afternoon,' she replied, shyly.

'Seen you before, haven't I?' he said.

'I expect so,' she said, blushing.

'Yes, I have, definitely,' he said, with the right eye twinkling away. 'What are you working on now?' And he had a look while she explained. Then he told her briefly what happened to the part she was making, where it went in the plane and what it did. And the whole business at once became more sensible and more important when he explained it. Probably that was why they kept him coming round to see them.

Death in a Factory

THERE was no pain where Elrick was now, but it was a long way off, darkish and getting colder and very lonely. He didn't like this loneliness, though he knew it was reasonable enough, for he realized that for all these people, these faces and voices and movements that no longer meant anything much, things were still going on, there was today to finish and tomorrow to wonder and worry about, whereas for him it was all over now. Their time was still running on, and they were hurrying with it, but his time was nearly done, only the faintest beat and lightest pulsing shadow of it remained with him, so that he no longer had to do any hurrying but could be quiet and still.

One of the faces – and he saw quite clearly that it was grimy and tear-stained – suddenly stood out from the others, and he knew that it was a good face, and important to him, and now he recognized it.

'Why, Gwen –' he said.

And it seemed not only to her but to several of the others there that when Elrick said that, with surprise and delight in his voice, and with a look that brightened before it faded for ever, he was not going away but arriving somewhere, not ending but beginning. But where he was arriving and what he was beginning, they would never know, because he did not speak again and in a little while was dead.

Sunday Morning

AT first this Sunday morning in Dunbury was like all the others, so quiet that the sun might have suddenly bounced up the sky in the middle of the night and caught everybody napping. It was a nice fine morning, with a bit of mist round its edges. Not many people came out to enjoy it. Some whole streets were so empty that they were like theatrical sets waiting for a harlequinade. At a few places in or near the market square the startling placards of the Sunday newspapers had been set out in a row, together with piles of the papers themselves, in which important journalists emphatically affirmed what they had equally emphatically denied two or three Sundays before, members of the peerage described their beautiful women friends, and the smallest piece of gossip from Hollywood was given far larger type and far more space than the combined arts and sciences and philosophy of Great Britain. For those who preferred the spoken to the printed word, the enterprising young minister of the Norfolk Road Congregational Chapel was preaching on 'Traffic Signals on the Spiritual Road'; and the Rev. S. A. Philips, B.A., of the North Dunbury Wesleyan Church had arrived at 'Your Problem and the Bible: 3'; and our friend the rector from West Dunbury was allowing his curate, a keen sound young fellow who had bowled a very useful off-break all summer for the Dunbury second eleven, to try his hand at 'St Paul and Appeasement'.

Here and there were the usual solitary men, standing at corners, smoking short pipes, and ruminating. What thoughts are theirs, as they survey these empty Sunday streets, nobody knows; they may be meditating upon doomsday, or wondering whether to make it a glass of mild at the 'Lion' or half a pint of bitter at the 'Bull'. A few pairs of sedate elderly men walked out of town to look at the yellow autumn fields and the golden mists and to discuss cottage property and the retail coal trade. A few packs of small boys, returning from Sunday School, jeered at each other, kicked stones to ruin their best shoes, and pointed and shouted at every passing car. But there was not much traffic: a bus or two, with a leisurely Sunday air about them; a few of those overcrowded little family cars wobbling and wandering uncertainly towards the country; and now and then an impatient fast car, thick with the dust of some distant county, knowing and caring nothing about Dunbury, but roaring on to some mysterious remote destination, and leaving behind it a deeper quiet and emptiness that had some hint of irony.

Even after half-past twelve, when church- and chapel-goers were about the streets, and groups of young men, like football teams in mufti, appeared from nowhere, and pairs of girls, either very solemn or giggling, flitted by, and solid citizens massively emerged to enjoy a pint before tackling the roast-beef-and-Yorkshire, even then, at the peak of morning, the town was still quiet and empty. There seemed hardly any life in it. But of course you could not see all the housewives, with wisps of hair falling over and tickling their hot shiny faces, who were having their weekly wrestle with kitchen stoves or gas-ovens, to produce that roast-beef-and-Yorkshire and a nice apple pie to follow. Plenty of activity among them, of course, and, indeed, Nature can show us few creatures more active, cracking and sparking with a more furious energy, than women who have spent a warmish morning in an under-sized kitchen cooking a dinner they do not particularly want to eat themselves. Sheer exasperation seems to give them a higher voltage. It is at these times when husbands and children, who now seem like so many idiotic passengers who have suddenly invaded the engine-room, are apt to hear something unpleasant about themselves. Barbed words come whizzing out of the kitchen. Vast edifices of masculine sham now crumble at a blow. Mines that were set in position weeks before are now exploded, in a flash, between setting down the gravy and picking up the custard. If you want a revolution to begin among the English lower-middle-class, you have only to call out all the women at about ten minutes to one on any Sunday. Anything left standing after they had done would most certainly be destroyed by the crowd of hungry and embittered husbands.

PEOPLE

The Pessimists

LAST Sunday they were in magnificent form. They had been walking all Saturday, and had managed to cover an odd ten or twelve miles that very morning. They bellowed their news and stretched themselves in my sitting-room, sang and splashed in the bathroom, and then came down to put away the lunch of six. My bottled beer went winking down their throats. My coffee disappeared between two epigrams. They filled their youthful and aggressive pipes, blew out great blue clouds of old matured Virginia and young raw satisfaction, and then accompanied me into the garden, where we lounged and smoked through the afternoon. We watched the sunlight fall upon the ripening pears. Across the lawn, the seven-foot hollyhocks stood like girlish grenadiers. The poppies blazed among the distant weeds. From somewhere close but mysterious there came a murmuring of doves, and far away an old bell jangled faintly. The afternoon went rustling by in blue and white. Well-fed, glowing, their strong young limbs outstretched, my guests leaned back, and after smoking idly for some time with half-closed eyes, at last began to talk. The moment was ripe for a symposium, and Epicurus himself would not have disdained the situation. Naturally enough, they grew philosophical.

Objecting to some timid remark of mine, A. pointed out that all our efforts are probably futile. His companion loudly and cheerfully agreed, and together, with raised voices, they hunted down man's foolish strivings and little sentimentalisms, hallooing as they went. Their sparkling eyes saw inward visions of this life as a desert, marked only by the whitening bones of wasted effort. They roared together over our pitiful illusions. Politics and art and religion and love were whirled away on gusts of laughter. Our whole civilization might perish at any moment, if, indeed, it was not perishing already. Gleefully, their faces alight, they pointed out to one another the unmistakable signs of this collapse, and upon me they rained evidence. They kicked out in ecstasy as flaw after flaw was discovered in this structure of ours. But now there arrived a difference of opinion between them, which resulted in the jolliest argument imaginable and all the pointing with pipe stems and the frequent striking of matches that accompany such jolly arguments. B. emphatically declared that the sooner this civilization was nothing more than a memory, the better it would be for all of us. A. was positive that it was doomed, but thought we had probably made a mistake in letting it go, if only because our next state would be immeasurably worse. For this he was heartily chaffed by B., who said that he would not have suspected his friend of such obvious sentimentalism. Then they both began to examine the situation more closely, making fewer concessions to mere human weakness and broadening the base of the discussion, so that by the time we had sat down to tea they were in full flight.

'The fact is, of course,' cried A., dealing heartily with his fifth sandwich, 'the universe is entirely indifferent to any of our concerns. A minor planet goes rotten and begins to breed all kinds of queer creatures, and after a time these creatures have the impudence to imagine that their affairs are important, that what they want is what the universe wants. As a matter of fact, though, that's wrong because the universe doesn't want anything. It will just grind away till it stops, and we might as well recognize the fact. We can make up our minds that the whole show will be blotted out sooner or later – and, on the whole, a jolly good thing, too! What do you say, B.?' And he beamed at us, and passed his cup for the third time. 'I don't mind how weak it is,' he remarked. 'I'm still thirsty enough for anything.'

B. cut himself a hearty chunk of cake and patted it lovingly. 'I don't agree with you,' he began. 'You're nothing but an old materialist. You're years out of date, you and your mechanical universe! I don't mind telling you, too, that you're a jolly sight too optimistic. The universe is alive all right and knows what's going on here. But why? –' And here he paused and A. reached out for a cigarette. 'To make an unholy mess of it, of course. The old idea was right all the time. We're just a droll spectacle for the gods. If there's a supreme deity, then you may depend upon it, he's probably a sadist.'

A. considered this view and clearly found it attractive, but was compelled, perhaps a trifle reluctantly, to reject it. He went on to draw a picture of man, doomed to perish with all his little notions of beauty and goodness, standing erect, his head lifted to the pitiless stars; and so warmed to the task that he quite forgot to finish his tea and keep his cigarette alight. Dancing with impatience, B. finally cut in with his own view of things, and showed us this life of ours as a tragedy of marionettes, with a dominating principle of evil, a malicious and omnipotent power, pulling the strings. We were allowed to develop so that our capacity for suffering might be increased. His companion declared that this view was far more rosy and sentimental than his, because 'people would rather have an evil spirit than none at all.' B., on his side, humorously incensed at the notion that he was at the old trick of pandering to human weakness in his revelation of truth, waved away what he called 'this pleasant little idea of the machine universe', and added more crimson and black to his own picture of things. The cottage resounded with the flushed and eager pair of them, but the talk had gone little farther before it was time for them to be off, for they were catching the 6-25 back to town, to end their happy week-end jaunt with a pleasant little dinner somewhere.

I was genuinely sorry when they departed, roaring down the road in farewell, for bereft of their high spirits the cottage seemed vacant, lifeless. It is really these evenings in late August that make the season, or brief interlude between seasons, so depressing. The long daylight has dwindled, but yet it is too early to light lamps and draw curtains. Fires are not to be thought of, yet there is a chill in the air. It is the drear little interval between the two magics of summer and autumn. Its long pallid face stares in at the casement, whispering that something is ending for ever. The sky looks like the window of an empty house. In this light, dimming to a dusk without warmth and kindness, Chehov's people chatter quietly and break their hearts. By the time the owls were hooting round the eaves and the room was ghostly with moths, I was more depressed than usual at such an hour and was sorry that I had not pressed my friends to stay or gone up to town with them, laughing and chattering away, on the 6-25. I saw them, in a wistful vision, sitting down to that pleasant little dinner, rubbing their hands, ruddy and bright of eye, preparing to round off the day and then march happily on towards the new morning.

Last of the Dandies

WITH them and their like was perishing, miserably and obscurely, an old tradition. Though they did not know it, they were in truth the last of a long line, the last of the Macaronis, the Dandies, the Swells, the Mashers, the Knuts. Their old home, the West End, knows these figures no longer; their canes and yellow gloves, their pearl-buttoned fawn overcoats, their brilliantine and scent and bouquets, their music-hall promenades, and their hansoms, their ladies, with elaborate golden coiffures, full busts, and naughty frills, all have gone, all went floating to limbo, long ago, on their last tide of champagne; and some foolish and almost forgotten song, in perky six-eight time, of 'Boys and Girls Upon the Spree, In Peek-a-deely or Le-hester Squer-hare', is their requiem. But just as a tide of fashion, raging fiercely in Mayfair for a season, will go rolling on and on, depositing black vases or orange cushions in drawing-rooms more and more remote year after year, so too the tradition of dandyism and lady-killing, after it had forsaken its old home, lingered on in towns like Bruddersford and among such young men as Leonard and Albert. They lived for dress and girls, above all – not having the opportunities of a Brummell – for girls. They ogled and pursued and embraced girls at the Bruddersford dances and socials, in all the local parks and woods, picture theatres and music halls; they followed them on the Bridlington sands, along the Morecambe piers, into the Blackpool ballrooms, and even went as far as Douglas, I.O.M., to treat them to eighteen-penny glasses of champagne and other notorious aphrodisiacs; they knew, and frequently discussed among themselves, the precise difference between the factory girls of Bruddersford and the factory girls of Bradford or Huddersfield, between the tailoresses of Leeds and the shop-girls of Manchester; they were masters of the art of 'picking up' and, young as they were, already veteran strategists in the war against feminine chastity or prudence, and were untiring in the chase, tracking these bright creatures for weeks through the dark jungle of West Riding streets, but apt to be either bored or frightened by the kill. In the end, most of them – as they said – 'got caught', and were to be seen walking out of their old lives, those epics of gallantry, pushing a perambulator.

The Dulvers

No one knew better than Miss Elsie Longstaff herself that, at that very moment, it was touch and go with the gentleman who has been somewhat unfairly introduced to us as Pink Egg. Mr Herbert Dulver was a gentleman friend of some two years' standing, though for the greater part of that time he had occupied a lowly place in the hierarchy of Elsie's gentlemen friends. Indeed, there had been periods when he had been as completely out of mind as he was out of sight. Shortly after *The Good Companions* had arrived at The Triangle, however, Mr Dulver had turned up again, for he was managing an hotel owned by his father, a substantial old place about fifteen miles out of Gatford and on the main London road. All the Dulvers – large, pink, and brassily cheerful persons – were landlords or bookmakers or something convivial or sporting. Herbert had been managing an hotel at the seaside when Elsie had first made his acquaintance, and now, having acquired in a mysterious Dulverish manner a considerable sum of money, he proposed not only to manage but also to own another seaside hotel. He was a bachelor about forty who liked to clothe his pink plumpness in sporting tweeds, wore a fair clipped moustache, and looked at the world out of prominent light-blue eyes that had about them a kind of hard amiability. His manner and phraseology suggested the confidential, but his voice was loud and carried far and he made full use of it, so that he always gave the odd impression that he was bellowing out his innermost secrets. Actually, however, he had no difficulty in keeping to himself whatever was best known only to himself, and was in reality a far more astute man of business than he appeared to be, like all the Dulvers, who for several generations now had been ordering drinks all round and slapping everybody on the back and talking at the top of their voices while they quietly contrived to feather their nests. And this Mr Dulver had the traditional attitude towards women. Outside business, in which he demanded and took care to receive his money's worth, he was very chivalrous and gallant towards 'the Ladies', and both masterful and saucy with 'the Girls'. Elsie, who liked being one of the Ladies and one of the Girls too, understood and appreciated both these attitudes, but that did not prevent her from telling herself from the first that Mr Dulver would want watching. Not that this stood in his way at all, for in her heart of hearts Elsie admired a man who wanted watching ...

The next day, Elsie became a Dulver. From all parts of the country there came Dulvers to welcome her, the males all large, shining, pink, hoarse, and brassily convivial, the females all large, blonde, and elaborately coiffured and upholstered. It is difficult to imagine what the Dulvers would have made of a christening or a funeral, because it is difficult to imagine a Dulver either coming into this world or going out of it; but there could be no doubt they were designed by Nature to celebrate weddings. The customary festivities, all the eating and drinking, the healths and back-slappings, sledge-hammer compliments and naughty jokes, might have been invented for them. Elsie was inspected by all manner of Dulverish relatives, who looked as if they were quite capable of having her stripped and weighed, and of pinching her in sundry places to make sure she was a sound article. After being thus inspected, she was approved. The general opinion obviously was that, with her shape, colouring, and disposition, it was only a matter of time – with some further coiffuring, upholstering, and the sipping of small ports – before she became a very good specimen of the female Dulver, fit to queen it in any hotel. And Bert was proud of her. Bert's father and mother, two fine heavy Dulvers, were proud of Bert. All the relatives were proud of somebody or something, if only of their appetites – 'I'm sixty past,' one gigantic purple Dulver told everybody, 'and I can eat and drink with the best yet.' Thus they were all happy.

Mr Dulver senior, in the business himself and now the host of so many professionally convivial persons, had no alternative, could not have found one even if he had looked for it: the thing had to be done in style. The style he had chosen he called 'the slap-up', but it might also be described as the Late Roman, so great was the crowd of guests, so lavish the feast. The immense wedding breakfast that awaited them in the long room upstairs drew a tribute even from the old masters, the purple Dulvers.

The Addersons – in a Depressed Area

WHEN he left the bridge, sauntering anywhere simply to kill time, he began to think about these relations of his, and not without shame, for they had been very good to him when he was a boy and he had thought little about them lately, had not thought about them at all these last few days. His Aunt Nellie, one of those dark, wiry, tireless little women, had always been the merriest of all his relations. She liked nothing better than to see a lot of young folks enjoying themselves. She had always had a knack of getting a party going in lively style. Of course there had been plenty of money about in those days. He remembered old outings and beanfeasts, and caught a glimpse of his aunt's little face flashing through them all, the darkest and the brightest there. This had seemed a big roaring city then, with everything in it you could want. There didn't seem any connexion between that place and this decayed town. Charlie thought about his uncle, Tom Adderson, and thought about him with some affection and a great deal of respect. Tom Adderson was quite different from his wife, very quiet, rather stern, and in some queer way, which Charlie did not attempt to define, a bit religious. He was no chapel-goer, Tom Adderson wasn't, yet you always felt he was a bit religious in his own grim way. As a boy Charlie had been in awe of this tall bony engineer, and he wasn't prepared to say even now that he wasn't a little bit frightened of him. Then there were their children, his two cousins, Johnny and Madge. Why, Johnny, who was only a few years younger than he was, would be twenty-two or three now; and little Madge must be about twenty. He had a clear picture of them both in his mind – Johnny, dark like his mother, tall and bony like his father, and Madge with her curly brown hair and fine blue eyes, a proper little madam – but only as they had been seven to ten years ago. There was a Christmas once he had spent with them here ...

Now they lived at 18 Fishnet Street. He had not been there before, but after enquiring he found it was in a fairly familiar part of the town, not very far from the river. It all had a broken-down look. You knew at once that there was no good money coming in here. About nine o'clock. They would be up now. He could risk it.

An elderly man answered his knock at Number 18, a very shabby, stooping man wearing steel spectacles. He was a grey figure, for his hair was grey, there was a thick grey stubble on his chin, and his hollow cheeks had a queer greyish look.

'What d'you want?'

'It's me, Uncle. Charlie – Charlie Habble.'

'So it is. Nay, lad, I didn't recognize you. Come inside.'

This was a lot worse than standing on that bridge. What had they been doing to Tom Adderson that he could look like that? If this was his uncle, what would his Aunt Nellie look like?

*

Johnny was inside, a very different Johnny from the lad he had known seven years ago. He was a strapping fellow now, but for all that he didn't look right. He was too thin; he slouched; he was very shabby; and his eyes and mouth were bitter. He was surprised to see Charlie.

'I thought you were a great man in London, Charlie,' he said. 'Hero – and all that. What's made you come up here?'

'Because I asked him to, lad, that's why,' said his father. 'Your mother'd like to see him.'

'Well, I don't blame her,' Johnny replied, with a sharp glance at Charlie. 'He'll be a nice change from some of us. All right, Charlie lad, no offence. But we're not used to seeing people all dressed up to kill – like you.'

'Where is she – my Aunt Nellie?' asked Charlie, wisely deciding to ignore Johnny's remarks.

'She's upstairs in bed,' his uncle replied, lowering his voice. 'No, she's no worse. We've a job to keep her i' bed, but doctor's told her to lay up a bit, and I've told her, and for once she's doing what she's told. Now listen, lad – before we go any farther. She's heard a lot o' talk about you, and she's been fretting to see you, but she doesn't know I wrote, and you mustn't go and tell her else she'll play war wi' me. Let on you thought of it yourself. That'll please her and get me into no trouble.'

'Yes, I see. How is she?'

'Well, she's poorly. I'm not going to say she isn't.'

'What is it that's wrong?'

'Well, lad' – and his uncle hesitated – 'doctor says it's one or two things –'

'I can tell you what it is – and sharp,' Johnny broke in harshly. 'It's bloody starvation, that's what it is. Doing without to let us have it – that's what it is. And worry.'

'All right, lad,' said his father. 'Keep it down, keep it down. You're not shouting at the club now. And there's been some a lot worse than we've been.'

'Well, what if there has?' Johnny retorted.

'Where's Madge?' Charlie asked.

'She's working.'

'The only one that is working,' said Johnny. 'Got a job in a shop. She gets eighteen bob a week. It isn't much, but it's a damned sight more than I can earn. And even then we don't get it.'

'How d'you mean?'

'Why, they deduct eleven and six from our transition pay because she's bringing in eighteen bob. We're no better off.'

His father stood up. 'Yes, we are. We've got somebody working. That's something. I'll go and see if your aunt's awake, Charlie.'

Johnny was quiet for a moment. Then, looking more friendly, he said: 'Well, I'm glad you're here, Charlie. It'll brighten my mother up a bit. She's been reading about you, and she'll want to know all about what it feels like to be called a hero up in London. Are you staying a bit?'

Charlie said that he was and explained that he had left his bags at the station. He added a remark about getting lodgings just near.

'Oh, that'll be easy enough,' said Johnny. 'I know one or two places myself and I expect my mother knows a lot more. Here, I'll go and get your bags. Oh – that's all right. It'll give me something to do.'

'Got any fags, Johnny?'

Johnny grinned ruefully. 'About two ends.'

'Get some, will you?' said Charlie, as if he were asking the other to do him a favour. And he handed over a shilling.

To Charlie's relief, his cousin simply nodded, then put on his coat and scarf, which had been hanging over the back of a chair, found his cap, and departed. Charlie looked round the room, which was full of things, most of which he remembered. He was pleasantly surprised to find that their home was anything but bare, though everything was very shabby and worn. Obviously, nothing new had been bought for years. On the other hand, they hadn't been reduced to wholesale pawning. That was something.

'I was just thinking, Uncle,' he said, a minute later, 'I remember most of these things. You've kept the home together all right, haven't you?' He sounded brisk, cheerful.

His uncle shook his head. 'Nay, lad, most o' these things would have gone long since if we could ha' found anybody to buy 'em. You can't pawn anything but bedclothes in Slakeby these days. Pawn-shops were full up long since. We all want to sell, and there's nobody to buy.'

Charlie's face fell. 'I didn't think o' that.'

'There's a lot o' things you don't think of, lad, till the time comes. You live an' learn. At least you learn, I'm none so sure about living. Well, will you go up and have a word with your aunt? And don't forget what I said.'

As he went up the dark little stairs he heard Aunt Nellie's voice, a thin excited cry, calling him, and he suddenly felt all weak and queer, as if the heart inside him had turned to water. The first things he saw in that room were her eyes, the same merry dark eyes, but bigger than ever now.

'Why Charlie – Charlie!'

'Aunt Nellie!'

She rose up from her pillow, took hold of him, laughed and cried. He himself had not been so near to crying for years. There was plenty to cry about here. She looked so much older, so yellow and shrunken, so very thin. Every gay memory of her, all the fun they had had, returned to him in a lightning flash and then shrivelled to this miserable moment. 'By God!' he was saying inside, 'it's wicked, it's wicked.'

'Now don't look at me like that, Charlie,' she cried gaily, 'I know I'm all skin and bone, but your poor old auntie never was much more, y'know, just like a fourpenny rabbit. Oh – but I'm so glad to see you, Charlie. You're looking so well, too. D'you know, you've more of a look of your mother than ever you had. And wouldn't she have been proud of you? She would that! And I'm proud of you, Charlie – we all are – with pieces about you in the papers and your photograph and everything! And look at your clothes, too. I'll bet our Johnny was jealous, wasn't he? Poor lad, it's just how he'd like to look – and he could look too if he had a chance. Isn't it a shame? Boys now haven't a chance of anything, not up here they haven't. Well now, Charlie, you've got to tell me all about it. But what made you leave all them grand folks to come and see us?'

He told her it was because he had wanted to see them all again and that this had been his first chance for a long time. Then he had to tell her all that had happened to him in London, and the pleasure she took in this recital, her face brightening with every new triumph of his, was wonderful to see. Nor could he cut it short, for she would have everything told, what he ate and drank there, the very feel of the bedclothes in the grand fairy-tale hotel.

'Now that's enough about me,' he said finally. 'It's all a lot o' palaver about nothing. I want to hear about you.'

Her face lost some of its brightness. 'Well, we're carrying on, y'know, Charlie. We're not dead yet, eh? Doctor keeps coming and having a look at me. Nay, I can't help laughing. He comes in and tells me I've got to keep quiet, and then in a few minutes he's shouting his head off, like a big bull.'

'What about?'

'Nay, you needn't look like that, lad. He's one of the best friends we have, doctor is. We've known him for twenty-five years. He shouts because he gets so mad about things. He can't get me into the convalescent home, because they've a waiting list as long as your arm. Not that I want to go, with two big soft men and a flighty lass to look after. But doctor says I ought to go, and he can't get me in and we can't afford to pay, so that's that. You should hear him go on about everything. Proper Red he is – like our Johnny. Red in the head and red in his ideas – that's our doctor. But he's a right good sort. He looks in to see me, and he knows we can't pay him and we're off the panel now.'

'Off the panel! How's that?'

'Because your uncle's been out o' work more than three years. After that, you get no more panel or anything. They give you up as a bad job after that.'

'And my uncle's been out over three years?'

'Three years! He's only had five months' work in six years. Think o' that, Charlie. Your Uncle Tom – Tom Adderson – who was one o' the best engineers Sturks ever had – and everybody knew Sturks' engines all over the world – to come to this! You remember him as he was, don't you, Charlie?'

'Yes,' Charlie confessed, 'he's changed a bit.'

'He's changed a lot, lad. He's twenty years older than he was when you came here last time. It's breaking him, properly breaking him. It's not going short – though that's bad enough – but it's being idle and feeling useless that's done it. I know we oughtn't to grumble, for we've pulled through so far and some I know has been a lot worse off – but he's said sometimes, when it's got him properly down, "Nay, Nellie, I might as well be dead. My day's done." And I tell him not to talk so soft. Life's sweet, I tell him, life's sweet. And we're not finished yet.'

'What about Johnny? What's he doing?'

'Johnny served his time, like his father, and all the work he's had since he finished is a month on the road for the corporation. He's worse off than his father, poor Johnny is, for his father's known what it was to work regular and earn good money, but Johnny's never had a chance from the start. Some of them young chaps don't know what it is to work. Your uncle says some of 'em wouldn't know how, though I'll bet our Johnny'd work fast enough if he'd the chance. What I'm frightened of is that one o' these days he'll have to get married. If he does, then they'd have to come here. Some women I know like that. Their sons get married – or their daughters – and then they have to come and live with the old folks. and these women just boss the lot, and won't let their own daughters or daughters-in-law bring up their own babies. You see that happening all round here, Charlie. Like bossy old gypsy women, they are. Well, it's nothing in my line, and I'm frightened to death our Johnny'll march up one fine morning with some lass he's got into trouble and they have to start a family in the next bedroom. And you can't blame 'em, can you, lad? Even if they are out o' work, they're human – they're young and they've got to have a bit o' fun somehow.'

'I haven't seen Madge yet. How's she getting on?' Charlie asked.

'She's got a job now, working in a toffee shop in Churchgate. Eighteen shillings she gets, and I tell her I bet she eats another eighteen shillingsworth. We're no better off because she's working – we're worse off, because transition goes and deducts what she's making, as if she gives us every penny o' that eighteen shillings and it didn't cost anything to send a girl out to work all day and half the night. Nay, Charlie, I'm as worried about our Madge as I am about our Johnny. She says she's had enough of Slakeby – wants to go off as a waitress or something o' that sort – some of her friends have gone and they keep writing to her – and I can't blame her for wanting to go, for there's nothing here for a pretty young lass like her. Oh – yes, she's nice-looking enough, Madge is, a proper picture when she's dressed up. That's the trouble, Charlie. If she were a bit plainer I wouldn't bother so much, but she's always had the lads – men too – after her, and as her father says, she gets her ideas about life from the Hippodrome and the Electric Palace. There isn't a bit of harm in her really – but you know what they are at that age, young lasses – not a bit o' sense in their heads – always thinking about clothes and chaps and pictures, and I don't know what might happen if she got off on her own, a long way from home. Her father won't hear of it, properly puts his foot down – sometimes them two play war with one another – but I fancy it's me that keeps her here. Who's this? Sounds like Johnny.'

It was Johnny. He announced that he had brought Charlie's

two bags from the station, and then asked his mother where Charlie could best find lodgings.

'I'm vexed you can't stay here, Charlie,' cried his aunt. 'But we simply haven't room in this house.'

'That's all right,' said Charlie. 'I didn't expect it. We'll easily find a place just near.'

His aunt spent an anxious but delightful minute tackling this problem. 'Mrs Crockit,' she cried finally, in triumph. 'Lives just down the street. She's a widow and only got one lad at home now, and she's a right decent little body. She'll only be too glad to get somebody, for she's been terribly hard put to it just lately to keep a home together. Has her Harry got his trousers yet?' she asked Johnny.

Johnny grinned. 'Yes, I saw him in 'em yesterday. They're about three sizes too big for him, otherwise they'll do. And I believe he's getting a job either this week or next.'

'Poor Mrs Crockit,' cried Aunt Nellie. 'We had to laugh, but it was a shame. The only trousers her lad Harry had, a week or two back, was a pair of moleskins, and when he went out in 'em all the other lads laughed at him and then he was so shamed he'd only go out at night. So his mother went all over trying to get him another pair o' trousers, and before she'd done she'd been to the mayor himself, telling him her lad had to have a pair of trousers. And now they've found him a pair.'

'Here, that'll do,' said Johnny reproachfully, 'you're tired. Isn't she, Charlie? Time she had a bit o' peace. Come on.'

The Salters

THIS girl should not have been as wholesome, comely, even beautiful, as she was. The fact runs counter to all our accepted knowledge of what is good and bad for human beings. All the conditions of her twenty-year-old life had been monstrous.

From earliest childhood she had been denied sunlight, good air, proper food and exercise. She ought to have been a premature hag, with a crooked spine, gummy eyes, rotting teeth. Yet somehow out of this dreadful mess of rubber teats, sinister teething powders, dirty linen, over-heated rooms, pastry, fish and chips, dubious laxatives, dreadful patent medicines, ignorance, swinishness, savagery, had emerged this healthy and handsome young creature. Nature had found a way to circumvent the idiocy of half-civilized Man. Or perhaps this was a legacy from her ancestors, Salters who had been hard moorland shepherds or labourers on the great wheat farms in the plain of York, whose wholesome red blood still flowered – it might be for the last time – in this evil industrial soil. Feminine beauty ought to be the prerogative – as so many other things are – of the privileged and carefully nurtured classes, yet, as the records will show, it has an odd trick of springing from the nameless mob beneath, suddenly blossoming in perfection out of stinking ghettoes, bug-ridden tenements, dockside lodging houses. Rose was not one of these astonishing beauties, who now so often coin their straight little noses, the fine curve of their cheeks, into millions of dollars in distant Hollywood; nor was her home in Slater Street, a respectable dingy street, the Yorkshire equivalent of those ghettoes and tenements; but nevertheless she was a surprise, a stroke of luck, a happy chance we do not deserve.

It would be easy and impressive to show the girl, workless now in a community where work was hard to find, returning to a home of despair and slow death, a family of tight-lipped suffering proletarians. But it would not be true. The Salters were not like that. As a family they had a notable capacity for enjoying themselves. They belonged to that section of the workers which is the despair of the austere revolutionary, who can understand neither their hoggish blindness nor their ability, which he lacks, to come to easy terms with each passing day. He sees them swallowing with evident enjoyment each new dose of capitalist dope. They seem to thrive on it. There is no persuading them that under these present conditions life is not worth living because obviously the fools are having a good time with it. Including Rose there were six Salters crowded into the little house – two rooms below, three above – in Slater Street; father, who was a warehouseman, a cunning bowls player, and a figure at the East Haliford Working-men's Club; mother, who was fat, jolly, and a very sketchy shopper and meal preparer; George, who was in a dyeworks by day and in the sporting life by night; Fred, who did a variety of jobs and just now had wangled something mysterious for himself at the Greyhound Racing Track; Nellie, in a toyshop in Market Lane, for ever getting herself engaged and then disengaged and telling you all about it with tears in her eyes and laughter on her lips; and Rose herself, the youngest, considered the quiet and rather deep one of the family, who had been known to sit with a book – not a picture or racing paper but a real book – for a whole hour together. Every meal at the Salters was a long-drawn-out noisy picnic. There was more shouting, more hustle in this little house than there is at most railway stations. Every member of the family had friends who continually popped in and out. The wireless set worked at full blast. The females were always making one another cups of tea; the males were always opening bottles of beer or slipping out for a jug of old ale. Every week-end with them seemed like Christmas. One or other of them attended all football and boxing matches and other sporting events, the one local music-hall, the more important films of the town, all public celebrations; and one or other of them tried a hand at all the competitions run by popular papers or commercial firms, so that the postman might bring a fortune at any hour. The family finances were so complicated, everyone borrowing from everybody else, that they could never be straightened out. Sometimes George and Fred were existing, in shirt-sleeves, with half-closed eyes over a cigarette and the sporting columns, on their mother's and sisters' bounty; and at other times they burst in like millionaires from the gold mines, slapping dirty pound notes and heaps of silver on the kitchen table and proposing to take everybody to Blackpool (their favourite resort) for the week-end. Rose did not set herself against all this; she was fond of her family; but there were times, and there had been more and more of them lately, when she found herself wanting something different, not quite so noisy, so Halifordish. She never protested, unless she wanted to be quiet and was not left alone, never sneered; but more and more, inspired by what she saw in picture papers or at the films, she entertained thoughts quite foreign to the other Salters.

She arrived home to find her mother, large, hot, dishevelled, doing some of her sketchy cooking. The fact that it was a warm day and would be a close evening had not deterred Mrs Salter from attempting a very hot and heavy meal, for she took no notice of the weather but catered by immediate inspiration, so that in January she might offer you cold pork pie and tinned pineapple, in August fried steak and a suet pudding. This seemed reasonable to all the family, except Rose, who was – they said – 'a bit pernickety'.

'Mother,' she announced at once.

'Yes, love?'

'I've got the sack.'

'Well, you silly monkey!' cried Mrs Salter, lifting her large round red face from the low oven. 'Whatever for?'

Rose told the story of the afternoon as well as she could, blaming neither herself nor the company. Her mother did not clearly understand what it was all about, but by this time she had given up trying to understand what all these things were about. Every other day one of them brought home some fantastic tale. But she was neither cross nor worried. She was even pleased. This was drama of a kind; and the Salters liked drama.

The Holt-Ibstocks

All four looked as if they had been kept in cold storage a long time and had then never been properly thawed out. Sir Edwin

Holt-Ibstock, who was a Member of Parliament and a very important personage who sat on committees and received deputations and who was very much on the Blue side and dead against the Red side, was very tall and thin and had scanty grey hair and a close-cropped grey moustache and a high complaining voice. He did not look quite as blue as his wife, perhaps because he could wear more clothes in the evening, but nevertheless he was thoroughly frosted. Mr Raymond, the son, was also tall and thin, a rather colourless young man, but was not so bad as the other three because he went out and played games. Miss Diana, only twenty-three, was perhaps the worst of the lot. She was thin but not so tall as the others, and she had chilly blue eyes, pale hair, and a little button of a nose that was nearly always reddish, no matter how much powder she put on it. When Rose saw her in evening clothes, with bones and gooseflesh showing all over the place, rather like a plucked turkey on a frosty Christmas Eve, Rose could have cried out in pity, and wanted to wrap her in hot blankets. Miss Diana's voice was the highest and most complaining of them all. All their voices, high-pitched, clear and loud, were cold too. They were like people out of a refrigerator. Rose felt very sorry for them at first, because they seemed to get so little cosiness and comfort and fun for their money. And they were always grumbling. Sir Edwin grumbled about the state of the country; Mr Raymond grumbled about the City, where he worked, and golf and such things; Lady Holt-Ibstock complained about 'the servant class' – even when it was handing her potatoes and listening to her – and the vulgar pushing people there were about nowadays; and Miss Diana, who was always rushing in and out and telephoning and writing notes and cancelling one engagement and accepting another and quarrelling with her friends and making it up again and saying she had nothing to wear and then complaining because she had to go for a fitting, was the most dissatisfied of them all and was always screaming that everything was 'foul'. Except in the matter of Miss Diana's clothes, Rose did not envy them at all. They had nothing like the fun and jokes her family had at home. They hardly ever seemed to do anything because they liked doing it. Even their amusements, which must have been very costly, appeared to be forced on them, like a sort of homework.

Cowboys

It was here in Arizona that I first met cowboys. Many of these cowboys now spend more time taking parties of ranch guests out for a morning ride than they do in rounding up cattle. Nevertheless, they are genuine cowboys. As a rule they have known nothing but ranch life, and they have all the accomplishments of the legendary cowboy, except perhaps that famous marksmanship with a Colt. When not at work, they practise for forthcoming rodeos or entertain themselves, and you, with that melancholy music, those long lugubrious strains, for which all men who lead an active open-air life seem to have a strange passion. Sedentary men may need gay cynical little tunes, but the cowboy, the sailor, the soldier, and their kind, ask for nothing better than a gloomy ballad of true love cut short by early death. The cowboy, who is a man of tradition, keeps the traditional tone in song, an odd and rather nasal little tone, which would drive any singing master mad but somehow pleases the rest of us. And like all healthy primitive males, the cowboy is a dressy fellow. Most of his pay still goes, as it always did, in tremendous hats and high-heeled boots, in belts and saddles and gaudy shirts. He is a peacock of a chap, unimpressed by any defeatist urban nonsense about quiet, respectable, drab clothes. The male in his natural state likes to show off, to blind the coy female, to stun her into admiration; and that is the cowboy. He has the luck to live in a simple world. There are certain things he must be able to do well, or it is all up with him, and they cannot be faked, as politicians and professional men and directors of companies so often fake things. He cannot pretend to ride and rope, and get away with it. He has to be able to ride and rope really well, and to do a few other things too; but once he has acquired the necessary skill and the courage and endurance that match it, all is well with him. He lives a natural healthy life in a healthy uncomplicated world. He does not go to bed to worry himself sick about what the public, the debenture-holders, the board of directors, the departmental boss, will say. He does not feel like a piece of straw in a whirlpool. He does not grow fat and apoplectic, or thin and cancerous, at a desk, wondering what exactly it is that has wasted his manhood. He has not much money but then neither has he many taxes, mortgages, insurance policies and doctors' bills. If he has a wife, she does not regard him as a sagging, moody fraud of a fellow, whose mysterious and probably contemptible activities during the day have robbed him of all bright masculine virtue; but she knows exactly what he has to do, and respects him for the obvious skill and courage he brings to his tasks. If he has young children, he shines in their sight as a wise hero, and is therefore the perfect father. His life may be infinitely narrower than that of a saint or a philosopher, an artist or a scientist, but can it be said to be any narrower than the existences of all those pale-faced millions who go day after day to factories, warehouses, offices and shops, the victims of all the cunningly deployed forces of publicity and salesmanship, of rubber-stamp opinions and artificially stimulated wants?

He is at peace with himself because his work allows free play to the strongest instincts of man. Unlike so many other men, he has not to pretend to be a short-sighted, deaf cripple all day to earn his living, and then to try and catch up with himself as a vital human being during the short hours of leisure allotted to him. His work is not without danger, and he is sustained by a sense of this, knowing that he has a certain fundamental dignity. This is true of other kinds of men, such as the miner and the sailor, men who are shabbily treated by the community they serve, but are often inwardly sustained by their sense of being engaged in an heroic calling. This is joined in the cowboy to an outward picturesqueness and a magnificent stage setting. There is still a good book to be written about the legend of the heroic West and the cowboy. The author would have to be a social philosopher as well as an historian. The legend has not been with us long. That West had a very short history. It did not begin until the 'sixties, and its Homeric age was over before the century ended. It was created by a passing set of economic circumstances, by cheap open grazing land in the south-west, and good prices on the hoof in Kansas City. It could not survive the invention of barbed-wire. Yet what a legend it has created! Cheap melodrama, whether in fiction, plays or films, soon claimed that legend; yet there always remains a faint gleam of Homeric poetry, not in the monotonous and incredible fables of very good men and very bad men and doll-like heroines, but in the enduring image they give us of a man riding in the wilderness of desert and mountain, the solitary heroic figure. Here is one who seems to have escaped the economic slavery and universal degradation of our time; who does not compete except with charging animals and the hostile elements; who is seen as the strong free male, careless and smiling and bronzed, that essential male for whom all women have a tenderness. He is a man of our world who has contrived to live his life in an epic simplicity impossible to the rest of us, caught in a bewildering tangle of interests and loyalties.

The Actors

WHEN I was a lad and regularly took my place in the queue for the early doors of the gallery in the old Theatre Royal, Bradford, the actors on their way to the stage door had to walk past us. I observed them with delight. In those days, actors looked like actors and like nothing else on earth. There was no mistaking them for wool merchants, shipping clerks, and deacons of Baptist chapels, all those familiar figures of my boyhood. They wore suits of startling check pattern, outrageous ties, and preposterous overcoats reaching down to their ankles. They never seemed to remove all their make-up as actors do now, and always had a rim of blue-black round their eyelids. They did not belong to our world and never for a moment pretended to belong to it. They swept past us, fantastically overcoated, with trilbies perched raffishly on brilliantined curls, talking of incredible matters in high tones, merely casting a few sparkling glances – all the more sparkling because of that blue-black – in our direction; and then vanished through the stage door, to reappear, but out of all recognition, in the wigs and knee-breeches of *David Garrick* or *The Only Way*. And my young heart, as innocent as an egg, went out to these romantic beings; and perhaps it was then, although I have no recollection of it, that the desire was born in me to write one day for the Theatre. Now, after working on so many stages, I know all about actors, and I doubt if the very least of their innumerable maddening tricks and absurd egoisms has escaped my observation; but, quite apart from the work we do together and without reference to the needs of my profession, I have a soft spot for actors, and probably it is because of that old delight I used to feel as they went swaggering past us on their way to the stage door. And indeed I sometimes wish they would swagger more now, buy bigger overcoats and wilder hats, and retain those traces of make-up that put them outside respectability and kept them rogues and vagabonds, which is what at heart – bless 'em! – they are.

Sam Oglethorpe

YES, Sam was in, and glad to see him, and together they went down to the run and looked at hens. The two had worked side-by-side for years in the waggon department of Higden and Co., but two or three years ago they had parted company, for Sam had come into money, having been left four hundred pounds by an uncle who had kept an off-licence shop, and had boldly walked out of Higden's, never to return. He was now 'on his own' at Wabley, the proud proprietor of a large hen-run, a little cottage, and a sign that said 'Joinery and Jobbing Work Promptly Attended To'. That was why Mr Oakroyd regarded his friend with admiration and envy, for he too would like to walk out of Higden's for the last time, to have done with wages and foremen and the tyrannical buzzer. Deep in his heart was a sign about Joinery and Jobbing Work. The hoisting of that sign, proclaiming Jes. Oakroyd, the independent craftsman, to the world, was one of his constant dreams. And he was a better craftsman than Sam, too; give him a saw, a hammer, a few nails, and he could do anything. But Sam, assisted by the off-licence uncle, had managed to scramble out, while he was still in, in up to the neck, and lucky perhaps to be keeping on at Higden's at all.

Now, the last hen dismissed, they were cosily talking over pipes and a jug of beer. They were not in Mr Oglethorpe's cottage, which was simply a place to eat and sleep in and not meant, as anybody in Wabley would tell you, for social life. No, they were sitting snugly in Mr Oglethorpe's combined hen-house and workshop, with the jug of beer on a bench between them. If you want to know what independent men in Bruddersford and district think about life, you must listen to the talk that comes floating out of hen-houses at night. A man can afford to let himself go in a hen-house. Sam had been letting himself go, enlarging upon his plans and prospects, his hens, his Joinery, his Jobbing, to all of which Mr Oakroyd had been listening with deep and admiring attention. It was now time he had a look in, and Mr Oglethorpe, like the good fellow he was, knew it and gave him his cue.

'Ay,' said Mr Oglethorpe, who had the slow meditative manner that properly belongs to Jobbing Work, 'that's what 'appens i' this sort o' business i' Wabley, ay, and i' Bruddersford too. Did you give it any ittention, Jess, when you was down South? It'll be a bit diff'rent there, I'm thinking.'

Mr Oakroyd's face lit up at once. This 'down South' was the cue. This was where he came in and more than held his own, for if, in this company, Mr Oglethorpe was the independent man, the owner of hens and a sign, the craftsman at large, who could smoke his pipe when he liked, Mr Oakroyd was the travelled man, who had knocked up and down a bit, who could talk of what were to Mr Oglethorpe, who had never been anywhere, foreign parts. It was only in the company of his friend Sam that Mr Oakroyd felt that he really had seen the world. He had not often been away from Bruddersford, though he had had a few little holidays at Morecambe, Blackpool, and Scarborough, had been on football trips to Manchester, Newcastle, Sheffield, and had once gone on a wonderful midnight excursion to London and had actually seen St Paul's and London Bridge before he fell asleep in an eating-house; but it happened that for a whole six months he had worked in Leicester, where his firm had a branch, and ever after he had referred to this exciting period as the time when he was 'down South'. It was another of his dreams, companion to that of the hoisted sign, this happy business of travelling, of knocking about, of seeing this place and that, of telling how you once went there and then moved on somewhere else, and although he knew he had seen nothing much yet and probably never would now, yet he was able, nourished as he was by his secret dream, to capture the manner of the true wanderer.

During his six months in Leicester, he had lodged in a street that could hardly be distinguished from his own Ogden Street, had worked in another Higden's mill that was just like the one in Bruddersford except that it was smaller and cleaner. Yet when he said 'down South', he seemed to conjure up a vast journey towards the tropics and at the end of it a life entirely alien, fantastic.

'Ay, it's different there, Sam,' said Mr Oakroyd, puzzling his brains to discover some proof of this difference. 'It's altogether different there, it is.'

''Old on a bit afore you tell me,' the other cried, reaching for the jug. 'There's another sup i' this for both of us, I'm thinking. Nah then!' And he put a match to his pipe and looked across at his friend, his honest red face aglow.

'Well, then you see,' began Mr Oakroyd, but thought better of it and drank some beer instead. Then he reflected a moment. 'Well, what I'd say is this. Yer asking me how this sort o' trade, Joinery and Jobbing, 'ud go down South, aren't yer?'

'That's right, Jess.' And Mr Oglethorpe looked very profound as he said this.

'Well, what I'd say is this; that ther mayn't be so much of it down there but what ther is 'ud be a better class o' thing. D'you follow me, Sam?'

Sam did follow him and looked more profound than ever as he slowly puffed at his short clay pipe. Nothing was said for a minute or two. Then Mr Oglethorpe proceeded to light a very old and evil-smelling paraffin lamp that hung from the roof, and when he had done this, he broke the silence. 'It'll be all different I'm thinking, Jess. I could nivver settle to it. But I'll bet tha liked it.'

'I like a bit of a change, Sam.'

'I'll bet tha'd like to be off down there ag'in next week,' said Mr Oglethorpe, with an air of great artfulness, as if he had caught his friend at last.

'I might an' I might not,' replied Mr Oakroyd, who was not for giving himself away at once, not even in Sam's hen-house. But then the hour and his mood worked together to fling down his reserve. He leaned forward and looked at once eager and wistful. 'I'll tell you what it is, Sam. I'd give owt to see a bit more afore I'm too old.'

'Yer've seen summat already, Jess,' Mr Oglethorpe spoke proudly, as if his friendship gave him a share in these vast migrations.

'Nowt much when you look at it.'

'Why, look at me,' cried Mr Oglethorpe. 'I've nivver been farther ner Wetherby, to t'races there. Nay, I'm lying; I have. I once went for a day to Southport to see t'sea, but I nivver saw it, not a drop. It were a take-in, that.'

'I'd like to knock up an' down a bit,' Mr Oakroyd went on, 'an' see what there is to see afore I'm too old an' daft. I've gotten fair sick o' Bruddersford lately, Sam, I have that. I'd like to get on t'move.'

'Where d'yer want to go, Jess? Down South ag'in? What is't yer want to see?'

'Nay, I don't know,' said Mr Oakroyd, gloomily. 'I'd like to see summat fresh. I'd like to have a look at – oh, I don't know – Bristol.'

'Ar,' said Mr Oglethorpe knowingly. 'Bristol.'

'Or I'd like to see – yer know – some of them places – Bedfordshire,' he added, at a venture.

The other shook his head at this. 'I nivver heard tell much o' that place,' he said gravely. 'Is ther owt special i' Bedfordshire, Jess?'

'Nay, I don't know,' replied Mr Oakroyd, a trifle impatiently. 'But it's summat to see. I'd like to go and have a look so I'd know if ther was owt there or not. And I'll tell you another thing, Sam. I'd like to go to Canada.'

'Yer nivver would, yer nivver would, Jess!' Mr Oglethorpe slapped his thigh in appreciation of this audacity. 'An' if yer got there, yer'd want to be back i' no time. Nowt to sup, they tell me, and snaw months and months on end. Plenty o' money I dare say, but nowt to spend it on. Nay, Jess, I'll nivver believe yer'd go as far as that.'

Mr Poppleby, Caterer

'MORNING.' The man shot up from behind the counter as if he were part of a conjuring trick. It could only be Mr Poppleby himself. All of him that was visible, his large round face, the top of his long apron, his shirt sleeves and the arms that came out of them, was the same shade – whitish and faintly greasy. Even his eyes were a pale grey, had a jellied look.

'Morning,' said Mr Oakroyd, still staring. 'Er – lemme see – er –'

'Tea-coffee-cocoa-bacon-and-egg-bacon-and-sausage-kipper-boiled-egg-plate-of-cold-meat-bread-and-butter,' said Mr Poppleby, keeping his prominent eyes fixed on Mr Oakroyd's with never a blink.

Mr Oakroyd gazed at him with admiration, then removed his little brown cap, possibly as a tribute. 'That sounds a bit of all right. I'll ha' a pot o' tea and you can do me two rashers and two eggs. And plenty o' bread, Mister,' he added.

'Pot-of-tea-two-rashers-two-eggs-four-slices-bread.' Mr Poppleby turned away.

''Ere, I say,' cried Mr Oakroyd. 'Can I have a bit of a wash afore I start? Been on t'road most o' t'night – wi' a lorry,' and he added this not without a certain touch of pride.

'Certainly you can 'ave a wash, my friend, certainly,' replied Mr Poppleby with impressive gravity. 'You just come this way and I'll find you a wash. I'm not saying it's usual – it isn't usual – but it's no worse for that, is it? You don't want to sit down to your food all dirty, an' I don't want to see you sitting down to it all dirty, and we're two feller men, aren't we? That's right, isn't it? Well, you come this way then.' And off he went, with Mr Oakroyd in attendance. They arrived at a tiny scullery, and Mr Poppleby waved a hand to indicate the presence of a little enamel bowl, a large bar of yellow soap, and a towel that had seen long and desperate service. ''Ere you are, my friend,' he continued. 'You can wash 'ere to your 'eart's content. And while you're 'aving your wash, we'll be dishing up your bacon and your eggs. That's fair dealing between man and man, isn't it? Give a man what he asks for – in reason, y'know, for there's reason in everything – but anyhow, *try* to give a man what 'e asks for – that's my motto.' And thus concluding a trifle unctuously, Mr Poppleby withdrew.

'Who does he think he is – Lloyd George?' muttered Mr Oakroyd as he took off his coat. He saw that the envelope was still safely stowed away in the breast pocket. 'To hear him talk, you'd think he was offering me a steam bath wi' shampoos an' finger-nail cutting to foller.' Nevertheless, when he had spluttered over the enamel bowl and had rubbed himself hard with the only corner of the towel that was not slippery, he felt twice the man he had been, and when he returned to the dining-room, passing on his way through a zone newly enriched by the smell of frying bacon, he gazed benevolently at the impressive figure of Mr Poppleby, who was engaged in depositing a pot of tea beside a plate of bread, a cup and saucer, a long pointed knife and a two-pronged fork.

'Your bacon and your eggs'll be ready in one minute,' said Mr Poppleby, returning to his counter.

'Good enough,' cried Mr Oakroyd, rubbing his hands. 'I'm fair pining, I can tell you.'

'We'll soon put that right.' And no consulting surgeon could have said this more impressively. 'So you've been on the road, eh?'

'I have an' all,' said Mr Oakroyd. 'Come down t'Great North Road last night.' But, somewhat to his surprise, this did not appear to impress his host.

'Well, what I say is this,' Mr Poppleby began even more weightily than before. 'It's all right if you take it all in the right way. What I mean is, if it makes you more yuman, it's all right. If it doesn't it's all wrong. If I've said it once to customers 'ere, I've said it a thousand times, just standing 'ere like I am now, talking to somebody like yourself. "Does it," I said, "make you more yuman? 'Cos if it doesn't, keep it." I take a broad view, and when I say yuman, I mean yuman. I believe –' and here he fixed his prominent eyes unwinkingly upon Mr Oakroyd – 'in yumanity.'

'That's right, mister,' replied Mr Oakroyd heartily but with a certain philosophical sternness. 'I see your point and I'm with yer.' He would have been better pleased, however, he admitted to himself, to have seen the bacon and eggs. A knocking from some place behind suggested that they were now ready.

'What I say is, ask yourself all the time "Is it yuman?" If it isn't, don't touch it. Let it alone. Pass it by. That's my motto – yumanity first – and that's the rule 'ere, as you saw right off when you asked for a wash. Take the yuman line, I say, and it'll pay you every time.' He now condescended to hear the knocking, and brought out the bacon and eggs. 'There you are, my friend,' he said, and he said it in such a manner that it was impossible to believe that he had merely carried the dish a few yards. He seemed not only to have done the cooking but to have gathered the eggs from distant roosts, to have cured the bacon himself, to have made the very crockery.

Mr Oakroyd, after telling himself that he wished the cooking had been done by some one a little less human (for the eggs were fried hard), ate away with the utmost heartiness and despatch. Every mouthful seemed to be taken in under the auspices of Mr Poppleby, who leaned over the counter and never took his eyes off his solitary customer. By the time he had arrived at his third slice of bread, Mr Oakroyd was ready to open the conversation again. He felt friendly, expansive.

'What allus beats me,' he announced, 'is this here "Cyclists Catered For". What's difference between cyclists and t'other folk as comes?'

''Am chiefly,' replied Mr Poppleby thoughtfully. 'Cyclists is great on 'am. I've seen the day when one of these cycling clubs would run me right out of 'am by six o'clock Saturday. Mind you, I'm not talking about last week, nor the week before, nor last year, nor the year before that, I'm talking about before the War. Properly speaking, there's no cyclists now, not to call cyclists. You might get one now and again, coming on a bike, but there's no real cycling, couples off together, and clubs, and suchlike. That's gone, that'll never come back. When I started 'ere, it was all traps and carts and what not on week day, and then cyclists – with a few regular locals coming in, of course – at week-ends. Now, it's all cars and lorries. And what 'appens? They don't stop at a place like this but goes on to big towns and stops there. That's what's hit this business so 'ard, my friend. It isn't what it was, I can tell you.'

'Nowt's what it wor,' said Mr Oakroyd with a kind of cheerful melancholy. 'I've seen some changes i' my time. You take textile trade nar –'

But Mr Poppleby was not taking it. 'That is so. And what's it amount to, what's the real difference between them times and these? That's the question I always ask.'

'And you're quite right, mate, to ask it,' Mr Oakroyd put in warmly.

'And what's the answer? What's the answer?' And Mr Poppleby hurried on so that he could supply it himself. 'It's less yuman, that's the difference.' And he paused, triumphantly, gazing at Mr Oakroyd, who was busy lighting the pipe for which he had long been waiting. Secure on a foundation of bacon and eggs, *Old Salt* was again delicious. Mr Oakroyd slowly sent a few of its kindly blue clouds rolling through the air, and waited for Mr Poppleby to continue.

'I've no need to tell a man like you what I mean by "yuman",' Mr Poppleby went on. 'I mean there's less of the good old man-to-man spirit. It's take what you can get and run, nowadays. Money and grab and rush, that's what it is. When you're running a business like this, you see life, you know what's 'appening in the world, you talk to all sorts. Of course there's some men in the catering that's as ignorant as you like – and why? – 'cos they don't make use of the hopportunities of the business; they see a customer come in, gets 'is order, serves it, takes the money, and finish. I like to live and learn. I talk to my customers and they talk to me, and that's 'ow I go on. I'm learning from you.'

'Ay,' said Mr Oakroyd, who could not help wondering, however, what it was that the other was learning from him. 'He doesn't gi' me a chance to tell him nowt,' he told himself, and, feeling that he had had enough of Mr Poppleby's conversation, he said, 'Well, what's t'damage?'

'Lemme see,' replied Mr Poppleby. 'Pot-of-tea-two-rashers two-eggs-four-slices-bread. That'll be one and eight. *And* a fair price if you ask me.'

'Ay, I dare say,' said Mr Oakroyd, who thought it stiffish. He felt in his pockets and once again produced the solitary sixpence. 'I shall ha' to ask you to do a bit o' changing for me,' he remarked, producing the envelope from his breast pocket.

'We'll try to manage that,' Mr Poppleby made a noise that faintly suggested he was laughing. 'You want the change and I want you to 'ave it, and we're both satisfied and nobody's the worse. That's the yuman line, isn't it?'

But Mr Oakroyd was staring in front of him open-mouthed. The envelope was not empty, but all that it contained was a dirty half-sheet of paper on which was scrawled 'Wishing you a Merry Xmas & a Happy New Year. XXX.' All four banknotes had disappeared. He ran through all his pockets, hoping against hope that somebody had merely played a trick upon him. But no, they had gone. He had been robbed. And now he understood why he had been given the sofa to sleep on last night, why Nobby and Fred had departed so early, why the landlady had hustled him out of the place before he had time to think.

''Ere,' he cried, 'I've been robbed. Look at this. I'd twenty pound i' there last night, fower five-pound notes, and sitha, there's nowt there but a bit o' paper. I've been robbed and I know who did it.' But when he looked at Mr Poppleby, he saw that that gentleman was regarding him coldly, with raised eyebrows.

'It'll be one and eight,' repeated Mr Poppleby.

This made Mr Oakroyd very angry. 'I tell you I've been robbed o' twenty pound. I haven't one and eight. I've got sixpence, and there it is, and that's all I have got. And I know who did it and where it happened too. It were two fellers wi' a lorry at t'Kirkworth Inn last night.'

'Are you trying to tell me you lost twenty pound, four five-pound notes, at the Kirkworth Inn last night?' demanded Mr Poppleby. 'Because if you are, I'm going to ask you what you was doing with so many five-pound notes and at such a place.

It sounds fishy to me. But that's no business of mine; you go your way and I'll go mine – though the sooner you get back to where you come from, the better, I think, my friend; but in the meantime you owe me one shilling and eightpence, whichever way you look at it. And that's what I want from you – one and eight.'

'And that's what you can't get from me, Mister,' cried Mr Oakroyd, exasperated. 'Aren't I telling you that I've nobbut sixpence in t'world? 'Ere, look 'ere.' And, rising to his feet, he turned out his trousers pockets. 'Twenty pounds I've lost, all I'd got but this here sixpence. Eh, but I was a gert blunderhead!'

'You're not the first that's tried it on,' said Mr Poppleby, steadily.

'Ar d'you mean?' cried Mr Oakroyd. 'I'm not trying anything on. When I come in here, I thought I'd twenty pound i' my pocket. I didn't know I'd been robbed.'

'And I didn't know, neither,' observed the other, eyeing him suspiciously. 'This has happened before 'ere, I'll tell you. And I go on trusting people. You come in 'ere and you 'ave my eggs and my bacon and my tea –'

'Ay, and your bread and your lump o' washing soap and your mucky towel and your drop o' water,' Mr Oakroyd added with great bitterness. 'Go on, go on. You've lost one and eight and I've lost twenty pound, and it's bad luck for both on us, but it's a dam' sight war for me. 'Ere, there's sixpence, and that knocks it down to one and two. Well, I'll settle wi' thee, lad.' And Mr Oakroyd, in a frenzy of irritation, rushed to his bag of tools and took out a chisel. 'You see that chisel? It's worth more ner any one and two, is that, and you can ha' that for your one and two. And when I can pay your fowerteen pence, I will, for I'd rather ha' that chisel than all t'shop you've got. Ay, even if you cleaned it up,' he added vindictively.

Mr Poppleby came forward, picked up the sixpence and examined the chisel. 'A chisel's no good to me,' he said slowly, 'but I suppose I'd better let you go. I like to take a yuman line –'

'Yuman line! T-t-t-t. Yuman nothing!' Mr Oakroyd was very scornful as he gathered his things together.

'That'll do, that'll do.' Mr Poppleby's philosophical vanity was hurt now. 'But let me tell you, my friend, you can't do these sort o' things 'ere. Don't try it again. I tell you, you can't do it.'

'And let me tell you summat, Mister,' said Mr Oakroyd, moving to the door. 'There's summat you can't do, neither.'

'Ho, indeed! And what's that?'

'You can't fry eggs.' And Mr Oakroyd, chuckling, closed the door behind him.

Miss Thong, Dressmaker

THERE can be no doubt that Miss Thong really was a clever, cheap dressmaker and that she worked miracles for them those few days, but that is not the reason why she deserves a little space to herself. We must glance at Miss Thong because the image of her haunted Miss Trant at odd moments throughout that winter. Miss Thong has a part in the homely epic; it is a very tiny part – no more than that of a whispering ghost – but we cannot say it has no significance. Miss Trant remembers her to this very day.

She went with Elsie, who knew the way. They walked the length of an unusually monotonous street of little brick houses, which ended in some waste ground, a melancholy muddle of worn turf, clayey holes, wire-netting and ramshackle fowl-houses made out of orange boxes, and a few dirty and listless hens. The last house on the left was detached from the row, but was yet so close to it, so obviously still a part of it, that Miss Trant felt that this house had just been sawn off, as if it were the crust of a long loaf. It looked like a slice too, for it was severely rectangular and only one room in breadth, being indeed the very narrowest house she had ever seen. It was not old; it was not dingy; it was newish, had a bright glazed look, and was immediately depressing. There were two little brass plates on the door: one said *Midland Guardian and Widows Fire and Life Assurance* and the other whispered *Miss Thong – Dressmaker*. The door was opened to them by the Midland Guardian, who had watery eyes, a drooping grey moustache, carpet slippers, and a coat and waistcoat that had seen far too much gravy and egg. Yes, yes, his daughter was in, and they could see her; but she was busy; she was always busy these days, always in great demand; and she wasn't too strong, not really strong enough for all the work that came. One of these days, he told them as they went into the tiny sitting-room, he would have to put his foot down, the girl was doing too much. And he shuffled out, to tell her they were there. 'I know the sort of foot he'll put down,' Elsie whispered. 'I'll bet she keeps him going all right. If he makes enough out of his insurance to keep him in whisky, I'd be surprised. Silly old blighter! But she isn't strong, either. She's a queer little thing.'

She was a queer little thing: no older than Miss Trant herself, perhaps, but very small and crooked, with thin hair pathetically bobbed, hollow cheeks, and a long nose that seemed to flush in a most unhappy manner. Her eyes were bright enough but she had hardly any eyelashes and the lids were slightly reddened. Perhaps she was consumptive. She looked as if she might have anything and everything wrong with that frail body of hers. It seemed as if one winter's night would extinguish her for ever. Nevertheless, as soon as she saw Elsie, her face lit up and she plunged at once into a gasping prattle that never stopped all the way up to the front room upstairs that was her workroom. When she learned that the troupe was to be re-formed under the direction of Miss Trant, she was genuinely delighted, almost in an ecstasy. She insisted upon telling Miss Trant all about the two performances of the Dinky Doos she had seen when they had been giving the show the first week.

'It was such a treat to me, you can't imagine,' she gasped. 'And then when Miss Longstaff came here – and I'd seen her only two nights before, singing and dancing there and looking prettier than a picture – well, well, it was a surprise! I stared at her, couldn't believe my own eyes! I must have looked a sketch.' Here Miss Thong laughed heartily at herself. 'Didn't you think I did, Miss Longstaff? Never mind, so did you, when you came on as that little girl in the choir. That was a skit, that was. Laugh! – you ought to have heard me. And that Mr Nunn – he's a comic, if you like. The way he went on telling everybody they was late! And then betting five pounds with that other one – who was it? – that fine sing-ger – yes, that's him – Mr Brundit – oh, that was good! And that Miss Susie Dean! Isn't she a card? The way she took people off! Really enjoying herself, she was, you could tell just by looking at her. So pretty too! And what high spirits! Now don't you go and be jealous, Miss Longstaff, because I'll say the same for you. I'm not going to quarrel with the prettiest customer I've got, and a real famous actress too – no, no, no!' And Miss Thong cocked her head on one side, looked very arch and very cunning at one and the same time, and then laughed at herself so heartily that she burst into a fit of coughing and hastily put a handkerchief to her mouth.

Miss Trant stared out of the window a minute, then said: 'I'm glad you enjoyed the show so much, Miss Thong. At least, I imagine you did,' she added, with a smile.

'I haven't enjoyed anything so much, I don't know when,' cried Miss Thong. 'I went twice – did I tell you? It's not usual for me to go even once, but twice – then it's got to be extra special. I said to Pa – he doesn't like me going out much, you know – but I said to him "I know I'm very busy," I said, "and I know it costs money. But I must go again," I said, "because they're so good they've taken me right out of myself, what with their sing-ging and lovely dancing and their comics and all," I said. And when I heard they'd gone and broken up – oh, the news soon gets round in Rawsley! – well, I could have sat down and cried. And then Miss Longstaff told me how they'd been treated, Miss What's it – Miss Trant, I beg your pardon. "What a shame!" I said. There I'd been sitting here, thinking how lovely they looked and trying to hum some of the songs and telling myself they hadn't a care in the world, and there they were all feeling as miserable as anything, not knowing where to look, you might say, and me here with my nice little business. And that only made me feel more miserable. You know how you can get sometimes?' And Miss Thong laughed again. 'But to think that you're beginning all over again!'

'And going to be better,' said Elsie. 'We've got two good new men.'

'Just fancy!' cried Miss Thong delightedly. 'It just shows you, doesn't it? You never know what's waiting round the corner, as I tell Pa. He'll never believe in anything. Oh, these business men, I say! He never would believe we'd get this house. But here we are. And isn't it nice here, Miss Trant?' She almost pushed them both over to the window with her. They looked out at the bald turf, the half bricks and tin cans, the huddle of box lids and wire netting and hens.

'Very nice,' said Miss Trant. Then, with an effort: 'Very nice indeed.'

'Isn't it?' cried Miss Thong. 'It's so open. You're in the town and yet *not* in it, I say. Especially up here, looking right out. That's where all the boys down the street play – cricket and football – and though they're a bit noisy, I don't mind it – quite cheers you up to see them running about and hear them shouting. It's a bit of life, isn't it? I'm glad you think it's nice here. It's made such a difference to me having such a lookout. What with this house and the dressmaking doing so well, they'll be telling me soon I'm getting above myself. Perhaps I am, what with actresses coming too, eh, Miss Longstaff? Somebody said to me, the other day, when I told them, they said: "You'll be going on the stage yourself next, Miss Thong." "And a fine sketch I'd look!" I said.' Here Miss Thong laughed and coughed again, and Elsie laughed a little too, and Miss Trant tried to laugh, but found it easier to turn away and undo the parcels they had brought with them.

They told her what they wanted, and she frowned and gasped out questions and nodded excitedly and busied herself clearing the worktable. 'There, you can go away,' she cried to the vanishing pieces of material, 'and so can you, and you, and you. Coat and skirt – blue serge and braid – for Mrs Moxon – that's the last of you for a bit and I don't care if you *are* promised. Semi-evening for Miss Abbey – wants it for whist-drives – and *you'll* have to wait. Yes, I'll do it for you, Miss Trant, Miss Longstaff, but don't – oh, don't – breathe a word to any one in Rawsley I'm doing it, or my custom's gone! You see, I've promised and promised and better promised – and they come round and ask and ask – just as if a girl had twelve pairs of hands. But I'll do it for you. I don't care. They can all wait, that's what I say.' The little crooked creature grasped the edge of her table, stood as erect as she could, and, with cheeks paler than ever but with her great nose flushing triumphantly, she seemed to defy a host of clamouring Moxons and Abbeys, coats and skirts and semi-evenings. 'So there you are,' she cried. 'If I've to lock myself in this room, give out I'm ill again, I'll do it. Let's have a bit of life, I say. Now tell me what you want and show me what you've got.'

'We want a harlequin effect in some of the dresses,' said Elsie. 'We've got all sorts of remnants and lovely odd bits. Look here. Sateens and light silks and crêpe-de-Chine and velvet.' And the next minute, the worktable had disappeared, and in its place was a crazy garden of fabrics, a rainbow carnival.

'Oh, I say! O-o-oh!' After this first rapturous cry, Miss Thong breathed hard, quivered with delight, pressed her hands together, and stared and stared, as if her eyes had long been thirsty and could at last drink their fill. Then she fell upon the glowing heap. 'Oh, look at this – and this – and these two together,' she babbled ecstatically. 'Here's some apricot velvet – lovely cap it would make, wouldn't it? And that old rose – let me smooth it out – look! – put that with it – wait till I get some pins – hundreds of pins – oh, aren't I silly?'

'I was like that the other day,' said Miss Trant, laughing.

'I'm always like that,' said Elsie, who was indeed nearly as excited as Miss Thong. 'They go to my head, I can tell you. Look at that, Miss Thong. Isn't it lovely?'

'Isn't it! Oh, deary dear! It's all lovely, and I don't know where to start or whether I'm on my head or my heels or laughing or crying, I don't really. Now aren't I silly?' And it certainly looked as if something dreadful would happen to Miss Thong, who was trying to laugh and cough and blow her nose and pick up some of the silks and fill her mouth with pins all at the same time. At last, however, she quietened down, the professional dressmaker taking the place of the enraptured woman, and they discussed the dresses they wanted. It was arranged that Elsie should help her when she was not wanted for rehearsal, during the remaining two days at Rawsley.

It was Wednesday evening when Miss Trant called there again. The thin little house, now besieged by the curiously melancholy dusk of autumn, that smoky blue into which the green and gold of summer has vanished, it seems, for ever, looked forlorn enough, but its glazed brightness had gone and there was something cheerful and brave, a hint of the indomitable, about that lighted upstairs window. Elsie was there, looking very pink and rounded and robust by the side of Miss Thong, who in the searching gaslight seemed frailer and uglier than before, like a worn-out witch, with that great nose and her dimmed eyes peering between their reddened lids. She was obviously tired out, yet greeted Miss Trant triumphantly. Two dresses were completed.

'And Miss Longstaff's is one of them,' she began.

'Elsie, I told you,' said that young lady.

'There now!' she cried to Miss Trant, nodding her head. 'She wants me to call her Elsie. Aren't I getting on? And it seems only a minute since I saw her on the stage. Well, then, Elsie's is finished and it's the loveliest thing you ever saw, Miss Trant, it really is. Do put it on, Elsie. Slip into my bedroom and put it on. Just to please me.'

After an interrogative glance at Miss Trant, Elsie nodded, went out, and returned in an incredibly short space of time an entirely different person. In that soft shimmer of blues and greens she looked almost beautiful.

'But what a lovely dress you've made!' cried Miss Trant

with genuine enthusiasm. 'It's like a wood full of bluebells.' She turned to Miss Thong to congratulate her.

But Miss Thong's gaze was still fastened mistily upon Elsie. Her lips were quivering a little, and her long clever hands were clutching and twisting. 'Oh – Miss – Miss – Elsie,' she faltered, moving a step or so towards her. 'You do look beautiful in it. And I made it, didn't I? And to think of you – wearing it – sing-ging and dancing in it – going all over – thousands of people. Oh, I am silly – but – just to think –'

Elsie put an arm about her, held her for a moment, then stooped and lightly kissed her on the cheek. 'You're not silly, you're very clever,' she said softly. 'There. Isn't she clever, Miss Trant? We shall have to put her name on the programmes, won't we? Dresses by Madame Thong of Rawsley.'

'Oh, go on with you,' gasped Miss Thong, dabbing at her eyes and laughing and crying. 'I really must be tired. I don't know when I've taken on so. You must be thinking "She's a ridiculous little thing." Now aren't you? Never mind, we're all a bit silly sometimes. Best thing I can do is to put in a bit at Mrs Moxon's coat and skirt, that'll bring me to my senses. Two yards of braid to put on, plenty of machining, that's what I want. There now, let's talk about the other things.'

So they settled down to talk about the other dresses and were very business-like. It was when Miss Thong began to discuss sending them on and to ask about addresses that Miss Trant, who was moved by the thought of their leaving this little woman and never seeing her again, had an inspiration.

'Tomorrow morning, you know,' she began, 'we leave for a place called Dotworth –'

'That's the three-night stand I told you about,' Elsie put in, nodding at Miss Thong.

'And then next week we go to a seaside place on the East Coast called Sandybay,' Miss Trant continued. 'Now if all the dresses will be finished by about next Monday or Tuesday, why don't you bring them yourself – you needn't carry them, you know; we can arrange about that – and then you can try them on.'

'And I could see you all on the stage too, couldn't I?' cried Miss Thong eagerly, her face lighting up.

'Of course you could. And it would be a nice little holiday for you too, after all your hard work. You could stay a day or two.'

'Oh, wouldn't that be lovely! Going to the seaside and trying on the dresses and seeing them on the stage perhaps and hearing it all again and better than last time and – oh – everything!' For a moment she saw it all, fastened on it in pure rapture. Then the light died out of her face. 'But I couldn't do it, Miss Trant. Oh, I wish I could, but I really couldn't.'

'Why not?'

'Oh! – so many things. There's – I don't know – I couldn't begin to think of it.'

'Of course we should pay your expenses,' said Miss Trant casually. 'Naturally, when you're working for us. It's the usual thing, isn't it, Elsie?'

'Done every time,' replied Elsie promptly and with a grateful glance at Miss Trant. Then she looked severely at Miss Thong. 'Now you're being really silly. I don't believe you want to see me in my dress. You come along. I'll get you in my digs.'

'Yes, of course, Elsie, Miss Trant, I know – but – oh, don't ask me! There's Pa. He'd never let me go, I know he wouldn't.'

'Where is he? Is he in now? Downstairs? All right, you leave him to me,' said Elsie grimly. 'If it's only Pa that's bothering you, I'll soon settle Pa.'

And off she went, there and then, leaving Miss Thong – as she admitted – 'downright flabbergasted'. It took Elsie exactly five minutes to settle Pa, and there could be no doubt – as a glance at her face promptly informed them – that on this question the Midland Guardian was settled once and for all.

'And didn't he mind then?' cried Miss Thong in wonder and delight.

'Not a bit,' said Elsie, still grimly. 'He liked it. And he'll keep on liking it.'

'Well, I'll come then. Yes, I will. I'll work and work and get them all finished and I'll bring them. I know there's an excursion from here to Sandybay – four days or something –

and that'll make it cheaper. I don't know how I'll get all the dresses to the station.'

'I do,' said Elsie. 'Pa will take them.'

'And I shall be able to come in and see you all for nothing, won't I?' cried Miss Thong. 'And perhaps go behind the scenes.'

'Of course! Madame Thong, dressmaker to *The Good Companions*,' said Elsie. 'Can't we put it in the programmes, Miss Trant?'

'We can and we will,' she replied, rising. 'We must finish making the arrangements now. I've still got heaps and heaps of things to do. I wondered at first how I should find anything to do, but now I seem to be busy from the crack of dawn.'

'I'm sure you like it, don't you, Miss Trant?' said Miss Thong. 'It's a bit of life, isn't it? That's what I feel about doing these dresses. Give me a bit of life, I say.'

And that was one of the things Miss Trant did not forget.

Stanley, Office Boy

THE frosted glass door that opened from the little space in which inquirers were kept waiting for a few minutes, now swung back to admit into the general office the body of a boy about fifteen, whose eyes were focused upon a paper, folded into a very small compass, that he held about four inches away from them. This was the office boy or very junior clerk, Stanley Poole, who had just come all the way from Hackney, which remained with him as a combined flavour of cocoa and bread dipped in bacon fat that still haunted his palate. His body, which was small and thin but sufficiently tough, and was crowned by a snub nose, some freckles, greyish-green eyes, and some unbrushed sandy hair, had been in the service of Twigg and Dersingham for the last twenty minutes, when it had boarded a tram and a bus and had walked down several streets. Now it had arrived in the office. But his mind had not yet begun the day's work. Even now, when the very threshold had been passed, it was still in the wilds of Mexico, enjoying the heroic and exhilarating companionship of Jack Dashwood and Dick Robinson, the Boy Aviators, the terror of all Mexican bandits.

'So you've come,' said Mrs Cross, putting back that wisp of hair again. 'It's about time I was 'opping it if you've come.'

Stanley looked up and nodded. With a sigh, he withdrew from the world of the Boy Aviators and the Mexican bandits. He tried to fold his paper into a still smaller compass, before cramming it into his pocket.

'Read, read, read!' cried Mrs Cross derisively. 'Some of yer's always at it. What they find to put in all the time beats me. What's that yer reading now? Murders, I'll bet.'

''Tisn't,' replied Stanley, balancing himself on one leg for no particular reason that we can discover. 'It's a boys' paper.' He made this announcement with a kind of sullen reluctance, not because he was really a sullen lad, but simply because he had discovered that when his elders asked these questions, they were usually not in search of information, but were trying to get at him.

'Penny bloods, them things is.'

''Tisn't,' said Stanley, balancing himself on the other leg now. 'This is tuppence. I buy it ev'ry week, have done ever since it come out. *Boy's Companion*, it's called. It's got the best tales in,' he added, in a sudden burst of confidence. 'All about boys who fly in airplanes an' go to Mexico an' Russia an' all over an' have advenshers!'

'Advenshers! They'd be better off at 'ome – with their advenshers! You'll be wantin' to go an' 'ave advenshers yer-self next – and then what will yer poor mother say?'

But this only goaded Stanley into making new and even more dangerous admissions. 'I'm going to try and be a detective,' he mumbled.

'Well now, did y'ever!' cried Mrs Cross, at once shocked and delighted. 'A detective! I never 'eard of such a thing! What d'yer come 'ere for if yer want to be a detective? There's no detectin' 'ere. Go on with yer! 'Ere, yer not big enough, and yer never will be either 'cos yer'd 'ave to be a pleeceman first before they'd let yer be a detective, and they'd never 'ave yer as a pleeceman.'

'You can be a detective without being a bobby first,' replied Stanley, scornfully. He had gone into this question, and was not to be put off by a mere outsider like Mrs Cross. ''Sides, you can be a private detective an' find jewels an' shadder people. That's what I'd like to do – shadder people.'

'What's that? Follerin' 'em about, is it? Oh, that's nasty work, that is. Shadderin'! I'd shadder yer if I caught yer at it, my word I would.' And Mrs Cross took up her brush and dust-pan and gave them a fierce little shake, almost as if she had just caught *them* at it. 'Now you just get on with yer work like a good boy, and don't you go tellin' anybody else yer want to be shadderin' else yer'll be getting yourself into trouble. Yer can't expect people to 'ave any patience with shadderers. If Mr Dersingham knew what was goin' on in that 'ead of yours, 'e'd tell yer to go straight 'ome and 'ave nothing more to do with yer, and yer'd find yerself shadderin' for another job, and that's all the shadderin' *you*'d get.'

Left to himself, Stanley, with the contemptuous air of a man who is meant for better things, began his morning's work. After taking off the two typewriter covers, dumping a few books on the high desks, and filling up all the ink-pots and putting out clean sheets of blotting paper (which duty was a little fad of Mr Smeeth's), he remembered that he was a creature with a soul. So, grasping a short round ruler in such a way that it remotely resembled a revolver, he crouched behind Mr Smeeth's high stool for a few tense moments, then sprang out, pointing his gun at the place where the great criminal's bottom waistcoat button would have been, and said hoarsely: 'Put 'em up, Diamond Jack. No, you don't! Not a move!' He gave a warning flourish of the gun, then said casually, over his shoulder, to one of his assistants or a few police sergeants or somebody like that, 'Take him away.' And that was the end of Diamond Jack, and yet another triumph for S. Poole, the young detective whose exploits were rivalling even those of the Boy Aviators. And having thus refreshed himself, Stanley replaced the round ruler and condescended to perform one or two more of those monotonous and trifling actions that Messrs Twigg and Dersingham demanded of him at this hour of the morning. These left him ample time for thought, and he began to wonder if he would be able to get out during the morning. Once outside the office – even though he was going to the post office or the railway goods department or some firm not four streets away – he could enjoy himself, for the affairs of Twigg and Dersingham faded to a grey thread of routine; he plunged at once into the drama of London's underworld; and as he hopped and dodged about the crowded streets, like a sandy-haired sparrow, he was able to do some marvellous shadowing. There also loomed already, early as it was, a problem that would become more and more disturbing as the long morning wore on and he became hungrier and hungrier. This was the problem of where to go and what to buy for lunch, for which his mother allowed him a shilling every day. He always ate his breakfast so quickly that his stomach forgot about it almost at once and left him hollow inside by ten o'clock and absolutely aching by twelve. He often wondered what would happen to him if, instead of being the first to go to lunch, at half-past twelve, he was the last, and had to wait until about half-past one. There are innumerable ways of spending a shilling on lunch, from the downright solid way of blowing the lot on sausage or fried liver and mashed potatoes, say at the *Pavement Dining Rooms*, to the immediately delightful but rather unsatisfying method of spreading it out, buying a jam tart here, a banana there, and some milk chocolate somewhere else; and Stanley knew them all.

T. Benenden, Tobacconist

Mr Smeeth was one of T. Benenden's regular customers, a patron (perhaps the only one) of T. Benenden's Own Mixture

(*Cool Sweet Smoking*). 'No,' he liked to tell some fellow pipe-smoker, 'I don't fancy your ounce-packet stuff. I like my tobacco freshly mixed, y'know, and so I always get it from a little shop near the office. It's the chap's own mixture and so it's always fresh. Oh, fine stuff! – you try a pipeful – and very reasonable. Been getting it for years now. And the chap I get it from is a bit of a character in his way.' Saying this made Mr Smeeth feel that he was a connoisseur of both good tobacco and human nature, and it gave an added flavour to his pipe, which could do with it after being charged with nothing but T. Benenden's own mixture. It is hardly possible that he was right about the tobacco being 'freshly mixed', for though mixed – and well mixed – it may have been, it could not come from T. Benenden's little shop, with its hundreds of dusty dummy packets, its row of battered tin canisters, its dilapidated weight scales, its dirty counter, its solitary wheezing gas mantle, its cobwebs and dark corners, and still be fresh. On the other hand, he was certainly right when he described T. Benenden himself as a bit of a character in his way.

T. Benenden's way was that of the philosophical financier turned shopkeeper. He was an oldish man who wore thick glasses (which only magnified eyes that protruded far enough without their help), a straggling pepper-and-salt beard, one of those old-fashioned single high collars and a starched front, and no tie. When Mr Smeeth first visited the shop, years ago, he was at once startled and amused by this absence of tie, jumping to the conclusion that the man had forgotten his tie. Now, he would have been far more startled to see Benenden *with* a tie. He had often been tempted to ask the chap why he wore these formal collars and fronts and yet no tie, but somehow he had never dared. Benenden himself, though he was ready to talk on many subjects, never mentioned ties. Either he deliberately ignored them or he had never noticed the part these things were now playing in the world, simply did not understand about ties. What he did like to talk about, perhaps because his shop was in the City, was finance, a sort of Arabian Nights finance. He sat there behind his counter, steadily smoking his stock away, and peered at old copies of financial periodicals or the City news of ordinary papers, and out of this reading, and the bits of gossip he heard, and the grandiose muddle of his own mind, he concocted the most astonishing talk. It was difficult to buy an ounce of tobacco from him without his making you feel that the pair of you had just missed a fortune.

As soon as he recognized Mr Smeeth, T. Benenden very deliberately pulled down his scales and then placed on the counter the particular dirty old canister set apart for his own mixture. 'The usual, I suppose, Mr Smeeth?' he said, picking up the pouch and then smoothing it out on the counter. 'I saw your chief this morning, the young fellow – Mr Dersingham. Came in for some *Sahibs*. Got somebody with him too, new to me, well set up gentleman, with a good cigar in his mouth, a very good cigar. You'll know who I mean?'

'He called this morning at the office,' said Mr Smeeth.

'Well, I didn't say anything,' Benenden continued, very seriously as he weighed out the tobacco. 'It's not my business to say anything. I *don't* say anything. But I keep my eyes open. And I said to myself, the minute they went out, "This looks to me as if Twigg and Dersingham's are moving on a bit. This has the look of a merging job, or a syndicate job, or a trust job. And," I said, "if Mr Smeeth does happen to come in for the usual, I'll put it straight to him. It's no concern of mine, but he'll tell *me*. I'll test my judgement," I said.'

'Sorry, Mr Benenden,' said Mr Smeeth, smiling at him, 'but I've nothing to tell you. I don't rightly know what's happening, but you can depend on it, it's nothing in that line.'

'Then,' cried Benenden, quite passionately, rolling up the pouch and then slapping it down on the counter, 'you're wrong. I don't mean you, Mr Smeeth, I mean the firm. That's the way things are going all the time now, Mr Smeeth, big combinations – merging away till you don't know where you are – and sweeping the deck, until – dear me – there isn't a picking, not a crumb, left. You see what I mean? Now there's a bit here in one of the papers – I was just reading it when you came in – and I don't suppose you've seen it. Just a minute and I'll find it. Now here it is. Suppose, Mr Smeeth, just suppose,' and here T. Benenden leaned across the counter and his eyes seemed colossal, 'I'd come to you a fortnight since, a week since, and said to you, "What about picking up a bit on South Coast Laundries?" – what would you have said?'

'I'd have said it takes me all my time to pay my own laundry bill,' Mr Smeeth replied, much amused by this retort of his.

T. Benenden made a slight gesture of contempt to show that this was mere trifling. Then he looked very solemn, very impressive. 'You'd have said, "I can't be bothered with South Coast Laundries. I'm not touching 'em – don't want 'em – take your South Coast Laundries away." And you'd have been right – as far as you could see, *then*. But what happens, what happens? Read your paper. It's there, under my very 'and. Along comes a big merger – a bit of syndicate and trust work – and up they go, right to the top – bang! Now – you see – you can't touch 'em. And there's a feller here – you can see it in the paper – who's been clearing anything out of it – a hundred thousand, two hundred thousand – a clean sweep, made for life. And he's not the only one, not a bit of it! And we sit here, pretending to laugh at South Coast Laundries or whatever it might be, and what are we doing? We're missing it, that's what we're doing, we're missing it.' Here, a dramatic pause.

'And if your Mr Dersingham isn't careful,' Benenden concluded, still impressive even if a trifle vague now, '*he's* going to miss it. He wants to keep his eyes open. There's one or two bits in this paper I'd like to show him. Let's see, what was it you gave me? Half a crown, wasn't it? That's right then – one and six change. And good night to *you*, Mr Smeeth.' And T. Benenden, after stooping down to the tiny gas-jet to relight his pipe, retired to his corner to ruminate.

Mr Ramsbottom

WILLIAM saw a stout man of about fifty approaching them. He was very broad and heavy, but nevertheless he seemed to bounce along. As he drew nearer, he beamed upon them. His rimless spectacles glittered with a jovial recognition. His clean-shaven face, almost as wide and flat as a dinner-plate, shone with his appreciation of this happy moment. Introduced as Mr Ramsbottom, he shook William's hand with enthusiasm.

'Very pleased to meet you,' he cried, stepping back and looking at William with the greatest interest, as if William's whole appearance was both remarkable and beautiful. 'It's good of you to come. It is. It's good of you. And don't mind me, Mr Dursley. Ah'm Lancasheer, you see – a Lanc'sher lad, if you like – and Ah say what Ah think and it all comes out, like emptying a chest o' drawers – and you mustn't mind me. That's right, isn't it, Commander? Well, we're all here.' Then suddenly his enormous smile vanished, and he looked earnestly from one to the other. 'Mr Dursley, Commander, you'll both take a drop o' something before we start? What's it to be? Cocktail or drop o' sherry or what?'

'I don't think I want anything, thanks,' said William.

'Nay, you must have something,' cried Mr Ramsbottom reproachfully. 'So must you, Commander. 'Ere, Albert –' and he called a waiter, to whom they were compelled to give an order.

'Do you know that waiter, too?' asked the Commander.

'Who, him? Yes, Ah know him. Albert, his name is. Only been 'ere a week. He used to be at the Metro. at Blackpool, Albert did. Ah knew him well there. You ask him. He's got a little girl that's won five prizes with the concertina, and she's going on the stage with it. He was telling all about her yesterday. Ah'll tell you her name in a minute.' Mr Ramsbottom tried to think of her name, but catching sight of the Commander's smile, he laughed and then turned to William. 'He laughs at me 'cos Ah know all about everybody, but Ah say –

damn it all, if you're stopping at a place you might as well know the other folk and Ah don't care a brass button whether they're waiters or barmaids or what they are so long as they've got a civil tongue in their heads. And if it hadn't been for the staff 'ere, Ah'd have gone days and days dumb and speechless.'

'Have you been here long?' asked William.

'Nearly two months,' replied Mr Ramsbottom, looking solemn. 'Ah came for my 'ealth. Doctor told me to come 'ere. Ah'd two doctors and a specialist.' At this moment, the waiter arrived with the drinks, and Mr Ramsbottom immediately sat up and became bustling and genial again. 'Well, 'ere we are, gentlemen. That's yours, Mr Dursley. That's yours, Commander. Well, 'ere's the best. That's good stoof.' He smacked his thick lips appreciatively, nodded his head, and beamed at them through his glasses. 'Now what was Ah talking about?'

'You were talking about your health,' William prompted.

'So Ah was.' And instantly Mr Ramsbottom began to droop and dwindle; the light faded from his eyes; his cheeks fell in; his whole figure sagged; he was a sick man. 'Well, Ah'd two doctors and a specialist. Ah couldn't eat and Ah couldn't sleep. Dizziness, too – oh dear, awful dizziness! And Ah'd a pain in my back – just round there – no, a bit lower down – there – oh, dear, dear, dear, Ah didn't know what to do with myself half the time. Chaps I knew in business or at club said to me, "Nay, Johnny Ramsbottom, you're looking bad." And Ah told 'em. Ah said: "Ah, an' Ah'm feeling bad." Couldn't eat, couldn't sleep, couldn't attend to my business properly. Ah'd got a buzzing in my 'ead like a circular saw. And trouble with my bladder, too – on the run every ten minutes. Ah said to myself, "If this goes on, Ah might as well hand my checks in. Life's not worth living." Mind you, Ah'd always had a bit o' bother with my inside. Anyhow, Ah went to one doctor, and he says, "It's your kidneys. That's what's wrong with you – your kidneys." Wait a minute. Dinner's up. We might as well go and peck a bit.'

On their way to the dining-room, Mr Ramsbottom continued his recital, and without troubling to lower his voice. 'Well, Ah went to another doctor, and he said, "Ah'm sorry to say, Mr Ramsbottom, it's your heart that's at fault." Ah wasn't surprised either, 'cos Ah'd always had an idea my heart wasn't all it should be. Ah'd noticed it knocking a bit for years, you might say. However, Ah saw a specialist too, best man in Manchester, and he pretended to make light of it, and he sent me to Harrogate first, and then when Ah went back, he told me to get some medicine to take, put me on a diet, and said if Ah could afford it Ah'd to knock off business for a year or so, and get out o' Manchester and find some fresh air. Then Ah went back to my own doctor, and he said come down 'ere. So Ah did.'

'I hope you're feeling better now,' said William politely.

Mr Ramsbottom halted at the dining-room door to give this question his full attention. 'Well, am Ah? It's a question, that. In a way Ah am, Ah dare say. Ah've lost that buzziness and dizziness and Ah eat and sleep better, but Ah'm not right, you know – oh dear no! Ah'm not right. and Ah never will be. Ah'll have to look after my inside. An' Ah still get that pain i' my back. Just a sharp twinge, you know, Mr Dursley, a right sharp twinge now and again, like as if somebody might be running a red-hot knitting-needle into me. Excuse me a minute.' He turned aside, in the dining-room, to greet three melancholy girls in black, who evidently constituted the Permanent Resident Orchestra. They smiled at him wanly above their instruments. The pianist was arranging some music, and the violinist and the 'cellist were tuning up. It was the 'cellist, the most melancholy of the melancholy trio, whom Mr Ramsbottom addressed.

'Have you heard from your mother, Miss Grierson?' he enquired.

'I had a letter to-day, thank you, Mr Ramsbottom,' replied the sad musician. 'She's a bit better, but she'll have to spend another fortnight in bed.'

'That's nothing so long as she's better,' cried Mr Ramsbottom. 'Is it now? A fair answer to a fair question. No, of course it isn't. You tell her from me to sit up and get some good stoof into her, Miss Grierson. And play us a few nice pieces to-night. Do your best.'

After this short exchange, he led the way down the room, which was large and nearly empty, to a table set for three near the fire.

'Didn't know you knew the orchestra too, Ramsbottom,' said the Commander, as they sat down.

'Oh yes, know 'em well by this time. Ah know all the pieces they play too, which is a pity. Ah'm getting a bit sick of most of 'em. That's Miss Grierson Ah was talking to, and her mother's poorly. She's been upset about it. She comes from just outside Birmingham, and she's a nice quiet girl, though she can't play that 'cello for toffee. You listen when they start. She gets so far off the note sometimes it brings tears to your eyes, like eating little green gooseberries. She's got no more ear than this table. What d'you think of the table? Done it nicely for us, haven't they? Ah told 'em Ah wanted it special to-night. And they're cooking a special dinner, too. They're careful what they give me now, Ah can tell you, Mr Dursley. Commander knows all about that, don't you?'

'I do,' said the Commander, suddenly producing fifty more fine little wrinkles round his eyes. 'Ramsbottom here is a great authority on food. He's an epicure, a gourmet.'

'Nay, Ah don't say that. But Ah do like good stoof. Ah've always been used to good stoof, and Ah know it when Ah see it and taste it, which is more than most people do. And Ah'm partly in the business, you know – 'cos Ah'm a wholesale grocer – and Ah take an interest in what Ah eat and drink. First two days Ah was 'ere, Ah just tasted what they gave me and said nothing. Then Ah went to see the manager. "Ah'm stopping 'ere some time," Ah told him. "Ah know you are, Mr Ramsbottom," he said. "But Ah'm not stopping another day if you don't give me better stoof to eat," Ah told him. "Why, what d'you mean?" he said. "We only use the best provisions, and our kitchen has a very good name." This made me laugh. "If you believe that," Ah told him, "then somebody's cheating you." He stared at me. "What's wrong with it?" he said. "Oh, Ah'll tell you," Ah said. And Ah did. Ah told him, to start with, the bread was poor quality, too much alum and potato in the flour, and they'd been putting a lot of margarine in his butter, and selling him the cheapest coffee on the market. Ah told him if they were going to get their soup out of tins, they'd better get some better brands, and Ah said they'd been using some bad fat in the kitchen and didn't seem over-particular about cleaning the pans, and that bits o' rock salmon shouldn't be called sole, and that their prime English beef must have been kidnapped and sent round the world because it had just been frozen. "And that cake you serve with afternoon tea," Ah told him. "If you're paying more than sevenpence a pound for that, you're being swindled." "Ridiculous," he said, "Ah'd like to see you buy cake like that at sevenpence a pound." "Oh you would, would you?" Ah said. "Well, Ah can let you have as much as you like of cake that quality at sixpence a pound, and Ah'll book the order now – much as you like. Only don't offer it to me at teatime, 'cos Ah don't eat stoof like that – it's muck. Ah like good stoof," Ah told him. "And you can't diddle me, Ah know too much about it." And Ah've not done badly since. They look after me. The dinner you're going to have now mightn't look as good on paper as the one they're offering everybody. But don't you believe it. It'll be plain and simple, but it'll be all good stoof, something to nourish you.'

William, staring at Mr Ramsbottom's great flat face and bursting shoulders, thought that nourishment was the last thing his host needed. He said nothing, being busy wondering, not without awe, what would happen if Mr Ramsbottom suddenly found himself grappling with the food at the *Lugmouth Packet*. Dare he ask him to a meal there? The idea fascinated him. He had a vision of Mr Ramsbottom, a knight-errant of 'good stoof', bearding the gloomy manageress in her cabbage-haunted cave. Meanwhile, the dinner they were eating proved that Mr Ramsbottom was not merely boasting. It was plain, but it was undeniably good stuff.

'That's the trouble nowadays,' Mr Ramsbottom observed, with the curious self-satisfaction that always accompanies this sort of statement; as if the speaker had been personally responsible for the Past, but had not been allowed to have any hand in shaping the Present. 'You can't get good stoof.

There's many an old working chap up in Lancashire or Yorkshire who's getting better stoof to eat than your millionaires. And why? Because he's got a wife who does everything herself and sees that he still gets some good stoof. Money won't buy it, unless you're taking trouble as well. Ah know. You'd be surprised. You know the Colossal Luxurious Hotel in the West End? All right. Well, you get good stoof there, don't you?'

'Yes, I suppose so,' said William, who had never been in the Colossal Luxurious.

'Well, you don't, then. It's all fancy and lah-di-dah, and maybe it looks well, but there isn't any good stoof in it. Ah wouldn't be paid to go and eat there – Ah wouldn't, Ah wouldn't be paid. Give me two tea-cakes – not the bits o' things you get down 'ere, but two proper big home-made tea-cakes – and some fresh butter, and a pot of tea that's mashed in the right way, with water just come to the boil and in a clean fresh teapot – give me that, and you've given me a meal Ah'd rather sit down to than anything they do at the Colossal Luxurious. And why? Because it'ud be all good stoof.'

Mr Tiefman – Tourist

AND then there was Mr William Ernest Tiefman, of Cincinnati, Ohio. He did not belong to any outer ring of vague people. Mr Tiefman was the strangest character on the passenger list, and during the first half of the voyage he proved to be a treasure and a joy, for he broke the ice for everybody, and everywhere he went he left behind him a rising tide of conversation. It was only later in the voyage, when everybody knew everything about him, that he became such an intolerable nuisance and people fled at his approach. Terry discovered him first – for he had an eye for a pretty face – and promptly shared him with William on the very first evening, and soon they were all gloating over him. He was nothing much to look at, being a short stoutish fellow of fifty, who beamed at the world through thick horn-rimmed spectacles. Nor was there anything remarkable about his history; he was born in the Middle West, of poor parents from somewhere in Central Europe, and after a long struggle had finally established himself in business, in the wholesale meat trade. It was as a traveller that Mr Tiefman was unique. Never having seen anything in his life, he had suddenly determined, five years before, that he would see everything worth seeing, and to this end he had begun to collect time tables, tourist guide books, and travel brochures, until at last he had an astounding collection of these things, referring to every part of the world that a tourist would wish to visit. 'Yes, sir,' he would declare proudly, 'I reckon I got the most complete collection in the States.' This was only the beginning. After making a thorough study of his collection, he started to compile an itinerary that would take him round the world and enable him to see everything of note in the shortest possible time. He determined to create an itinerary that would put all the tourist agencies to shame, and he did. It took him four years, but at the end of that time, he was triumphantly in possession of the *Great Itinerary*, in which all his movements for nearly a year were carefully set down, and, except for those periods, like this, when he was compelled to idle at sea, every waking hour of every day had its programme. This itinerary was a fair-sized volume, which he carried round with him and proudly exhibited, calling it his 'skedool' or, more often, his 'sked book'. His only reading was in this 'sked book' and you never saw him parted from it. 'Yeh,' he told everybody, on first acquaintance, 'this is my sked book. I got my itinerary in this. What's yours?' And he was constantly amazed – half proud and half disgusted – to find himself in a world of travellers who had only the vaguest notion of what an itinerary could be, who journeyed dreamily with the merest ghost of a 'sked'. Very soon it became one of the recognized ship's diversions to make Mr Tiefman delve into his itinerary, out of which the most astonishing details of touristry were forthcoming. 'But what about Java, Mr Tiefman?' some solemn wag would enquire. 'Surely you're not going to miss Java?'

'No, sir,' Mr Tiefman would reply, promptly and proudly, whipping open his 'sked book'. 'I got a wonderful skedool for Java, right here. Here it is. May 19th. Get up at 5 a.m. to see the scenery. 9 a.m. arrive at Sourabaya. Clear baggage through the customs and take an automobile to the Oranji Hotel (reservations made by letter dated November 23rd). See bank, photographers, and collect reservations on touring car to Batavia (reservations made by letter dated November 23rd). If time, visit bazaar before lunch. Have a rice taffle for lunch –'

But the enquirer, having had enough of it by this time, would clap him on the back and say: 'You've certainly got a wonderful itinerary there, Mr Tiefman.'

Another method was to ask him what he would be doing on a certain date. 'Now, Mr Tiefman, you talk a lot about that itinerary of yours, but I bet you don't know what you'll be doing on June 11th.'

At this, the innocent creature, beaming through his thick glasses, would instantly turn to the 'sked book', and begin reading the entry under that date. 'June 11th. Singapore. Get up at 5.45 a.m. Take an automobile to the Seaview Hotel and watch the sun rise, have a swim, and back to hotel. 9 a.m. breakfast. 9.30 a.m. visit the silk and curio shops in High Street. 10.15 a.m. visit Raffles Museum. 11.15 a.m. go to John Littles for a gin-sling –'

'Wait a minute, Mr Tiefman. Sure that's all right – I mean, about going to John Littles for a gin-sling?'

And Mr Tiefman would explain that it was the habit of residents of Singapore to go to that particular place at that particular hour for that particular drink. His itinerary made a special point of these details, and its accuracy could not be questioned. Wherever he went, it made sure that he did the correct thing at the correct time.

The more malicious wags, among whom his fellow Middle Westerners Burlecker and Stock were prominent, used to torture him by gravely discussing, in his presence, the chances of various boats being two and three days late. 'That's so,' Mr Burlecker would say to Mr Stock. 'That's the trouble, I guess, with these Eastern boats. Can't keep to time. Must be the typhoons. They think nothing of getting you in three days late.' For this, of course, was Mr Tiefman's nightmare. One delay would throw his whole itinerary out of gear, and from that time onwards he would be a lost man. The very thought of it made him look piteous.

But this was not all. Mr Tiefman had ideas of his own on the question of the amount of baggage to be carried by the really efficient world traveller. 'Yes, *sir*,' he told them all, 'if you ask me, baggage is the bunk. And why? Cuts down the efficiency of travel. You got to plan it, that's all. You don't catch me with these big wardrobe trunks. No, *sir*. Don't need 'em. I travel with two little suitcases, and I say it's enough for any man.' And then he would explain, at any length his listeners allowed him, his economical system. His raincoat, which was silk-rubber-lined, served as dressing-gown, rug, and overcoat. He had a wonderful combination of walking-stick, umbrella, and sword-stick. He had only one hat, one pair of shoes, and one peculiarly repulsive tie. He carried only two suits, both very ugly; one a dark chocolate, for evening wear, and the other a light striped yachting suit. And he had a special socks system, which was the joy of the ship. He had only three socks, not three pairs but three individual socks, all of course of the same pattern. Every night, before going to bed, he washed the sock he had been wearing on the left foot, and the next morning he put the spare clean sock on his right foot and transferred yesterday's right-foot sock to his left foot, thus wearing one clean sock every day and more or less achieving a clean pair every two days. All this he explained quite seriously to anybody who cared to listen to him, and for the first few days out, he did not want for listeners, having established himself as the ship's butt. His fellow Americans, including Terry, were especially assiduous and adroit in drawing him out and making him exhibit at full length his innocent folly, and to William, who became bored with the man as quickly as anybody, but to the last found something rather pathetic in his beaming idiocy, there was a disquietening touch of cruelty in the way in which they exploited and enjoyed his folly and then relentlessly flung him aside. Undoubtedly, Mr Tiefman, once you were thoroughly acquainted with his various systems, was a most outrageous bore. There were moments, however, when William envied him his cast-iron cheerfulness, his untroubled self-absorption. Others he bored, himself he could not bore. Such was Mr William Ernest Tiefman, of Cincinnati, Ohio, a man of ruthless efficiency, no doubt, but yet a man not without wonder and poetry in his composition, for through years of the wholesale meat trade in Ohio he had carried with him a vision of arriving at Sourabaya at 9 a.m. on May 19th, of going at 11.15 a.m. on June 11th for a gin-sling to John Littles in Singapore. A dream had come through the multitude of business.

Mr Drivnak

THEY landed on the larger island that William had first noticed. Its shore seemed absolutely barren, but then he discovered that the life on these atolls is away from the thundering open sea, on the inner shore, round the lagoon. And into this lagoon, in which pink forests of coral fell away into glades of emerald water, the *Hutia* cautiously entered, like a bewildered mortal tiptoeing into some shimmering world of dream and myth. The whole scene had an exquisite gauzy beauty, and carried with it not the remotest suggestion of the wholesale trade in vegetable fats, the margarine and soap industries, whose enterprise had actually sent the *Hutia* into this dim pearly fairyland. Ariel might have come whistling over the water to them; Caliban might have been seen scratching himself among the shells and hermit crabs; and Prospero himself, wand in hand, might have welcomed them at the water's edge. Instead, they found a crowd of natives, some lazy old ones and some very noisy and energetic young ones, an old snuffy bearded French priest, and Mr Drivnak, late of Seattle and once of Czecho-Slovakia.

Mr Drivnak was a small, round, bullet-headed man, with lively little black eyes, a lively little black moustache, and pores so large and open that he seemed in constant danger of sweating all his features away. He pounced upon Captain Prettel, but when they had concluded their business and the captain went away with the priest, an old friend of his, Mr Drivnak pounced upon William and Ramsbottom, first inviting them to have a drink at his bungalow, to which he marched them at a great pace, talking all the time. He had plenty of English, having been some years in Seattle, but he had a peculiarly thick and rasping voice. William had seen this place as a series of enchanting, luminous water-colours, and walking with Mr Drivnak and listening to him was like taking these water-colours and rapidly tearing them up. Mr Drivnak's bungalow was also the island store, and it was all neat and bright and business-like, but did not seem to be on the island at all.

'Id certainly is von big pleasure to me to meet you gentlemen,' cried Mr Drivnak, mopping his face, then beaming upon them.

They said it was a pleasure to them, too.

'I been here nearly two years,' continued Mr Drivnak, 'and how many fresh faces you think I've seen? How many? Now how many? Give a guess, just give a guess.'

They did not want to give a guess, but he was one of those tiresome people who insist upon your giving them a guess. So Ramsbottom said twenty, and William said thirty.

'Sigs,' Mr Drivnak shouted triumphantly, starting fresh rivulets of sweat at every pore, 'just sigs and no more. Sigs fresh faces in nearly two years. Id isn't good, eh? No, no, no, no, id isn't good.'

'How's trade?' enquired Ramsbottom, with a glance towards the other room, which was the store and seemed full of things.

'No good. Never will be good here, never, never, never. Why? No business enderprise, no developmend.'

William stared through the open window, past the cool

broad leaves, into a patch of sunlight where the dreamy coffee-coloured damsel who had just waited upon them was now gracefully reclining and doing something to her long, straight, black hair. She had a flat stupid face, not at all beautiful, but nevertheless at that moment she looked charming, idyllic. 'But did you expect any business enterprise and development here?' he asked.

Mr Drivnak was astonished at the question.

'Ah must say,' said Ramsbottom bluntly, 'you came to a queer shop for it.'

'No, no, no,' said Mr Drivnak, with great emphasis. 'No shob ad all. I open this store myself. In Seattle I work in a big store. I take a course. Yes, gentlemen, I take a course. I prepare myself. I take a big business course – by correspondenz. Some money is left to me by an aunt in Czecho-Slavachia. Id is not too much, but id is enough. I want independenz. I want room to develop. I say to myself I shall find id here. And here I am – a man of ideas, gentlemen, who has worked in a big store in Seattle and has taken a business course. I come here with the ideas and the energy. In Papeete I said to them, "Show me a good beautiful island where there is room for developmend."'

'Well, you got it all right,' said Ramsbottom, giving William a wink.

'Got id, yes. But nothing can be done here.' Mr Drivnak seemed to glare at them through a misty cascade of sweat. Hastily he mopped his face, as if he was wiping it all out and starting with a new one. 'Ideas came ad once. Why sell the copra? We will deal with it ourselves. What about planting coffee? And why not elecdrig light? And tourism. Why not tourism?'

Mr Drivnak paused, allowing the sounds of voices in song to reach them. The islanders were idly chanting, it seemed. Mr Drivnak listened for a moment, then exclaimed; 'You hear? Filthy stuff. Filthy, filthy stuff.'

'Why,' said William, 'it sounds vaguely like a hymn to me. Wait a minute. It is. I believe it's *From Greenland's Icy Mountains.*'

'And we can do with 'em,' said Ramsbottom.

'The tune no doubt, yes,' said Mr Drivnak hastily, 'but the vords – no. Native vords. Filthy, filthy. Yes, I think id is the von about the dirty fat woman. But what did I say before? Ah yes – about the tourism.' He jumped up, grabbed hold of them both, and promptly rushed them outside, where he began pointing this way and that. 'There, you see, gentlemen, a place for an hotel. An hotel there. Perhaps a casino – oh, just a little casino – down there, facing the lagoon. You have your factory – perhaps two factories, three factories – over there, on the other side. A place for your varehouse? Over there. Perfect. All perfect for every kind of developmend. I tell you gentlemen – this place robs me of my sanidy. I have the ideas – I burst and burst with the ideas – and I have the enderprize and the business knowledge – and nothing, nothing, nothing can be done.' He set off now at a brisk pace, shouting as he went. 'Here is your Main Streed.'

'Where?' puffed Ramsbottom, staring at the vague track ahead of them, winding between little native huts and coconut palms.

'Just where you are. Made for id. Id would go straight from the hotel to the wharf, keeping quite clear of the industrial section.' He waved a hand towards seven palm trees and two huts. 'That would be over there.'

When they left, next morning, all the islanders were there to say farewell: some were in little boats; some standing on the dazzling beach; others, the youngest, were plunging into the liquid gold of the lagoon; behind them was a shore of bright pink patches and violet shadows; farther behind still, beyond the palms, where the outer shore was, there was a faint mist of spray; and the sky was a piece of faded blue silk. It was, to William's eye, a scene of incredible, remote loveliness, and there in the middle of it, waving farewell with the rest, still beaming and sweating, but bidding them god-speed out of a great despair, was Mr Drivnak.

Captain Jary

'On dees,' said Captain Prettel, pointing across the lagoon, 'you find Englishman.'

An Englishman! They were interested at once. They had not found a fellow-countryman yet on any of the islands.

'Yais – Eenglishman. Vairy, vairy old. Perhaps he die. Cap'n Jary he is called. He see and 'ear *tupapaus* alvays. He is like a *tupapau.*'

Something stirred in William's memory. What was it? Then he remembered, and was back again in the study at Ivy Lodge, his uncle's papers before him, and there was the ghostly snapshot of the thin old man, with his uncle's writing on the back: 'Cap. Staveling up in the Manihikis just after hearing his big-headed Tupapau knock on the roof. Last time too. Never saw poor Cap. again.' It gave him a queer sensation to remember that. How far away from all this he had been then, and how he had clutched at its magical possibilities! And now here he was. But this was Captain Jary, not Captain Staveling, who must have died years ago. These islands seemed to have a fair supply of antique and spectral captains who were in the habit of seeing ghosts. But then it was natural for seamen to retire to these islands, and it might be equally natural for them to see ghosts, if they lived here long enough. Probably their imaginations came in time to be dominated by the imaginations of the islanders, who went in terror of the *tupapaus*. Then again, perhaps there *were* tupapaus, and you had to live a long time in these quiet remote places before you began to notice them.

There seemed to be only about a dozen huts on the island, but one of them was much larger than the rest, and was indeed a bungalow with a corrugated iron roof. But it was very shabby. It was a curiously shabby island, without any of the idyllic prettiness of most of the others. Even the palms had a very ragged and barren look, though they must have been fruitful enough, for there was a fair store of copra waiting for the schooner. The lagoon was unusually sombre in tint, and the coral of the place was rough and rather colourless. The name of this shabby island was Tapuka. On the beach, not far from the bags of copra, were three dead sharks, with their jaws all cleaned up and fixed wide open, ready for sale. They looked as if they were sardonically amused at life. Although there did not appear to be many inhabitants, yet the beach was alive with children, bobbing and splashing and screaming. At first, there was no sign of Captain Jary. A large native, who was wearing nothing but a pair of cotton shorts and a taxi-driver's cap, was in charge of the copra. When William and the others landed, however, a figure came tottering out of the bungalow with the corrugated iron roof. This obviously was Captain Jary. He was wearing patched old drill trousers and nothing else. He was an astonishing and rather repulsive figure, for he was very tall and horribly thin, had long white hair and beard, and a greyish mat of hair on his chest. Captain Prettel rushed forward to shake him by the hand, and the old man at once returned with Prettel to his bungalow, taking no notice at all of the three strangers. They concluded, correctly as it afterwards appeared, that he had not seen them. They hung about the beach, watching the loading and unloading of the copra and trade goods, and the antics of the children, and then, after an hour or so, Prettel, reeking of his own store of liquor, came along and asked them to pay the old man a visit in his bungalow.

At close quarters, Captain Jary looked even more dimly patriarchal than he had done at a distance, and not unlike a faded water-colour sketch of a prophet that had somehow acquired real hair. His eyes, a washed-out blue, were the dimmest thing about him, and this gave him a curiously unreal appearance. William never remembered seeing anybody before who looked quite so old. Nor had he ever seen any place before that seemed so remote as this bungalow. It was very neglected and littered with dusty odds and ends. There was the wreck of a mandolin; there were the remains of a set of dominoes; some carpenter's tools; a model ship with broken masts: three bound volumes of the *English Illustrated Magazine*, Lytton's *Last Days of Pompeii*, a Bible, and some books without backs that might have been anything; two long German pipes, half a flute, some ancient playing-cards, several springs for clockwork, and a stuffed monkey in a very unpleasant state of decay. In this dust-bin at the end of the earth sat Captain Jary, welcoming his fellow-countrymen. He wore a tattered blue coat now, but did not attempt to button it over his thick mat of grey hair.

'Yes,' he quavered rustily, 'Grimsby was my town. I left it in seventy-eight, and that's a tidy time since, gen'l'men, a tidy time it is. I was a Grimsby man, and my father was Grimsby before me. I was in sail for forty year. All over I was, in sail. None o' you gen'l'men been in sail?' He turned upon them his queer faded eyes, which were not quite sightless, and yet seemed as blank as the windows of an empty house. He did not wait for any reply. 'And then I was master of a steamer for fifteen year. And I came here – retired – twenty year ago or more – don't just remember. Came here to die, twenty-five year ago. And I've raised another family since then – got grandchildren here.' He produced the thin ghost of a chuckle. 'This is the third family I've raised, gen'l'men. I've got one in Wellington. But I don't come from New Zealand, not me. I'm a Grimsby man by rights, though I left in seventy-eight. Any o' you gen'l'men know Grimsby?'

Here there was a pause long enough for two of them to say that they knew it slightly.

The captain took no notice of them. 'If you didn't know it,' he continued, with a certain faint relish creeping into his tone, 'you never will now. Grimsby's gone. Hull's gone. Scarborough's gone. And they tell me Yarmouth's gone, though I don't rightly know about that. You haven't to believe all you hear. But I know them others has gone.'

'What d'you mean – gone?' demanded Ramsbottom, looking at him in astonishment.

'Smashed up, blown up, set fire to, burned out, beaten down, gone,' replied Captain Jary. 'All that coast's gone, you might say, for there's not one brick standing on another, they tell me. All done in this big war they had. Russians or Germans came along and smashed it all up, half the north-east coast, and they've never bothered to build them places again. No good me going back, even if I wanted to, is it? I'm a Grimsby man, and if there's no Grimsby, then there's no place for me to go to. That's right, isn't it, gen'l'men? That's sense. And they tell me half London went at the same time, though I didn't care about that, for I never took much stock of London. I ha'n't been there since nought-two.'

William and the Commander said nothing, for it seemed useless to try and put that wandering old mind right; but Ramsbottom could not contain himself. 'Nay, who's been telling you all this stuff?' he said, rather sharply. 'It's a lot o' nonsense. Grimsby and Hull and Scarborough are like they always were.'

Captain Jary shook his head, with good-natured contempt, like a man correcting a child. 'They're keeping it from you. You're not a Grimsby man, are you? Or a Hull man? No, I thought not. Well, there was this big war, you see – Russians and Germans and Dutchmen and so on – and they all came across and smashed up all them parts. I've not seen 'em myself, but I've talked with them that has. All gone. No fishing round there these days, that's all gone. You could get good fish out o' the North Sea too, one time. Better than you can get here – a lot better – more tasty-eating. I was always partial to a bit o' mackerel, even if it was a dirty feeder. And a nice fresh herring. That's all gone. And I've seen the day when you'd find more fish in Grimsby of an early morning than would keep 'em all for a week from here to Fiji. And tasty fish too. But I left Grimsby in seventy-eight. That's a tidy time since, gen'l'men, a tidy time it is. I was in sail for forty year.'

It seemed as if his talk was trapped in a circle, and that unless they broke away they would stand there listening to him going round and round. He returned now to his account of the desolated north-east coast of England, and William began to feel that if he heard it again, he would believe that Grimsby and Hull and Scarborough really had gone. Even as it was, he would have liked to have had a quick glimpse of them to reassure himself. Captain Jary did not mention *tupapaus*, perhaps because the fact that they were English had imprisoned him in this Grimsby circle: but he had no need to talk about ghosts to be ghostly. And quite suddenly, without giving any sign that he was about to stop talking, he did stop, and quietly fell asleep. When they tip-toed out, they might have been leaving behind them a dead man, he was now so quiet, so still, so bloodless. And the glare and bustle of life outside the bungalow was incredible; they might have been plunging into Piccadilly on a June morning, the contrast was so great.

'Poor old boy,' said the Commander, as they walked away. 'He must be ninety, if he's a day.'

'And better dead, if you ask me,' said Ramsbottom. 'He can't grumble. He's had a ripe old age, even if he's rotten now. He said he'd raised a family since he was seventy. There's plenty of time for you yet, Commander. But Ah'll tell you one thing. If you going to live to be that old and wrong in the head, you're better off here than at home. Nobody much to bother you, plenty o' sunshine, and the bit of fish and coconut you get to eat is about all you want, anyhow. Make a note of it, Dursley lad. When you're getting old and silly, see you make for one o' these places. Never mind about the ghosts.'

'I don't think you would,' said William. 'You're a ghost yourself then. It was all ghosts with that poor old captain.'

'Ay, he'd even turned Grimsby into a ghost,' said Ramsbottom. 'And that takes a bit o' doing.'

A Night With Sir George

TIMMY gave the bell another good pull and from far inside the house they could hear it jangling. But nobody came. And there was no sign of a light anywhere near the great front door. They stood there in almost total darkness, for now it was late – they had had to walk from the bus stop at Castle Claydon to Chilham Moss and then find this Manor House – and there was no moon. They had walked about half a mile up a drive, and the house looked enormous, a real mansion. Why, the front door was as big as three ordinary front doors.

'Nobody at home,' said Timmy, rather hopefully. He had always been doubtful about this call on Denberry-Baxter, and this mysterious gloomy grandeur did nothing to restore his confidence. He was hoping that they would have to go back to Castle Claydon and settle down for the night in some sensible little pub.

'There is somebody,' the Professor announced. 'I saw a light when we were walking up – it must be somewhere round the corner there – and I thought I heard music. Let us go and see.'

'Well, but if they won't answer the front door –' Timmy protested.

'It is a very large house and if the servants are out, then the others may not hear the bell. This way.' And the Professor turned to the left, to find his lighted room, and Timmy had to hurry after him. He had been right about the music. They could hear it now. Turning a corner, they found themselves looking through the open French windows of a large lighted room. The music was coming from a wireless cabinet and also from a violin, which was being played in an enthusiastic slapdash style by an immense stout old fellow, who was sitting very close to the wireless cabinet and actually had his music propped against the side of it. Although it was a cool autumn night, the old fellow was not wearing a coat or waistcoat, only a billowing chequered shirt above his vast baggy tweed trousers, and yet even with so little on he was sweating profusely. Timmy stared at him in amazement.

'It is the Schubert Octet in F Major,' said the Professor, stooping towards Timmy's left ear. 'He is playing the first violin part, and just finishing the second movement. He is playing it very badly, but after all it is extraordinary that he should be playing it at all. Let us wait. He will never last through the fourth movement – you will see.'

So they waited on the lawn, just outside the gold bars of light that stretched through the open window. The room was as odd as its occupant. It was crammed with stuff, all higgledy-piggledy, rather like a second-hand shop. The spoils of Empire seem to have been gathered there. It was a room that held the gorgeous East in fee. There were Burmese gongs, Chinese Buddhas, Indian elephants in brass and ivory, helmets, shields, swords and guns from Arabia and Persia and Afghanistan. Miscellaneous books and solemn quarterly periodicals were piled up everywhere, in every corner, in arm-chairs and settees and on top of the grand piano. It was a mystery how the old fellow, who looked a crimson mountain of a man and had a snowy summit of wild hair, ever moved about that room without bringing down piles of books, impaling himself upon a sword or two, or breaking his shins upon some shining Oriental trophy. And he looked like a mad old emperor, fiddling away there, trying to keep time with the eight invisible musicians in the wireless cabinet.

'Only in England could such a thing be seen,' exclaimed the Professor, during a long passage for the clarinet, when the violinist refreshed himself hastily from a giant tumbler. 'What a people and what a country! One minute it is all cheapness and dreary commerce, and the next minute it is Alice through Wonderland.'

They waited without moving for another five minutes, and then the old fellow, who had been finding it more and more difficult to keep up with the other first violin in the wireless cabinet, suddenly gave it up in despair. 'Damn your eyes, boys, you're taking it too fast for me,' he cried, put down his instrument, took another swig at what looked like a giant-size whisky-and-soda, and put a match to the very largest calabash pipe Timmy had ever seen.

The Professor stepped forward into the light. 'Sir,' he called, 'we have been ringing some time –'

'What's that?' roared the old fellow, struggling to his feet. 'Come in, come in.' He switched off the wireless set. 'Been ringing, eh? Well, Ketley's about somewhere. That's my man – Ketley. Must be in. Come in, come in, come in.'

'Mr. Denberry-Baxter?' the Professor began, formally.

'Sir George Denberry-Baxter, as a matter of fact,' said that gentleman, in a large off-hand manner. 'Glad to see you. Rum-looking pair, if you don't mind my saying so, but glad to see you. Sit down. Have a drink.' It was now obvious that Sir George had had many drinks already. His immense face, looking scarlet under its white thatch, was beaded with perspiration. It was a most formidable countenance, with a great nose that looked as if it had been badly broken at some time or other, for it was both dented and twisted; there was a deep angry scar on his right cheek; and he had fierce little bloodshot eyes. But at the moment he beamed hospitality and good cheer, and finding two odd glasses he poured out whiskies-and-sodas for them.

'I have here a letter,' the Professor began again.

'Never mind letters. Too late in the day for letters. Have a drink. Better make it a toast. Schubert!'

'Schubert!' they muttered, and drank with Sir George. The whisky was uncommonly strong.

'I thought they were playing the fourth movement too quickly,' said the Professor, with great tact.

'By thunder, you're right, too. Running away with it. They take everything at a devil of a pace nowadays. I can't keep up with 'em. Can't keep up with anything. Now why did that scoundrel Ketley keep you waiting at the front door? If he's gone out wenching again – he's fifty if he's a day, but the minute I bring him back home he can't keep his hands off 'em – I'll rip the coat off his back. Soon see if he's in, though. Listen!'

And Sir George gave the largest of the Burmese gongs an immense whack, so that the room seemed to shake and the whole night to hum with its unfathomably deep rich tone. A few moments later from somewhere within the house there came an answering note from a similar gong. 'There he is. Make him take that with him at night, wherever he is in the house – it's just an empty warren, this place is – just to prove he hasn't slipped out. You a musician?'

'In a very small amateur way,' the Professor smiled. Then he looked grave and formal again, and insisted upon pronouncing his name slowly.

'Timmy Tiverton's my name,' said the little man, shyly.

Sir George suddenly pointed a finger at him. 'Seen you before somewhere. Never forget faces. Any kind of faces, yellow, brown, black. Used to surprise 'em in the East. And I've seen you before. I'll remember soon, you see if I don't.' He turned to the Professor again, in his odd masterful fashion. 'Play the fiddle?'

'No. I play the piano. Or I did, in happier days.'

'Then, by crumpets, we'll have some music. We'll try one or two of the Mozart sonatas. Open that piano, while I find 'em.' He turned to Timmy now; he seemed to be a great chap for giving orders. 'You're the right size. See if there's a music stand under the piano, and drag it out. And finish your drinks, finish your drinks. It's one of those nights when you need a drink or two to cope with this damnable climate. Now then, gentlemen, a little Mozart.'

He bustled them round, and soon had the Professor, looking very impressive and very foreign, seated at the piano, and himself towering over the music-stand with his violin ready for action again. Timmy sipped his very strong whisky, and wondered what he was doing there, among unpredictable giants in this gigantic dark house. Sir George and the Professor, after some happy discussion, decided which sonata they would tackle, and they were just about to begin, and Sir George had his bow poised above the strings, when they were disturbed by a deep and somewhat very significant cough from the lawn just outside the window. All three heard it and turned.

'Now who the devil's this?' growled Sir George. 'Always the same. There's a kind of conspiracy to put something between you and Mozart or whatever it is that makes life worth living. What is it? Who is it?'

A police sergeant stepped into the room.

Timmy went cold. The Professor stiffened and then slowly rose. Sir George stared angrily, annoyed at the interruption. It was a large police sergeant, but he had a rather small head at the end of a long stiff neck, so that he looked not unlike a gigantic wooden doll. He looked hard at all three of them – and put Timmy's heart down into his boots – and then addressed himself to Sir George.

'I beg your pardon, sir –' he began.

'And I should think you do, marching in here just when we're going to enjoy ourselves! Here we are, miles from anywhere, just settling down to a bit of Mozart, and in comes the police force. And for two pins, sergeant, you'd ask to see a form or two, want to put a rubber stamp on some paper or other, all that sort of thing, eh? Now listen to me, sergeant. I'm Sir George Denberry-Baxter and I've had forty years of that sort of thing. I've governed islands. I've governed peninsulas. I've governed territories the size of England. I've had forty years of seeing that forms were filled in and properly stamped and documents put into the right despatch-boxes, and I've walked miles and miles up and down the ranks of soldiers and policemen, white, yellow, blue, and black. And by Christmas!' he roared now, having worked himself up into a gigantic passion, 'I've had my share of it, and I won't have any more of it. I don't want police sergeants. I want Mozart.'

He looked for a moment as if he were about to throw his violin at the sergeant's head, but then he put the instrument down, threw himself down into his enormous camp chair, and swallowed about half a pint of whisky and soda. Then he looked sternly at the sergeant and said: 'Have a drink.'

'Well, sir,' said the sergeant, still apologetically, 'I'm on duty, you know, sir –'

This did him no good at all. 'If you're on duty, my man,' Sir George thundered, 'then don't come in here. You've no duty that brings you into a gentleman's private house. So either come off duty and have a drink, or stay on duty and clear out.'

The sergeant decided to ignore this. In his wooden style, he looked the irate Sir George in the eye and said, as if submitting a report: 'A few minutes ago, sir, seeing the house all dark from the lane, I heard a loud noise, which might have been a sort o' signal –'

'It was that gong. If you hit it properly, you can hear it three miles.'

'Quite so, sir. Well, as we've had word that there's some very suspicious characters –'

'Suspicious characters!' Sir George, in his contempt, almost blew like a whale. 'I don't believe in your suspicious characters. Is he a suspicious character? Is he a suspicious character?' As he asked this, he pointed first at the Professor and then at Timmy, to their horror. For the sergeant, following the finger, took a careful look at them. 'Am I a suspicious character?'

The sergeant smiled. 'Not exactly, sir.'

'Then you're wrong,' cried Sir George triumphantly. 'I *am* a suspicious character. Have been for years. By thunder, if you knew the half of what goes on in my head, you'd have me handcuffed in no time. Eh? Well, you'd better have a drink.' And Sir George, puffing and blowing and snorting, found another odd glass, and poured out another very stiff whisky, not from a bottle but from a gallon jar. Timmy and the Professor exchanged careful glances.

'My respects, gentlemen,' said the sergeant, with enormous wooden solemnity. He took a tremendous pull at his whisky without blinking an eyelid. Then he felt that he ought to make a little conversation. 'It's these I.R.A. chaps that's giving us so much trouble. All over the place, they are. One of 'em blew up a statue this afternoon in Birchester.'

'Good for him,' cried Sir George, to Timmy's secret delight. 'If I'd my way, I'd blow up the whole of Birchester. Never saw such a damned place! Blow it up, blow 'em all up!'

'So you see, sir, hearing this noise, I just wondered what was going on here,' the sergeant concluded.

'What's going on here is music,' Sir George rose and waved a vast arm at the sergeant. 'So finish that whisky and pop off, sergeant.'

'Certainly, sir.' He emptied his glass, then suddenly looked quite sharply at Timmy, who by this time had relaxed and was now caught off his guard. 'Didn't I see you this morning in Claydon market-place?'

'Yes, I fancy you did,' stammered Timmy. 'Yes, I'm certain I saw you there.'

'Are you?' said the sergeant pleasantly. 'Well, that's odd, because I wasn't within forty miles of Claydon this morning.'

'Well, what of it?' demanded Sir George. 'You fellows look all alike in uniform. Now pop off. I want some music. Good night.'

'Good night, sir,' said the sergeant. Did he – or did he not – take a last quick look at Timmy and the Professor? Off he went, however, and Timmy put a hand to his forehead and discovered that it was cold and damp. He also discovered, the moment after, that the fierce little eye of Sir George was upon him. 'Seen you before somewhere, you know. Don't tell me. I'll remember. Not wanted by the police, are you, by any chance?'

'Me?' Timmy sat up straight. 'No – not really. Here, why should I be?'

'Why should you look as if you are, eh?' Sir George bellowed with laughter. 'Now then, you don't want Mozart – I can see it in your eye – so just go and find Ketley, tell him the two of you are staying the night, and tell him to bring some sandwiches in about an hour. Ham, and plenty of mustard. Try the billiard-room. Here, take a torch.' He plunged forward with a sweeping gesture to lay a hand on an electric torch, knocked over a bronze idol, a chain helmet and two elephants, blasted the whole room and hurled a curved dagger at the opposite wall, where it stuck quivering, then put the torch into Timmy's hand and almost swept him out of the room.

Timmy went slowly down a long cold corridor, musty and smelling of moth-balls, and all he could hear out there were the rats and mice scampering and scratching behind the woodwork. He had never been in a house this size before, and now in its dark emptiness it seemed to him a crazy terrifying place. At the end of the corridor there were stairs going up and stairs going down, and after a little hesitation he decided that the billiard-room would probably be downstairs, so down he went. At the bottom of a short flight, he had to go along another corridor, which seemed colder and mustier than the one above; and by this time he felt such a long way from anywhere, and everything seemed so completely unreal, that he was ready to bolt through the nearest door back into the outside world. But then he heard the *click-clack* of billiard-balls and saw a band of light under a distant door. He hurried along to this door, and was about to open it when it was suddenly opened from inside, nearly knocking him down; moreover, a monstrous thing was standing there, a thing that had dark trousers and shoes but an upper part, both body and head, that consisted only of a large dark-metal disc; and then this monster let out such a clang that Timmy could feel the sound knocking him back into the corridor. All this turned out to be the man Ketley smacking the other Burmese gong.

He was a cool card, this Ketley, a lean, darkish, old-soldier sort of man, who was wearing a dirty striped house-coat and smoking a black cheroot. He nodded and said: 'Well?'

'He says,' Timmy panted, 'we're staying the night – there's two of us, an' will you bring some sandwiches in about an hour. Ham, and plenty of mustard.'

'There isn't any ham. It'll have to be tongue.' Then Ketley took out his cheroot to make a reproachful sound at the back of his teeth, sent the gong and its stick skimming into a corner, and continued: 'The gov'nor must be good an' bottled, isn't he?'

'I suppose he is – really. I thought at first,' said Timmy carefully, 'he was barmy.'

'He *is* barmy. Sunstroke started it. *And* lifting the elbow. He was well on when I left him. Who's the other fellow with you?'

'He's a sort of foreign professor.' Timmy felt he had to go cautiously here. 'An' his son's wife was an old friend of this Mr Denberry-Baxter and gave him a letter to him, if you see what I mean.'

'Not sure that I do, chum,' said Ketley in his soldierly style. 'But what I'm sure of is this – that isn't the gov'nor – for he's Sir George and has been for twenty years. It's his nephew you want. This is his house, not the gov'nor's. He's in East Africa. If I was you, I'd push off to-night.'

'I never wanted to come here,' Timmy explained. 'But it's a bit late now, y'know, and they seem to be settling down to a musical evening.'

'That's 'cos the gov'nor's bottled.' Ketley sounded very gloomy. 'You wait till to-morrow morning.'

Timmy did not like the sound of this. 'Why, what about to-morrow morning?'

'Never mind. Play you fifty up. Or snooker, if you like.'

Timmy hadn't played billiards for a long time, but he used to play in his earlier days, and he elected for the fifty up. Ketley, who seemed to do himself very well, was drinking bottled beer, and insisted that Timmy should join him. They began playing in an easy careless fashion.

'Isn't there anybody else here but you?' asked Timmy, who had been wondering about this for some time.

'There was. Eight servants when we took over. They all left. Couldn't stand the gov'nor, chum. You'll see what I mean. We've only a deaf old woman who comes in every morning. Place is going to rack an' ruin. There'll be hell to pay when the owner comes back. But the gov'nor doesn't care. When he isn't plain barmy, he's bottled. I've had so much of him now, I'm not so sure I'm all there myself. One of the girls who left was a lovely piece,' continued Ketley, missing an easy cannon. 'Talk about curves! But there's one at the farm here – Ruby – who's as good. Artful little devil too. You ought to have gone for the red there, chum.'

After an hour of this they took a long dark walk to a pantry, where they cut some sandwiches, loaded themselves with more bottled beer, and then set out for the music-room, which apparently was the one room downstairs that Sir George used and into which he had crammed all his own possessions. By this time even the Professor was somewhat flushed and untidy and Sir George was now like a crimson mountain in eruption. He was using an Oriental shawl as a towel.

'And about time, too, Ketley. Music always gives me an appetite. This isn't ham, you blockhead. I said *ham.*'

'That's right, gov'nor,' replied Ketley in a very easy

familiar style. 'But there isn't any, see? You'll have to put up with tongue.'

'I've seen *you* before,' said Sir George, once more pointing straight at Timmy's nose.

'Course you have,' Ketley told him. 'You sent him along to tell me about –'

'I don't mean to-night, you wooden numskull,' bellowed Sir George, throwing the damp shawl at his henchman. 'I mean years ago – years and years ago – before we all went off our heads. Now don't tell me.' He stared hard at Timmy, then finally let out a whoop. 'I've got you. A pound to a penny I've got you. On the halls.'

'Quite right,' said Timmy, delighted to be recognized. 'And Timmy Tiverton's the name. Comedian.'

Sir George patted him on the shoulder. It was like being patted by an oil furnace that had been burning whisky. 'Knew I'd get you. Timmy Tiverton, eh? Good man, good man. Why, you used to sing that song about not giving father any shrimps.'

'Cockles,' Ketley corrected him.

'One of these days, Ketley, I shall throw you straight through the window. Don't be so damned impertinent. Though I believe you're right.'

'He is,' said Timmy smiling proudly. 'It was one of my most successful numbers. *You Can't Give Father Any Cockles.*'

'*And you can't give Mother any gin,*' Sir George sang loudly. He turned to the Professor. 'Play *You Can't Give Father Any Cockles*, doctor.'

The Professor raised his hands apologetically. 'I am sorry, but I do not know this *Cockles*. Perhaps I pick it up though.'

Sir George had reached over for his fiddle and began humming the tune, with some expert assistance from Timmy. A minute later, Sir George could play the chorus, and two minutes later the Professor, who didn't look that kind of pianist at all, but who nevertheless seemed to have a knack that would have earned him a living in many a public-house singing-room, had contrived a good rousing accompaniment on the piano. Standing among the spoils of Empire, Timmy, doing his act as he had done it nearly thirty years before, doing it well, but feeling like a man in a dream, sang the verse, with the help of a few vamping chords from the Professor, and then went swinging into the refrain, with Sir George not only fiddling variations on the melody but lending his voice to Ketley's as Timmy's chorus. All together, they roared:

You can't give Father any cockles;
You can't give Mother any gin;
Auntie's a sport,
But don't give her port,
You never know what she'll begin ...

The words might have been foolish and vulgar, but the tune had a confident jolly swing, which any man in his senses could enjoy. These men did enjoy it. And when they had had enough of that song, Timmy remembered another of his old successes *Roly-Poly For Mrs Moly*, and then a later one, just after the War, *You Know What To Do With Your Rhubarb.* They seemed to sing themselves back into another and happier world. Timmy had not been so happy for a long long time; the years that stood between him and his youth and success now seemed only like the flying soundless years of a dream. The noisy male companionship and the drinking deep into the night made the Professor forget that he was an elderly exile and almost turned him into a rowdy student again. As for Sir George and Ketley, no doubt they too returned in spirit to an earlier and happy time, and in any event there had descended upon them the same fine uproarious mood. At the end of the third song – after many repetitions, with the gigantic glistening Sir George urging them to make it louder each time – the odd quartet was like a little band of brothers. Even Ketley, the coolest and probably the most sober of the four, seemed ready to swear eternal friendship.

'Sir George,' cried Timmy hoarsely, with his face all screwed up as if he did not know whether to make it laugh or cry, 'believe me or believe me not, but you've done something for me to-night I didn't think any man could 'ave done for me again. Sir George, you've made me happy. Poor old

Timmy Tiverton, Sir George, you've made him feel like a man again. An' I'll – I'll say to your back now what I'd never say to your face – Sir George, you're a great gentleman. You are. An' for God's sake, put a coat on, you're sweating like a bull.'

'Ketley,' said Sir George, 'you'll have to take the little man to bed in a minute because he's tired and he's had too much to drink. And look after him, look after him, because in his own way – and a very good way it is too – he's an artist.'

'Very good,' the Professor smiled. 'Quite true. An artist. And we must cherish our artists.'

'And our scholars, our philosophers, our thinkers,' added Sir George, almost sternly. 'Among them our friend here Dr Krudiebacker from Vienna –'

'Thank you very much,' said the Professor modestly, 'although I am really Professor Kronąk from Prague.'

'Don't let's have any pedantry, doctor,' cried Sir George reproachfully. 'Don't imprison the soaring creative human spirit in a cage of pedantic forms. Remember Mozart. remember Schubert. Remember Mrs Moly and her roly-poly. Just hand me those two elephants, Ketley.'

'You're bottled, gov'nor,' Ketley reminded him, as he passed the two bronze elephants.

If his master heard this, which is doubtful, he chose to ignore it, and now, with an elephant in each hand, he drew himself up to his full height and addressed the other three as if there were at least three thousand of them. 'Gentlemen, it is my custom on such felicitous occasions,' he began, in splendid form, but stopped to sneeze and did not trouble to complete this fine opening sentence. 'It is my pleasure to welcome you here under the ancient roof of the Denberry-Baxter family, a family that, with the solitary exception of myself, who have recently retired after a brilliant career in the Colonial Service, a family, I say, that has left no mark whatever in our national history. But – but, gentlemen,' he continued, just as if he were making some superb debating point, 'though you have made no mark whatever, you are just as welcome under this roof as any great minister of state – in fact, a damned sight more welcome. Unless it should be the elder Pitt, the great Lord Chatham. It was said of Chatham, gentlemen, that when he was Minister of War nobody left his presence without feeling a braver man –'

'That is curious,' the Professor put in, 'for the same was said of our own great statesman –'

'But the last thing we wish to do now,' Sir George went on, with a stern glance at the Professor, 'is to explore the morass of political life. We have here with us a scholar, philosopher, and musician. I refer to our friend Dr Krudiebacker from Vienna. Also an artist, no other than Tommy Tupperton, late of the Tivoli, Oxford, Empire, and Middlesex music-halls. And to celebrate this occasion, though I trust you will be with me for many weeks to come –'

'Hear, hear!' This was from Timmy, who felt at that moment ready to stay for months.

'I present to each of you, as a personal tribute, a bronze elephant of fine design and workmanship. Dr Krudiebacker, your elephant! Tommy Tupperton, your elephant! And welcome, a thousand times welcome, to the Manor!' And with a final hospitable wave of the hand, Sir George Denberry-Baxter took a deep breath and then marched straight out into the night.

Daisy Barley

It was still raining but Timmy let down the window for a breath of fresh air. There was plenty of noise coming from this 'Dog and Bell', including the *thud-thudding* of a little dance band. Miles and miles away from anywhere, in the middle of ten thousand wet fields, and yet they could keep a place like this blazing with light and run a dance band in it. Timmy still did not care tuppence about the place, but for all that he couldn't help feeling a bit out of things. He was cold too and damp. The eccentric costume, short black coat with no lapels, a red waistcoat, and baggy light check trousers, had not been chosen to travel round in on wet autumn nights. A stiff whisky and perhaps a bite of something savoury and hot would be more than welcome. If this thin chap had been a human being, he would have brought something out himself. So Timmy shivered, brooded, and cursed in his dark corner of the car. Dunbury, with the Professor and Hope and Mr Hassock and everybody there, seemed to fade right out, and he felt as if this was a direct continuation of his horrible day in Birchester. He was the same unwanted man, and not any more comfortable now because he had landed himself here in full make-up and costume.

'No harm in taking a look,' some woman shouted. Let her shout and take looks. But not at him, he hoped, and bunched himself still smaller.

But the door was opened and an electric torch was flashed full in his face. He turned and made it even fuller in his face. He was startled and annoyed. 'Here, what –' he began, almost snarling.

'Lord love a purple duck! Either I'm going barmy or it's Timmy – Timmy Tiverton!'

'Well, yes,' he began stammering, half recognizing the voice out of the past.

But now the torch was switched off and a plump little woman had hurled herself into the car beside him, was putting her plump little arms round his neck, was kissing him and laughing and gasping and wetting his cheek with tears. 'My God – what a thing to do to a woman, Timmy, turning up like this out of the blue – and dressed and made-up to go straight on! Oh – Christmas! – Timmy – when I suddenly saw you there, just as if you were waiting to go on, just like the old days, I tell you my poor old heart turned right upside down. I'll have indigestion for a fortnight. An' I don't believe you know me yet, you silly ol' comic –'

'Yes, I do, dear. You're Daisy – Daisy Barley.'

'Of course I am,' she cried, hugging him again.

'Then why the hell didn't that chap say so?' cried Timmy, not knowing whether to laugh or cry himself. He had to explain that remark, and then he told her, very simply and quietly, how he'd been thinking and wondering about her, and she clutched his arm tight, and choked and sniffed and damned herself for a silly ol' woman.

'You see, Timmy,' she explained when he had done, 'I married a chap called Fillans out in Australia – he died out there, so then I came back – and here they call me Mrs Fillans. And what we're staying out here for, I don't know – with you shivering away – poor ol' Timmy! Come on – inside.'

'What. Like this?'

'We'll run through the back and straight up to my little sitting-room,' she cried, 'an' I'll have you out o' them things and a drink an' some hot supper in front of you – in a jiffy. You don't know me now, Timmy. Business woman. An' I boss 'em round here like a female Hitler. My goodness me – come on, dear, stir yourself; we're going – but I'm glad I listened when that chap said he'd got a comedian stowed away in his car! If I'd known afterwards you'd been shivering out here – with me in there, just talkin' to those bits of nonsense – I'd have gone out of my head. Now in there, Timmy, an' straight up the stairs. Here,' she shouted to somebody, 'tell Walter I want him upstairs – sharp.'

She rushed him into a cosy little room that was crammed with photographs of the profession and souvenirs and knick-knacks and feminine rubbish. And she never stopped talking. He still felt too dazed and shy to say very much, and deep inside he was much moved, as if there was another Timmy in there who had to cry over this strange meeting. She was sadly changed, of course, after all these years; the red curls were still there but obviously owed a lot now to the hairdresser and the chemist; the saucy little face had filled out and was heavily lined in spite of its rather thick make-up; the pretty legs had vanished with so many other pretty and amusing things; and this plump little middle-aged woman, over-dressed and wearing too much jewellery and a make-up almost as startling and unreal as a clown's, seemed at first sight only a distant connexion of the bewitching and saucy Daisy Barley who used to set her curls and heels twinkling at the enraptured boys and had been known to turn even the fellows in the band into her slaves. Yet it was Daisy all right. Her eyes had not aged and tired. In their reckless greeny-hazel depths the fire and fun and devilment still burned. Agents, managers, sulking audiences, marriages, Australia, none of them had got her down. She had winked and shouted and danced her way, through God knows what, into this sitting-room, where she now sat kicking her legs excitedly and looking at him as nobody had looked at him for years and years, as if she could eat him, as if she truly loved him.

'Daisy,' he told her, hardly knowing what he was saying, 'you ought to have seen that wet little blonde in that car.'

'What for? Don't tell me you've gone an' fallen for some messy little piece you've just –'

'No, of course I haven't,' he almost shouted at her. 'But I was just comparing you. They don't make 'em like you any more, Daisy. That's what I meant. They're like half-drowned kittens. You're alive – you're – by thunder! – you're wonderful.'

'Now you're talking, dear. I wondered what had come over you. Ah – Walter!' A stout little oldish chap had come in, with the look of an old pro about him. 'Now look who's here!'

'Blimey!' cried Walter, staring at Timmy as if he was a ghost. 'Wait a minute! Don't tell me. It's Timmy Tiverton. You remember me? Walter Shafton – you remember – the Shafton Brothers?'

Timmy, still dazed, found himself shaking this fellow droll warmly by the hand. Shafton Brothers used to be a very good turn indeed. Hadn't heard of them for donkey's years.

'Now, Walter,' cried Daisy briskly, 'I asked you to come up because I want you to take Timmy up to your room and lend him some of your clothes – you're about a size except you're a lot fatter. That's what comes of working for me. I believe the whole damn lot of you have put on about three stone each since you came here – an' what we'll all look like in a year or two, God only knows. Off you go, Timmy my boy, an' clean up – an' I'll have something waiting for you down here that'll make you feel like a two-year-old.'

A girl put her head round the door. 'Mrs Fillans, Mr Johnson and his friends are asking for you in the cocktail bar.'

'You tell Mr Johnson and his friends, dear, that one of my very oldest and dearest friends has just arrived – so I'm busy. Now pop off. That kid's Lottie Carwell's daughter – you remember poor Lottie? That time we had with her in Liverpool just after the Grand National. Now go on, Walter, don't stand gassing there.'

Walter explained it all upstairs, while Timmy was changing into a suit much too large for him, Walter's best, too, a Harris tweed so gaudy and so hairy that you wondered which Harris had made it. 'Yers,' said Walter, 'there's 'alf a dozen of us 'ere, boy. When Disy gits back from Austrylia, what 'appens? First thing, she finds a lot of her ol' pals can't get a job. Eh? Right. Next thing, when she tikes this big brand-new boozer, what 'appens? She can't get staff. Eh? Right. So what does she do?'

'She goes round England on a bicycle,' said Timmy.

Walter, like many drolls, was a very solemn fellow in private life and had only a professional sense of humour. 'I'll buy it, ol' boy,' he said anxiously. 'I 'aven't 'eard this one. All right then, why does she go round on a bicycle?' And he put on an expectant look he had used for thirty years as one of the Shafton Brothers.

'Never mind, Walter,' and Timmy patted him on the shoulder. 'Some other time. So Daisy decided to take you all on the staff, eh? And how does it work?'

'A treat. Look at me. I do odd jobs before we open – plenty of odd jobs in a plice this size – an' then help to wite in the smoke-room – or if necessary' – he concluded with a fine flourish – 'elsewhere.' Now he surveyed Timmy with almost paternal pride. 'Suit's a bit big, I don't deny, but the general effec' is classy – classy in what you might call a country style. I'll pop your costume, boy, into this li'l bag. This w'y, Squire.'

A very promising table for two had been laid in Daisy's sitting-room. Daisy herself was not there, but a waiter brought in a loaded tray and a fine smell of roast chicken. He was a real waiter, not an old pro. 'Would you like a gin and It, sir?'

'No, thanks, I don't like gins and Its,' said Timmy, 'but now that you're asking me, I'd like a little whisky, because I feel a bit shivery.'

'An' you're going to have some whisky, dear.' Daisy bounced in. She must have been redecorating herself, and seemed to have added a good deal of bright magenta to her lips and cheeks, and now could not have been put into the shade by a sunset above a Californian flower-show. 'Pop off, Clarence! We'll serve ourselves. You go an' serve the customers.' Out of a well-stocked cupboard she brought a bottle of whisky, and poured out two hefty ones. '*Highland Pride*, this is. It's about as Highland as I am, but it's got a hell of a kick in it, an' that's what we need at our age, eh? Not that I'm anything like as old as you, Timmy.'

'Certainly not, of course,' said Timmy gallantly. 'Why, I'm fifty-five.'

'Doesn't Time fly?' cried Daisy, now attacking the chicken with a very professional-looking carving-knife. 'But of course you're years an' years older than me. I was younger than poor Betty, y'know. I was nothing but a school kid when I first made my name. Fact is, I'm only forty-six now.'

Timmy nodded encouragingly. This was reasonable of Daisy, who must be now about fifty-four. If she took only eight years off, nobody could grumble. 'Daisy, all the best! Why, this is wonderful, meeting you again! Never thought I'd have such luck.'

'It's not been too good, eh, Timmy?' Her fine eyes suddenly misted above the glass she was holding up. 'I thought it hadn't. Asked an' asked about you, my dear, but nobody seemed to know anything. You're going to tell me how you come to be sittin' in the back of a car in your make-up, an' all about it, but not now, not just yet, dear. Just tuck in, first. My God! – but I do like eating, these days. I can remember the time when I'd just peck at this an' try a bit of that – y'know how girls go on, silly little devils – but now I just like to plant my feet under the table an' gobble, gobble, gobble.

Little greedy-guts, that's me. Have some more chicken, dear. I'm having some more.'

'Walter Shafton was telling me you've got a lot of old pros on the staff here,' he remarked, content to give her a cue.

'That's right. Killing two birds with one stone. You'll see some of 'em soon. I told 'em to come up an' have a look at you. They're a bit slow on their pins, some of 'em, an' one or two are inclined to lift the elbow too much an' talk the customers right out of the place. But you can't have everything, can you? This is my show, y'know, Timmy.'

'I wondered. That chap in the car I came in talked as if you just managed it.'

'That's all right. I want most of these chaps to think that, 'cos if I've to put my foot down – y'know, you've got to watch some of these devils, they'd have you standin' there before the Bench in no time – then I blame the owners. "Can't help it, boys," I tell 'em. "It's the owners." You've got to watch out with all these chaps that come to a place like this an' spend money. Got to flatter 'em all the time, while pretending not to. Don't you run away with the idea I don't know what I'm doin', Timmy, just because I used to be a bit wild in the old days – an' believe me, boy, if I'd known what was coming – well –'

'You'd have been a bit more careful,' he prompted her, grinning.

'I'd have been a damn sight wilder,' she cried, 'just to make sure I got it all in, before I went and landed myself in Woolloomalloowalloo – or whatever the rotten place was. No, Timmy, I'm not playin' round. I've got all I brought out of Australia sunk in this house. I thought of tryin' a seaside hotel first – gingering it up, of course – but then I was told of this place, which they'd nearly finished building when the fellow who started it went broke. When I first saw it, I said to 'em: "Don't be silly. It's miles an' miles from anywhere." I couldn't see anybody comin' here.'

'I still can't see it,' said Timmy, who had been wondering about this for the last hour. 'Where do they come from?'

Daisy laughed, and helped herself to trifle that was only a

shade less gorgeous than she was. 'If this isn't plastered with good sherry, those perishers downstairs are doin' it on me, for they ask for enough of it.' She took a large spoonful, winked at Timmy, then returned to the main theme. 'You see, the trouble about you, my dear, is you're not up-to-date. Now, are you?'

'No, I'm not,' replied Timmy sturdily. 'I'm clean out o' date, and I don't care who knows it.'

'You little devil!' cried Daisy, regarding him with affection. 'You don't know how glad I am to see you again. Inside –' and she tapped her opulent bosom – 'I'm with you every time. But you've got to move on. Things change, an' you've got to change with 'em if you don't want to be left in the cart. I learnt a thing or two in Australia, an' when I came back I came through America – stayed about three months in California an' then another month with a cousin of mine in Chicago – an' I saw there which way things were going. What the Yanks did last year, we'll do next year, y'know.'

'I do know,' said Timmy, rather unhappily. 'But I don't see why.'

Daisy had her answer ready. Obviously she had talked on these lines many a time before. 'Because somebody's always in the lead an' setting the fashion. Fifty years ago it was us. Now it's the Americans. You can't get away from it, Timmy. Every new thing you see here nowadays is only a copy of something they've had for years in America. Look at this place. Road-house. Not near a town, but what does that matter? Everybody with money to spend has a car now, an' likes to use it. Here we collect chaps and girls from twenty or thirty towns. Yes, an' people who used to be content with a quiet country life – they come here, too. They can have a bit o' dinner or supper, a few drinks, dance, play some games – darts an' so on, an' we have competitions an' bits of nonsense. I'm putting in a swimming-pool for the next summer. You've got to keep up-to-date, see?'

A very fat, jolly woman, who looked as if she had just come up from the kitchen, now came in and advanced upon Timmy with an outstretched hand and a beaming smile. 'How was the chicken? An' I bet you don't remember me.'

'The chicken was wonderful,' replied Timmy, staring at her. 'Now – just give me a minute. I'll remember.' He meant it, too, for he knew he had seen those eyes before.

'He'll never do it, dear,' said Daisy.

'Isn't it terrible?' sighed the nice fat woman. But then she smiled again at Timmy. She was a fine woman, and not unlike a kind of gigantic roast chicken herself. But Timmy had to shake his head.

'Why, you fathead!' cried Daisy, 'You remember *Little Katie Sacker, the Singer By The Water Mill* – ?'

And of course he did. Back it came out of the past, accompanied by invisible orchestras and cheered by spectral gallery boys, this image of little Katie Sacker, with her sun-bonnet and her fair ringlets, with her water-wheel-effect set, trilling sentimental ballads in a swiss-milk-chocolate soprano. And this was little Katie!

'Yes, that water-mill's turned a bit too much since then, hasn't it?' said Katie. 'Lucky for me I'd always fancied myself as a cook. We've often wondered about you, Mr Tiverton. We have a cup of tea in the morning –'

'A cup! You have quarts, you mean,' cried Daisy. 'Some of your insides must be like ol' brown boots.'

'And we talk about the old times,' Katie continued. 'And we've often wondered about you. I'm so glad to have seen you again. And I know Daisy is. Aren't you, love?'

'Now don't start that, Katie. They made her sing so many of these kiss-me-farewell-by-the-old-mill-stream numbers when she was a kid that they got right into her blood. Talk about sentimental! She'd make a Christmas card look tough. Now go on, dear. You'll see him again. Hello, who's this?'

It was another of her staff, a grave oldish man, who was once the hind legs of a famous comic horse. Then Jimmy Flagg came up, to have a look at Timmy and to give Daisy a message or two from the cocktail-bar, over which he presided. Jimmy had toured for years as *Denga Din* (presumably related to the celebrated Gunga) the *Mystic Hindoo Illusionist*, and even now, in his trim white jacket, there was still a suggestion of the mystic Hindoo about him, and no doubt his cocktails appeared to be mixed and shaken by magic. He fixed his mournful dark eyes, which seemed to be permanently in the Hindoo line, upon Timmy's, and said he was damned glad to see him and had never forgotten, and never would forget, a postman act of Timmy's that had left him nearly prostrated with laughter in the wings. And all this, and more, was said in a soft sad voice that still suggested Bengal and not a back street in Wolverhampton.

'He's a big success in the cocktail bar, Jimmy is,' said Daisy. 'Aren't you, dear? Does a few little tricks now and then, an' they nearly pass out. These people now think they know it all an' think they're hard to please, but really they're money for jam. All right, Jimmy, I'm coming down.'

She took Timmy on a little tour of inspection. Still dazed by the fantastic events of the evening, and especially by this series of encounters with his old pals of the halls, Timmy did not take everything in very well, could not have described afterwards what he saw, but he took in enough to make him regard Daisy with a new respect. Amazing to think she should be running a place this size, and running it so well, too. Big kitchen, white-tiled and full of gadgets; a long dining-room, so determinedly Tudor that you might have been in Stratford-on-Avon, and indeed the head waiter, who had a manner that could turn any fish that Grimsby forwarded into Dover sole, had once toured with Benson; a dance-room that was a bit Spanish, a bit Viennese, and a good deal Metro-Goldwyn-Mayer, with a five-piece dance band consisting of two enthusiastic young men from Birmingham who were trying to look like love-sick Mexicans and three much older men, whom Timmy recognized as the masculine section of the former *Musical Wilsons*, a good act in its day; a cosy, leathery smoke-room in the Old English a-hunting-we-will-go style; and the cocktail bar, which had a vermilion colour scheme and was so hot and dazzling and queer that it made you wonder if you had a temperature; and it was here in the cocktail bar, which had forty or fifty people in it, that Daisy had to attend to business.

'Daisy,' Jimmy Flagg whispered, 'that chap–Mortimer–from

Melminster – he's here again with his pal and those two little pieces.'

'I'll have a word with him,' Daisy muttered; adding to Timmy: 'Now you'll see what this game lets you in for.' As Timmy followed her over to the group of four, he saw her detach one of the men, who were at least twenty years older than the girls they were with, and was in time to hear what she said to him.

'All the best!' she began, as he raised his glass. 'Glad to see you here again, Mr Mortimer. Y'know, I was over in Melminster the other day, an' somebody was saying very nice things about Mrs Mortimer to me. Why don't you bring her over an' let us have a look at her one of these nights? What about Saturday, if you've nothing better to do? We're having another Treasure Hunt. Yes, do!'

She watched him go back speculatively, then took Timmy into a corner. 'I've never heard anything about his wife – but I know he's got one – an' I'm tellin' him straight to bring her here instead o' these bits of typists. I know! I can see it in your eye, you little devil! You're thinking this doesn't sound like Daisy. But don't think I've changed. I want everybody to have a bit o' fun, but I don't like these kids being brought here by men old enough to be their fathers. If this Mortimer's wife just won't have a night out – all right, let him find somebody who will, somebody his own weight. But if you ask me, he's never asked her – an' I'll bet twenty to one she's sittin' at home now wondering why he always has to work so late these days – when he's spending his money – hers, too, for that matter – turnin' the head of some kid who ought to be havin' ninepenn'orth of pictures with a boy her own age. I tell you, Timmy, you may think it's no business of mine, but I'm not interferin' for interferin's sake. I want to run this show so's nobody'll curse the day I ever came here –'

She broke off because a middle-aged square man, with a close-cropped moustache and a bitter, bloodshot look, now came over, and greeted her.

'You're not dancing to-night, major. Thought you couldn't keep off that floor. Lost your partner?'

'Oh, no. She's here.' The major also had a close-cropped, bitter, bloodshot voice. 'Came over to talk to you about that, Mrs Fillans. Thought you'd better know. We left the floor for a good reason. May not be aware of it, but to-night you've got a gang of dirty little Jews dancing in there.'

Daisy looked at him steadily. 'Now, just a minute, major. What d'you mean by dirty?'

'What I say.'

'Let's have a look. Come on.' She led the way through to the entrance to the dance-room, where about thirty couples were swaying and shuffling. 'Now then, where are these dirty people?'

'Over there – see? Four of 'em. Can't mistake 'em. Jews all right.'

'Yes, I see. Matter of fact, I know them quite well. Nothing dirty about them, major. They're among the nicest people who come here.' And she still surveyed him steadily.

'So you're goin' to take that line, eh?' The major sounded unpleasant.

'Listen, major,' said Daisy earnestly. 'I'm not takin' any lines. You're takin' a line. An' I'll tell you frankly it's a line I don't like –'

'Whether you like it or not,' said the major sharply, 'you'll find more an' more decent people here are taking it.'

'If I thought so,' cried Daisy, angry now, 'I'd leave this country an' never come back. In the meantime the "Dog and Bell" is open to anybody who behaves properly, an' I don't care what shape their noses are, an' if you an' Hitler don't like it, major, I'm sorry, but you'll have to lump it. Good night.'

She swung away, an absurd little figure but now not without dignity, and Timmy joined her. They walked the length of the dance floor in silence. He knew that now she was feeling upset but he did not like to say anything. This was a new Daisy, a long way from the old madcap. 'I want to look in the dining-room again,' she said finally, 'and then we'll go back to my sitting-room so that you can tell me all about yourself.'

As they entered the dining-room, Timmy pulled her up short. For there, in the far corner, unnoticed before but plainly to be seen now, tucking away, was the thick-set, square-faced man who had followed him out of the Hall and cried 'Hey!' There was no mistake. It was undoubtedly the same severe, menacing fellow. At any moment, if he should look up from his plate, he might be crying 'Hey!' again, and before the night was out he might be heying Timmy into the nearest police station.

'Here, Daisy,' he muttered, 'I've got to get out of this – sharp.' And he hurried out, and looked for the stairs up to Daisy's sitting-room.

'I never knew such a rum little devil,' cried Daisy at his elbow, a trifle breathless. 'I believe you've been up to something, though what you could be up to, God only knows. This way, an' then tell Auntie Daisy all about it.'

Back among the photographs and souvenirs of professional life, Timmy began talking about himself, and he could not have had a better audience. When he arrived at the end of his depressing morning in Birchester, which had left him wondering about suicide, Daisy, half in tears, leaned forward and gave him a bright magenta kiss.

'I'm not surprised either,' she cried, dabbing at her eyes. 'I could never get on with 'em in Birchester. My God – how I used to hate that date! There's something *wrong* with 'em there – got dried peas where their hearts ought to be – or something. Poor ol' Timmy! Still,' she added, brightening up, 'you must have got out of it all right 'cos you're here, not buried in Birchester. Go on, go on!'

So he had to tell her then about the Professor and Mr Hassock and the girl Hope and all the doings at Dunbury and how it was by escaping from the thick-set square-faced chap, down in the dining-room, that he came to be at the 'Dog and Bell' at all. 'And that reminds me,' he concluded, 'I've got to get back to Dunbury to-night. Don't forget that.'

'Why have you? Stay here.'

'I'd like to sometime, Daisy, but –'

'Sometime! Sometime my foot! Fancy talking like that! There's plenty of room for you here. You're one of my oldest friends – a real ol' pal – why –'

'You've missed the point, my dear,' said Timmy quietly. 'I can't just walk out on these people at Dunbury. I don't know what they're going to do now, but whatever it is, I've got to see it through with 'em. Now, haven't I?'

'Yes, of course you have, if that's how you feel about it. But, you see, I feel that way about you, Timmy.'

'What do you mean?'

Daisy hesitated. 'Well, you see, Betty said – the very last time I talked to her – when they only let me have a couple o' minutes with her, an' I think she knew it was all up – she asked me then to look after you –'

He stared at her, his mouth wide open. 'She asked *you* – to look after *me* – ?'

'Now that just shows how much sense you think I have,' cried Daisy. Then she was quiet again. 'But you see, dear, she had to ask *somebody* – being a woman – an' she knew that I'd more gumption than I seemed to have – an' that you'd perhaps a bit less than you seemed to have. Yes, I know, I know. But you were always a fool to yourself, Timmy Tiverton. Why, with your talent – you ought to have been still right at the top. No, don't start mutterin' to me about films an' wireless. That's a good enough excuse for most of this lot I'm employin' here. But you're different. You'd something none of them 'ud got. In a different class altogether – like me. But you've just *let* yourself be pushed out, that's what's happened to you, Timmy. An' I believe poor Betty knew. So she asked me, an' I promised. And I didn't keep my promise, being so damn busy getting married an' unmarried and married again, runnin' round like a little mad hen. An' that's another reason why I've so often wondered about you, an' made so many enquiries since I came back from Australia, an' why I was so glad to see you. An' that's the plain truth – an' – an' – oh, give me another whisky.'

Uncle Rodney

It was queer up there on the landing outside his uncle's room. He could hear the gramophone inside and so he waited, leaning against the oak chest of drawers that had always been there, and staring at a large old water-colour of an incredible street scene in some Mediterranean port. The window, farther along the landing, was bright with racing clouds and blue air; but here in the corner there was a warm dusk, the day already dying. But what made it so queer was the music coming from Uncle Rodney's room. A woman – a deep throbbing contralto – was crying farewell to the earth. The strings thinly soared, broke, and fled. There was a faint sweet jangling of harps. The soft silver hammering of a celesta, scattered in the deepening silences, was like some dawn, far-off, pearly, indifferent to men in its pure beauty, stealing over a scene of ruined hearths and dead cities. '*Ewig!*' cried the woman softly, out of a lost Vienna. The last instruments murmured and died. The silences grew. '*Ewig, ewig!*' The blue brightens; the earth awakes in spring; but the last whispering farewell is heard no more, because man has gone to find his far long-lost home ...

'Steady, boys, steady,' Alan muttered, more moved than he cared to admit even to himself. And then went in.

His uncle, wearing an old shooting jacket and tweed trousers, was attending, with the huge deliberation of the run-down elderly, to the needs of a gramophone whose giant horn dominated the room. The windows were closed, and the air was sweet and thick with the smoke of Egyptian cigarettes.

'Hello, Uncle. I waited until it was over. Last movement of Mahler's *Lied von der Erde*, eh? And rather clever of me to recognize it after all this time.'

'I'm glad to see you, my boy,' said Uncle Rodney, shaking hands. He was still impressive, but a vast ruined figure of a man now. 'Good God, what have they done to you? It's that suit. Makes you look like a little insurance tout. Where did you get it? The damn thing's cut all wrong. Sit down.'

'Utility suit. Provided for members of His Majesty's Forces on demobilization.'

Uncle Rodney lit another of his fat Egyptian cigarettes, and promptly suggested a distinguished, world-weary diplomat of the 'Eighties. 'Give the thing away. Then, the next time you're up in town, you could pop round and see my fella – if he's still there. Can't tell you if he is or not, because I haven't had any new clothes made since this war began and don't propose to have any. Got a pretty good wardrobe, y'know, Alan – it'll last longer than I shall. Got used to that idea now, but at one time it gave me the creeps – that a fella's waistcoats and boots, hairbrushes and razors, all easily outlast him. Got used to the idea – but still feel there's something wrong somewhere.' He looked hard at Alan. 'Had a rough time out there, eh, my boy?'

'Some of it. Not many of the chaps from round here will be coming back.'

'Hm – sorry. You're a good lad, Alan. Wish I could do something for you, but I can't – no money, no influence, no anything. Like the gramophone?'

'Yes, but I didn't know you did.'

'No? New idea. Sold my coins a few years ago. Then sold my stamps – good price too. Couldn't decide what to collect – so thought I'd listen to some music. Very good instrument too – this – best there is.'

Alan agreed that it was. 'And what about Mahler?'

'Oh, this Song of the Earth thing. Thought it too fancy – and too damn Chinese – at first, but now I'm beginning to understand it. Heart-breaking stuff, really.' Uncle Rodney leaned back, produced one of his finest smoke-rings, and eyed it complacently. 'Like it now.'

'Diana says –' Alan began.

'No, no, my boy. I don't want to hear what Diana says. The girl's all tied into knots because her husband's been killed. Understandable, of course, though he seemed to me a dreary fella. But come to me if you want to know what I'm up to. Don't listen to Diana – or your mother. As for Gerald and that wife of his, they don't know what a man like me feels about things. They don't know any better than a couple of garage hands. That's why they'll be all right. They *are* a couple of garage hands, in a world that'll soon be nothing but a factory, a garage, and an aerodrome. The fact is, my boy, the real world – the one worth living in – is finished. These fellas – Mahler, Elgar, Delius, and the rest of 'em – knew it years ago. They saw it all coming; and before it was too late, they looked about 'em, saw what was gracious and charming and beautiful and knew it was all finished. Have a whisky? I've still got a bottle or two.'

'No, thanks, Uncle. But let me give you one, while you go on talking.'

'All right, thank you, my boy. Not too much now. It's as if you're in love with a woman – or have been in love with her,' said Uncle Rodney, who was known to have been in love with several beauties in his time. 'She's a lovely woman – a delicious creature, all delicacy and fire, which is how they ought to be – so don't get yourself tied up to one of these great lolloping land girls. Well, you go and see here – and there she is – beautiful as ever – but then you notice this and that, and suddenly you realize she hasn't long to live – she's doomed. And then – by God – you go away – and you sing it, you make the fiddles cry out, you set the trumpets sounding it – your old ecstasy, your love, your despair. That's what these fellas felt – that's what I feel – not just about women, of course – though they come into it, naturally – but about everything, about the whole damned drivelling world.' Uncle Rodney was quite excited now; the distinguished diplomat had vanished; he was no longer even the country gentleman who collected things, a part he had played successfully since 1938; but now he was a weird kind of clubman prophet, a Pall-Mall-and-Ritz Jeremiah; and he pointed a huge shaking forefinger at Alan. 'You must be nearly fifty years younger than I am, my boy, and let me tell you, quite plainly, I don't envy you. On the contrary, I'm sorry for you – especially as you're a sensitive, quick-witted sort of fella, not like this race of bloody mechanics and chauffeurs we're breeding now. Yes, I'm sorry for you. You'll get up, take your bath, brush your teeth, shave, and put on your clothes – for what? To go and drudge in some hell-hole of an office or factory so that you can come home to some numbered cubby-hole at night, gobble some mess out of tins, and either go to the moving pictures to see how pins are made or sit listening to some government bully on the wireless telling you to hurry up and fill in *Form Nine-thousand-and-thirty-eight*. Once a year you and your wife, who'll be as plain as a suet pudding, and all your brats, who'll have all been vaccinated against everything but stupidity and dreariness, will be given a ticket to a holiday camp, along with five thousand other clerks and mechanics and their women and kids, and there you'll have physical drill, stew, and rice pudding, round games, and evening talks on tropical diseases and aeroplane engines. And I'll be dead – and delighted.'

'You know,' Alan said, 'you're in fine form. I don't believe you know what you're talking about, but it's coming out in great style.'

Uncle Rodney smiled. 'The fact is, my boy, I'm very glad to see you. Haven't been talking to anybody lately, and your arrival has done me good. Not rushing away again, are you?'

'No. I don't know what I'm going to do yet. Too early to decide. But tell me,' Alan continued, 'if you think everything worth having is ruined and finished, what on earth have chaps like me been fighting for?'

'No, no, my boy,' said Uncle Rodney, wagging his huge white head, 'you can't catch me with that one. You fought to keep us out of the hands of the Gestapo and all the Hitler louts, to save us from the whole damned German lunacy. Had to do that. Done it myself if I'd been even thirty years younger. The irony is,' he continued, leaning back and preparing to enjoy himself, 'that if these Nazis hadn't been so impatient and greedy, if they hadn't thrown their weight about so much and provoked everybody, they'd probably have got all they wanted without so much as dropping one bomb. Mass production and mass meetings! Leadership talking over the wireless!

Nice little houses for nice little people! Strength Through Joy! See Italy or the Norwegian Fiords for eight pounds! That's what they were offering – and isn't it what the mob wants everywhere?'

'You old devil!' cried Alan. 'Sorry – but you know what I mean.'

'I take it as a tribute,' replied Uncle Rodney complacently. 'And the fact remains that the world worth living in is finished – can't be brought back. I can't grumble, for I've had my share. But all you've done, my boy, is to catch a last glimpse of it. That's why I'm so sorry for you. Let's have some more music. How about the Elgar 'Cello Concerto?' He rose ponderously.

Alan regarded him with mixed affection and irritation. 'You're like a talking dinosaur.'

'Don't be impudent, my lad. And wind this thing up, will you?'

So Alan stood there, winding up the gramophone to play straight through the concerto; and he looked across at his uncle who was taking the Elgar out of the record cabinet, and he noticed how everything about the old man – his cheeks and chins, immense shooting jacket, tweed trousers – now seemed to hang in great loose folds; and in that corner of the room which framed his uncle's stooping figure, there were white bookshelves piled high with gaudy memoirs and old French yellow-backs, and the little William Nicholson still life, and a Sickert of the Dieppe period; and it seemed to him, a moment later, before he had finished his winding, that the scene itself was turning into a picture, painted no doubt about 1903, exhibited originally at the New English, now perhaps hanging in the Tate Gallery. 'I've got you into the Tate, Uncle. But the record cabinet's wrong.'

Either Uncle Rodney did not hear this or he chose to ignore it. 'By the way, be careful of those women downstairs. If you don't look out, they'll probably have you married to some clean-living local wench, probably with hands and feet like a farmer's. Heard 'em discussing it, the other night. They may have a list by now. I'm warning you.'

'I told Mother,' said Alan lightly, 'that everybody here seems to be warning me against everybody else. What's the matter with you all?'

'Disintegration, my boy, sheer disintegration.'

Aunt Hilda and Uncle Miles

IF the house in Brigg Terrace seemed like home almost at once, that was not only because of my rather homeless childhood but also because my uncle and my aunt gave it that quality. I was equally fond of each of them, but they were so gloriously different that it was hard to believe they were not doing it deliberately, like an artful pair of comics. Aunt Hilda had no sense of humour at all, not the least glimmer. In the house she was extremely active, almost tireless: a passionate cleaner and indefatigable tidier-up, serving some ideal of spotlessness that was far beyond the sight or comprehension of Uncle Miles and me. But she was also a really superb cook, which was something we could understand. She had one maid, a plump and snorting lass called Alice, from a miner's family down Barnsley way; and there was also a charwoman called Mrs Spellman, who was small and skinny but had one of those shatteringly loud Bruddersford voices not capable of being modulated at all, so that her least sarcasm rang through the house, and any observations she made while scouring the front door steps could be heard the length of the terrace. Aunt Hilda drove these two hard, but drove herself harder still. But in company, dressed in dark rich stuffs and wearing a few ornaments that always had an odd funereal look, handsome in a pale, stricken fashion, Aunt Hilda always appeared to be recovering slowly from some terrible bereavement, and arrived at a picnic or a whist-drive as if attending the reading of a will. She had good features and a square pale face, with some hint of a marble monument about it; she was always pulling down her mouth, in pity and sorrow, and so lengthening her upper lip; and she had a deep mournful voice. Her favourite talk, when she was out to enjoy herself, was all of minor ailments leading to major ones, of operations and tragic breakdowns, of dissolution and death. But she was also fond of a gossip about house property, having inherited some herself (and I suspect that it paid most of our expenses in Brigg Terrace) and following a local fashion in talk – for in those days Bruddersfordians liked to discuss house property, and two oldish men, solid citizens, might easily go for a long afternoon's walk and never talk about anything else. Aunt Hilda liked to spend a fine Sunday afternoon walking round the huge cemetery beyond Wabley Wood (as did thousands of other Bruddersford folk), and there she could lead the talk from puzzling early symptoms to grave illness, and illness to death and burial, and burial to wills and house property.

Behind her mask of woe was an unfailing store of kindness. She was a most lavish hostess, and she kept to the good old-fashioned feminine idea that the male sex, nuisance though it might be, should always be promptly, generously, gloriously fed. At the same time she was extremely fastidious. And when I remembered this, I remembered also, after forgetting them for thirty years, the two Miss Singletons. They kept a small corner shop, a confectioner's, not far from the Merton Park end of Brigg Terrace. It was my aunt's favourite shop, representing her ideal of shopkeeping. The two Miss Singletons were timid and shrinking old maids, forever blushing as they told you they were sold out (and their little shop always appeared empty of everything but these blushes and apologies), but they were so devoted to some high fanatical ideal of baking and confectionery, which they shared with my Aunt Hilda and a few other fastidious matrons, that they only made and sold about a tenth of what was demanded of them. They would have driven all the recent advocates of high-pressure commerce and salesmanship to despair and suicide. In their determination to sell the best, and only the best, they turned that little shop into an unconquered fortress of taste and integrity. And if the universe is not simply an idiotic machine, grinding out nothingness, then in some queer but cosy dimension of it my Aunt Hilda is still trotting round to the Miss Singletons to secure the last brown loaf and the remaining six Eccles cakes.

Sitting there in my room in the Royal Ocean Hotel, with the wind howling at the turret and the Atlantic booming below, I heard again, after so many years, Aunt Hilda's reproachful: 'Now, Miles – really!' But as she said it – and of course she was always saying it – there was often just the very ghost of a twinkle in her dark hazel eyes. I can see now that while outwardly disapproving of so much he did and said, inwardly she must have relished and applauded every self-indulgent whim and caper; and he had a plentiful supply. As a boy of course I never gave their relationship a thought; it seemed to me then one of the great stable things of the world, companion to the Pennine Range; but now that I am about the age they were then, and move among the wrecks of marriage, I realize that it must have been an unusually good and happy relationship. They bickered now and then, but I never remember even the shadow of a serious quarrel. They were perfectly complementary. The hidden and unconscious life of each one was reflected on the very face of the other. The sad responsibilities, the sick-beds, the tombstones, all so airily banished by Uncle Miles, were the essential properties of Aunt Hilda's outward life; while all the easy self-indulgence and pottering and clowning so sternly suppressed by her were jovially flaunted by him.

Uncle Miles was a large comfortable figure of a man, steadily thickening, with one of those massively handsome heads, of a type often seen among old-fashioned American politicians, that promise more than they can perform. He had a fine mop of hair and an imposing moustache, dancing blue eyes and a fine pink shining face. (I have tried every shaving gadget that our recent ingenuity has contrived, but have never succeeded in being so exquisitely clean-shaven as he was with his single old cut-throat razor.) He had a mysterious little business of his own, something to do with manufacturers' remnants, that was perfectly contrived for an unambitious man who had plenty of other interests. If Yorkshire happened to be playing at Lords or the Oval, this business could take him even as far as London, and had always had nice little journeys for him; but if he wanted a week or two in Morecambe or Filey or up in the Dales, then apparently it never suffered at all; and even when he was attending to it, he had ample time for dominoes or chess in the various smoking-rooms of the cafés near the Wool Exchange. It was an ideal business for a happy-go-lucky man whose wife had some house property. And the textile trade in Bruddersford in those days, before the first war, seemed to be able to support hundreds of these independent lucky fellows. I can see them now, in their fragrant haze of Virginia and Latakia, at their dominoes and chess, or strolling towards tram or train to watch some cricket or to try for a trout in the Wharfe. All day Uncle Miles smoked his pipe – always Exchange Mixture from Porsons' in Market Street, and very good it was too: I wish I had some now – but over his toddy at night, perhaps sitting up to read W. W. Jacobs, he liked a good cigar. But then there were a lot of things he liked: a walk over the moors and then bilberry-pie and new milk; an afternoon in the sun with a good view of Hirst, Rhodes and Haigh; the clarinets and flutes of a Guards' band in the park tootling away at Delibes and Massenet; the Bruddersford Choral Society dealing roundly with Handel; Little Tich and Robey, the Six Brothers Luck or Fred Karno's knockabouts at the Imperial; roast pork and veal-and-ham pie, tea with a drop of rum in it, then playing what was regarded as a devilishly cunning game of whist, perhaps followed by some riotous charades; and a grand onslaught upon the Tories by Lloyd George or Philip Snowden or the leader writers of the *Manchester Guardian*. There was nothing of the bitter rebel about my uncle, and no revolution could ever have been of his making, but nevertheless he held strong progressive views, was always ready to defend them, and often surprised me by showing much skill and tenacity in argument. He still lived in that early optimistic Labour atmosphere, before anybody had sold out and before the party machinery had grown too elaborate. In those days

Merrie England, with more good cricket and W. W. Jacobs and Exchange Mixture and roast pork and bilberry-pie and June mornings in Wensleydale for everybody, still seemed just round the corner.

The Painter

THE *White Horse* was a nice old pub, at the Bruddersford end of the straggling village of Bulsden. Among the sensations I seem to have missed for years and years, sensations that appear to have vanished never to return, was the one I experienced then, that of plunging from the sunlight into the deliciously dark cool interior, smelling of beer and fresh sawdust and fried ham and eggs. And the last time I was up there the old *White Horse* had gone and in its place was a large road house, offering a dance band and bogus Martinis, and not until I arrive among the smiling hills of Paradise shall I see the original old *White Horse* again.

An odd-looking chap, with a long fattish body and a small head crowned by a mop of white hair, was standing at the bar, downing a pint. He had a painter's box and a light easel with him. 'Nah Jock,' he cried, grinning so that his weatherbeaten face seemed to crack all over, 'have a pint wi' me.'

Jock introduced us. He was Stanley Mervin, an artist, who chiefly painted landscapes in water-colour, and lived somewhere the other side of Bulsden. I knew him by repute, and had seen several of his drawings and sketches of the moors and Dale villages at the Alingtons'. They were very good, with much of the breadth and ease and masterly rapid statement of light and colour of the grand old tradition of English water-colour.

'We're going to the Alingtons',' Jock explained.

'So am I, lad, so am I,' cried Mervin. 'The missis'll be there this minute, wondering what the heck's become o' me. Well, we'll ha' this pint an' then be off. Ah've been out since early on 'aving a go at that little bridge at Broadstone Beck End. An' if Ah've had one try at that little beggar Ah've had a dozen. Never could get bloody tone right. But Ah think Ah've got it this time. 'Ere, you can have a look for your-selves, lads.'

He took us to the deep-set little window and showed us what he had done. There on the rough thick paper, reduced to their simplest possible terms, were the stream, glinting and dimpling, the stone arch of the bridge flushed in morning sunlight, the moor and the hills. It was the morning caught for ever. It was the time, the place, and a sensitive man's feeling about that time and that place, stated once and for all: it was art and a little miracle. I cried out my admiration, and wished I could buy the lovely thing then and there; and Jock solemnly added his approval.

Mervin nodded and grinned with some complacency. 'It's 'it or miss with this sort o' caper, an' Ah fancy this time Ah've rung the bloody bell. Gregory Dawson, eh?' He stared at me ruminatively out of small blood-shot eyes. ''Aven't Ah seen some little pieces o' yours in the *Bruddersford Evening Express* lately? Ay, well, they're not bad, not bad at all. Are they, Jock? Only – look, lad – don't try to be clever. Keep it straight an' simple. That's trouble wi' Ben Kerry, in my opinion. He's a bit of a Clever Dick, Ben is. Nah in a year or two, if you'll just keep it all straight an' simple an' don't try to show 'ow clever y'are, you'll be knocking spots off Ben an' a good many more. You're only a young lad yet, you've plenty o' time. Ah wish Ah 'ad – Ah'd show 'em summat – but Ah started late an' Ah'm gettin' on.'

'Not you, Stanley,' said Jock. 'You'll be climbing these moors and daubing away for the next thirty years.'

(But Jock was wrong for once. Stanley Mervin had a stroke in the autumn of 1914, and two years later, when I was out in France, I read of his death in a Bruddersford paper somebody sent out.)

Chuckling away, Mervin collected his apparatus, and the three of us went out into the dazzling village street. Mervin seemed to know all the men who were hanging about there, waiting for their roast beef and Yorkshire pudding, and exchanged greetings with most of them at the top of his loud hoarse voice. He was not at all my idea of an artist and, in my ignorance, I found it hard to associate this odd rough-spoken chap with those watercolours, at once so delicate and precise.

'Ah 'ope you've got summat to eat in that knapsack,' he said. 'Ah told the wife to tak' a few things down. Ah like John Alington an' his wife, but they're apt to be a bit fancy an' sketchy wi' their meals, an' Ah like summat solid, specially after gettin' up so early. Ay, Ah'm right peckish.'

Jock and I were too. But we assured him that there was a solid contribution in the haversack.

Mervin turned to me, grinning, as we came to the top of the village street. 'An' which o' them three lasses of his are you gone on, lad?'

'I've been wondering that,' said Jock.

'All three, I think,' I said, grinning too. 'But Joan's older than I am, and I'm afraid Eva's already out of my reach –'

'Well, that leaves young Bridget,' said Mervin. 'And she's best o' the three, to my mind, though Ah'm sayin' nowt against the other two. But Bridget's got most in her, you'll see. Ah'll back 'er against lot of 'em. Ah'm right fond o' young Bridget. Knows nowt about paintin' naturally, but for all that she knows what's what – an' picks out the good uns every time. She'll like this Ah've just done – you'll see.'

'She can't like it any better than I do,' I told him. 'I want to stare at it again.'

'An' so you shall, lad.'

'This may sound silly, but it isn't. I feel a lot better – more ready to try to do something good myself – now that I've seen that drawing of yours, Mr Mervin.'

He gave me a nudge in the ribs with the elbow of the arm that was carrying the paintbox. 'If that's silly, lad – it's sort o' silliness Ah like. An' there's nowt silly about it. Don't let nobody persuade you it is, neither. What is damn silly – an' Ah get sick to death of it – is all this bloody daft solemn talk round 'ere about merinos going up tuppence a pound an' crossbreds coming down tuppence a pound – an' so forth an' so on. Ah'd twenty years of it, doin' my paintin' at week-ends, an' then one fine Monday morning Ah says to the wife "Ah'm just wastin' my time." She says "Ah know you are, an' you'll be rare an' late for the office if you don't hurry up." Ah says "Nah look, Alice, Ah'm not going to any office. That's what Ah'm tellin' you. Ah'm wastin' no more o' my time in offices. If Ah go on much longer, Ah'll be dead an' buried afore Ah can turn round." She says "Well, tell 'em you're poorly an' tak' a few days off." Ah says "Ah'm goin' to tell 'em Ah never felt better in my life an' Ah'm goin' to tak' rest of it off." She says "Nay, Stanley, we can't afford it, lad." Ah says "We can't afford not to do it, lass." She says "We can't keep this house goin' on what you'll make sellin' your pictures." Ah says "Ah knows we can't, but what the hamlet do we want to keep this house goin' for? Let somebody else keep it goin'," Ah says to her. "Why, you're always tellin' me it's more than you can manage. Well, stop tryin' to manage it then," Ah says, "an' we'll tak' a cottage out Broadstone Moor way." An' so we did, an' Ah never went back, an' the first year or two it was 'ard goin', we must 'ave lived on a pound a week, but if Ah wanted to go out an' paint, Ah went out an' painted, an' if Ah wanted to stop in, then Ah stopped in – an' if you ask me, Ah've just about been 'appiest bloody man in Yorkshire ever since. Merinos can go up an' crossbreds come down till they're both out o' sight, for all Ah care. But Ah will say that for John Alington – he may be still in the business, but he talks about summat sensible, like a chap with his eyes an' ears open an' not like a talking white mouse in a cage, same as some of 'em.'

PLACES

Heidelberg in the 'Twenties

WHEN we went out, after our first lunch in Heidelberg, the gentle drizzle suddenly became a downpour, so we took refuge in a motor-coach that promised to spend the next hour or so wandering round the town. The only other passengers were four sad American women. In a few minutes the guide arrived, first to salute us and then to beam upon us. He was a spectacled, long-haired fellow in the inevitable peaked cap, and he looked like an unsuccessful student of metaphysics. His English was fluent but fantastic, and appeared to have been learned entirely from books. It sounded more foreign than German itself. Listening to him, you could never quite believe that this guide was a serious, real person and not an actor playing a foreigner in an old-fashioned farce. No sooner had the motor-coach started than he began bombarding us with queer syllables. 'Aboaf, vere you see now, zat eez 'Oly Ill, ven ze Chairman Beoples vairst begin.' This is how he opened his performance, and the American women, who – poor things – had been conducted and guided out of their senses, looked at him and at the Holy Hill in dumb despair.

I liked that guide. He was a man of temperament. Sometimes for a mile or two he would not say anything, but would simply sit there looking at the rain and no doubt pondering over the problem of the world as Will. Then, perhaps, after catching the eye of an American passenger, he would begin guiding us again. He would explain everything, the blossom on the trees, the very stones in the road. He might have been conducting us through a new solar system. Glistening with sweat and with his eyes flashing through his glasses, he would grow wilder and wilder in his English, every word of which, by this time, would be wearing spectacles and a peaked cap. 'Yaiz, yaiz,' he would cry, pointing, 'in zat building zere, ze vater of Cöln, ze shmelling vater of Cöln, makes zere – ze bedst shmelling vater – you know id?' And he looked imploringly at the American women; but they only stared blankly back at him, not being able to translate his fine phrases into eau-de-Cologne. To the end, they never understood his 'rococo', for which he had an enormous enthusiasm. We left him, saluting and still sweating, under the towering and becandled chestnuts near the Castle, where the rain made a pretty music among the leaves.

When, after the Day of Judgement, the earth is remade and all the things that have disillusioned us are hurled into the fiery pit, Heidelberg, I trust, will remain as it is now and have its place in that smaller world. Heidelberg is dead right. The moment I set eyes on it, a little bell rang in my mind. It is what I have always imagined an old German town would be. When they sing about a town in the *lieder*, they mean a place like Heidelberg. It is the right lovable mixture of the beautiful, the heavy grotesque, and the absurd. That vast, dark, strawberry-coloured ruin, the Castle, could not have been better devised. At one minute, when the mists blow across it like smoke from a cauldron and the wooded hills above are conjured into remote mountains, it is at once elfish and grim, a Nibelungen fastness, set to the thunder of Wagnerian trombones. The next minute, however, when the mist has vanished before the sun and there is a lovely blue beyond the tender green of the firs above, the place wears the look of an operetta back-cloth, is electoral, eighteenth-century, charming, and ridiculous, and could be introduced with propriety into that piece by old Johann Strauss we saw last night at the Stadt Theater. The town is as perfectly German, as, say, Wells or Oxford is English.

When you remember the sentimentality of the German, the further sentimentality of nearly all graduates, and the loveliness of Heidelberg in spring, it must, you will agree, be a terrific business for an old Heidelbergian to revisit the place. This morning I saw an old gentleman totter towards his waiting car, and he was wearing one of those fantastic hats of the students' unions. He must have been nearly bursting. What a town to be goldenly young and foolish in! Even I, who had never been in the town before, felt like an old Heidelbergian. I could have gone about the enchanted streets crying over my lost youth. It is not the situation of the place that works the magic, though its situation is almost miraculous; it is not the river, the Castle, the woods above, not the old buildings near the Rathaus and the Kornmarkt, though no doubt all these play their part; it is the blossom and the atmosphere. Here is a town smiling out of a garden in a wood. The chestnuts are bright with pink or white candles; the hawthorns are all in flower; the magnolia and laburnum are neighbours down every street; the villas of the professors are overhung with wistaria; and everywhere the rain is sweetening the lilac. I do not know what Heidelberg is like at any other season, but now it is a place filled with wet lilac. The Neckar winds smoothly between its steep, green hills; the mists, like puffs from a giant's cigarette, swirl about the red castle hanging above the town; and there, between them, are the little streets of wet lilac. I hope that among these students with the comic hats, which they are for ever raising, there are some poets, some good old-fashioned rhymesters, so that the purple and white blossom shall not go unsung. Let them raise their hats to the rain-drenched lilac.

I nearly burned my passport and my boats this morning. We had sauntered along the Leopoldstrasse, which is entirely filled with bright little shops, the greenest of green leaves, and this multitude of blossom, and as we walked along the rain shrank to a few glittering drops. We turned down and found ourselves in a little street just behind the Stadt Theater. A few people were hanging about, and they were listening to a good round baritone voice that was singing a jovial air and being excellently accompanied by a piano. It came, this voice, from the upper window of a villa, an oldish, slightly dilapidated but altogether delightful villa that had the spring itself blossoming in its courtyard. The jovial voice came rolling out above the shining leaves and the blossom. Obviously it belonged to a member of the Stadt Theater troupe, who was practising next week's operetta. There is nothing in all this, I admit; and yet, for a moment, there was everything in it. I said to myself: I will stay here for ever, for this is the town I have dreamt about when I have awakened to find myself miserable in my own world; I will wander along the Philosophen Weg across the Neckar and watch the mists above the Castle; I will eat my share of ragout of calf and fillet of swine's flesh at the Ritter and drink my Niersteiner and Goldberg at the Silver Harp; I will sleep in a bed that has everything on top, and will, if necessary, wear a comic hat and peer through spectacles at Gothic newspapers; and no doubt many pleasant things will be *verboten*; but here, in this enchanting town of mists and wet lilac and learning and operetta, I will stay. Probably I would have been bored in a fortnight, but nevertheless it was a great moment, and I believe I shall remain in spirit an old Heidelbergian.

The people are unusually pleasant, smiling, and attentive, but of course they do not live up to their town. Indeed, to be brutally frank, they are a plain lot and might have been plucked out of the streets and offices of Düsseldorf or Essen. This will not do. Germany ought to look to this. These people ought to have a picturesque, slightly fantastic air, with a suggestion of the romantic Eighteen-Thirties about it, something of the poetical-philosophical-mysterious-handsome-stranger-with-cloak-and-staff line of business. These streets should be filled with beautiful, tender maidens ready at any moment to go into a decline, and with men whose minds are fixed on Truth, Beauty, Goodness, Love, Tobacco, Drink, and nothing else. The place ought to have a Jean Paul Richter and early Carlyle flavour. The Eternal Yea – whatever that is – ought to be easily obtainable in the town. The place itself has this atmosphere, but not the citizens, who are making an all too successful attempt to look like all the other Germans. Only the students, magnificent and happy in their yellow, green, and scarlet hats, keep it up.

I do not know what *drang* is on in Germany now. The famous *Drang nach Osten* came to an unpleasant conclusion a few years ago, and if anything has taken its place, I do not know what it is. But I suggest – with all the usual apologies of the ignorant and interfering outsider – a new one, a *Drang nach Heidelberg*, that is, *nach* misty castles and rococo mansions and little steamers setting out pompously for nowhere and small towns where everybody knows the chief tenor and metaphysicians lost in the fumes of tobacco from huge untidy packets and solemn little societies with coloured hats and tender songs in the moonlight and sausage and beer and fireworks and waltz tunes in the woods. It can't be done, I suppose, for now there must be world politics and rationalization of industry and stunts in Persia and commercial campaigns in South America, together with large motor-cars and too much electricity and new buildings that look as if they were designed in Mars for a race of ambitious ants. The radio resounds through a host of steel and concrete electrified flats. This is a Germany one can respect. But give me the Germany I can smile at and love, with the Stadt baritone trolling above the wet lilac.

Bruddersford

THERE, far below, is the knobbly backbone of England, the Pennine Range. At first, the whole dark length of it, from the Peak to Cross Fell, is visible. Then the Derbyshire hills and the Cumberland fells disappear, for you are descending, somewhere about the middle of the range, where the high moorland thrusts itself between the woollen mills of Yorkshire and the cotton mills of Lancashire. Great winds blow over miles and miles of ling and bog and black rock, and the curlews still go crying in that empty air as they did before the Romans came. There is a glitter of water here and there, from the moorland tarns that are now called reservoirs. In summer you could wander here all day, listening to the larks, and never meet a soul. In winter you could lose your way in an hour or two and die of exposure perhaps, not a dozen miles from where the Bradford trams end or the Burnley trams begin. Here are Bodkin Top and High Greave and Black Moor and Four Gates End, and though these are lonely places, almost unchanged since the Doomsday Book was compiled, you cannot understand industrial Yorkshire and Lancashire, the wool trade and the cotton trade and many other things besides, such as the popularity of Handel's *Messiah* or the Northern Union Rugby game, without having seen such places. They hide many secrets. Where the moor thins out are patches of ground called 'Intake', which means that they are land wrested from the grasp of the moor. Over to the right is a long smudge of smoke, beneath which the towns of the West Riding lie buried, and fleeces, tops, noils, yarns, stuffs, come and go, in and out of the mills, down to the railways and canals and lorries. All this too, you may say, is a kind of Intake.

At first the towns only seem a blacker edge to the high moorland, so many fantastic outcroppings of its rock, but now that you are closer, you see the host of tall chimneys, the rows and rows of little houses, built of blackening stone, that are like tiny sharp ridges on the hills. These windy moors, these clanging dark valleys, these factories and little stone houses, this business of Intaking, have between them bred a race that has special characteristics. Down there are thousands and thousands of men and women who are stocky and hold themselves very stiffly, who have short upper lips and long chins, who use emphatic consonants and very broad vowels and always sound aggressive, who are afraid of nothing but mysterious codes of etiquette and any display of feeling. If it were night, you would notice strange constellations low down in the sky and little golden beetles climbing up to them. These would be street lamps and lighted tramcars on the hills, for here such things are little outposts in No Man's Land and altogether more adventurous and romantic than ordinary street lamps and tramcars. It is not night, however, but a late September afternoon. Some of its sunshine lights up the nearest of the towns, most of it jammed into a narrow valley running up to the moors. It must be Bruddersford, for there, where so many roads meet, is the Town Hall, and if you know the district at all you must immediately recognize the Bruddersford Town Hall, which has a clock that plays *Tom Bowling* and *The Lass of Richmond Hill*. It has been called 'a noble building in the Italian Renaissance style' and always looks as if it had no right to be there.

Yes, it is Bruddersford. Over there is the enormous factory of Messrs Holdsworth and Co., Ltd., which has never been called a noble building in any style but nevertheless looks as if it had a perfect right to be there. The roof of the Midland Railway Station glitters in the sun, and not very far away is another glitter from the glass roof of the Bruddersford Market Hall, where, securely under cover, you may have a ham tea or buy boots and pans and mint humbugs and dress lengths and comic songs. That squat bulk to the left of the Town Hall is the Lane End Congregational Chapel, a monster that can swallow any two thousand people who happen to be in search of 'hearty singing and a bright service'. That streak of slime must be the Leeds and Liverpool Canal or the Aire and Calder Canal, one of the two. There is a little forest of mill chimneys. Most of them are only puffing meditatively, for it is Saturday afternoon and nearly four hours since the workpeople swarmed out through the big gates. Some of the chimneys show no signs of smoke; they have been quiet for a long time, have stayed there like monuments of an age that has vanished, and all because trade is still bad. Perhaps some of these chimneys have stopped smoking because fashionable women in Paris and London and New York have cried to one another, 'My dear, you can't possibly wear that!' and less fashionable women have repeated it after them, and quite unfashionable women have finally followed their example, and it has all ended in machines lying idle in Bruddersford. Certainly, trade is still very bad. But as you look down on Bruddersford, you feel that it will do something about it, that it is only biding its time, that it will hump its way through somehow: the place wears a grim and resolute look.

Snow on the City

As he left the hospital, a clammy air of dissolution and mortality clung to him. Barbican and Golden Lane, through which he passed on his way to Old Street and Brown and Gorstein's, spoke to him only of decay. It was a curious afternoon, belonging to one of those days that are in the very dead heart of winter. The air was chilled and leaden. The sky above the City was a low ceiling of tarnished brass. All the usual noises were there, and the trams and carts that went along Old Street made as much din as ever, yet it seemed as if every sound was besieged by a tremendous thick silence. Cold as it was, it was not an afternoon that made a man want to move sharply, to hurry about his business; there was something about it, something slowed down and muffled in the heavy air, the brooding yellowish sky, the stone buildings that seemed to be retreating into their native rock again, that impelled a man to linger and stare and lose himself in shadowy thought.

Mr Smeeth found himself doing this, after he had left Brown and Gorstein's, and had turned down Bunhill Row on his way back to the office. He halted opposite that large building boldly labelled *The Star Works*, and wondered what was made there and whether it had anything starry about it. Then he turned round, idly, and stared through the iron railings at the old graves there. He had been this way before, many a time, in fact, but he never remembered noticing before that the earth of the burying-ground was high above the street. The railings were fastened into a wall between two or three feet high, and the ground of the cemetery was as high as the top of this little wall. There was something very mournful about the sooty soil, through which only a few miserable blades of grass found their way. It was very untidy. There were bits of paper there, broken twigs, rope ends, squashed cigarettes, dried orange peel, and a battered tin that apparently had once contained Palm Chocolate Nougat. This dingy litter at the foot of the gravestones made him feel sad. It was as if the paper and cigarette ends and the empty tin, there in the old cemetery, only marked in their shabby fashion the passing of a later life, as if the twentieth century was burying itself there too, and not even doing it decently. He moved a step or two, then stopped near the open space, where there is a public path across the burying-ground. He stared at the mouldering head-stones. Many of them were curiously bright, as if their stone were faintly luminous in the gathering darkness, but it was hard to decipher their lettering. One of them, which attracted his attention because it was not upright in the ground but leaned over at a very decided angle, he found he could read: *In Memory of Mr John Willm Hill, who died May 26th*, 1790, *in the eighteenth year of his age*. That had been a poor look-out for somebody.

''Aving a look at the good old graves, mister?' said a voice. It belonged to an elderly and shabby idler, one of those dreamy and dilapidated men who seem to haunt all such places in London, and who will offer to guide you, if you are obviously a stranger and well-to-do, but are quite prepared to pour out information for nothing to a fellow-citizen.

'Yes, just having a look,' said Mr Smeeth.

'Ar, there's some pretty work 'ere, if yer know where to look for it, mister. I know the Fields well, I do. Some big men 's buried 'ere. An' I'll tell yer one of 'em. Daniel Defow's buried in 'ere, boy, and I could take yer straight to the plice. Yers, the grite Daniel Defow.'

'Is that so? Now, let me see, who was he exactly?'

''Oo was 'e? Daniel Defow! Yer know *Rawbinson Crusoe*, doncher? Rawbinson Crusoe on the island and Man Friday an' all that? Thet's 'im. Defow – 'e wrote that. Cor! – think 'e did! Known all over the world, that piece, all over the wide world.

Well, 'e's in 'ere, Daniel Defow, and I could take yer straight to the plice. Yers, that's right. Monument, too – ee-rected by the boys and girls of England to Daniel Defow 'cos 'e wrote *Rawbinson Crusoe* – in 'ere. I tell yer, boy, there's some big men in there – what's left of 'em.'

Mr Smeeth nodded and continued to stare idly through the railings of Bunhill Fields, where the old nonconformists are buried in mouldering eighteenth-century elegance, to which they had at least conformed in death if not in life; and where, among the divines and elders, not only Defoe, but also Bunyan and Blake, the two God-haunted men, lie in the sooty earth, while their dreams and ecstasies still light the world. As Mr Smeeth stared, something floated down, touched the crumbled corner of the nearest headstone, and perished there. A moment later, on the curved top of the little wall beside him was a fading white crystal. He looked up and saw against the brassy sky a number of moving dark spots. He looked down and saw the white flakes floating towards the black pavement. In all his life he had never been so surprised by the appearance of snow, and for one absurd moment he found himself wondering who had made it and who was responsible for tumbling it into the City. He hurried away now, and as he went the snow came faster and shook down larger and larger flakes upon the town. Before he had reached Angel Pavement, not only had it whitened every cranny, but it had stolen away, behind its soft curtains, half the noises of the City, which only roared and hooted now through the white magic as if in an uneasy dream. It was so thick that Mr Smeeth was no longer one of ten thousand hurrying little figures, but a man alone with the whirling flakes. The snow was storming the City and all London. In Twigg and Dersingham's, they had turned on the lights, but they could still see a queer dim scurrying through the windows. Mrs Smeeth, in her little dining-room up at Stoke Newington, watched it with delight and remembered her childhood, when they had cried, 'Snow, snow faster, White alabaster.' Mrs Dersingham, who had been shopping in Kensington High Street, had to shelter from it in a doorway, and was wondering if it had caught the children. The Pearsons, secure in their warm maisonette in Barkfield Gardens, stood at the window for a quarter of an hour, calling one another's attention to the size of the flakes, for there had never been anything like this in Singapore. Miss Verever, who had missed her usual visit to the Italian Riviera, wrote another angry little note to her solicitor, because it was he who had insisted upon her staying in London. Lena Golspie, in Maida Vale, watched it for a minute or two, then switched on one of the big shaded lights and curled among the cushions, with a magazine, voluptuously, like a sleek blonde cat. Mr Pelumpton was just prevented in time from making a bid of twelve and six for a marble clock (out of order), and stayed at home, in Mrs Pelumpton's way. Benenden, having dozed off, never knew it was there. For an hour it was unceasing, and all the open spaces on the hills, from Hampstead Heath on one side to Wimbledon Common on the other, were thickly carpeted, and everything in the City, except the busier roadways and the gutters, was magically muffled and whitened and plumed with winter, just as if it had been some old town in a fairy-tale.

'Rusty Lane'

THERE had been a sudden flurry of business in the metal trade, and my friend was going back to his office and warehouse in West Bromwich after lunch. I went with him, and on the way was shown, among other things, the last dairy farm in the district. It stood there surrounded for miles by the grim paraphernalia of industrialism; I had only a glimpse of it, a solitary surviving farmhouse in the wet fog, with a few ghostly fields on either side. My friend's warehouse was in – shall we say? – 'Rusty Lane', West Bromwich. He keeps sheets of steel there, and no doubt any place is good enough to keep sheets of steel in; but I do not think I could let even a sheet of steel stay long in Rusty Lane. I have never seen such a picture of grimy desolation as that street offered me. If you put it, brick for brick, into a novel, people would not accept it, would condemn you as a caricaturist and talk about Dickens. The whole neighbourhood is mean and squalid, but this particular street seemed the worst of all. It would not matter very much – though it would matter – if only metal were kept there; but it happens that people live there, children are born there and grow up there. I saw some of them. I was being shown one of the warehouses, where steel plates were stacked in the chill gloom, and we heard a bang and rattle on the roof. The boys, it seems, were throwing stones again. They were always throwing stones on that roof. We went out to find them, but only found three frightened little girls, who looked at us with round eyes in wet smudgy faces. No, they hadn't done it, the boys had done it, and the boys had just run away. Where they could run to, I cannot imagine. They need not have run away for me, because I could not blame them if they threw stones and stones and smashed every pane of glass for miles. Nobody can blame them if they grow up to smash everything that can be smashed. There ought to be no more of those lunches and dinners, at which political and financial and industrial gentlemen congratulate one another, until something is done about Rusty Lane and West Bromwich. While they still exist in their present foul shape, it is idle to congratulate ourselves about anything. They make the whole pomp of government here a miserable farce. The Crown, Lords, and Commons are the Crown, Lords, and Commons of Rusty Lane, West Bromwich. In the heart of the great empire on which the sun never sets, in the land of hope and glory, Mother of the Free, is Rusty Lane, West Bromwich. What do they know of England who only England know? The answer must be Rusty Lane, West Bromwich. And if there is another economic conference, let it meet there, in one of the warehouses, and be fed with bread and margarine and slabs of brawn. The delegates have seen one

England, Mayfair in the season. Let them see another England next time, West Bromwich out of the season. Out of all seasons except the winter of our discontent.

Tyneside in the Depression

My guide-book devotes one short sentence to Jarrow: 'A busy town (35,590 inhabitants), has large ironworks and shipbuilding yards.' It is time this was amended into 'an idle and ruined town (35,590 inhabitants, wondering what is to become of them), had large ironworks and can still show what is left of shipbuilding yards.' The Venerable Bede spent part of his life in this neighbourhood. He would be astonished at the progress it has made since his time, when the river ran, a clear stream, through a green valley. There is no escape anywhere in Jarrow from its prevailing misery, for it is entirely a working-class town. One little street may be rather more wretched than another, but to the outsider they all look alike. One out of every two shops appeared to be permanently closed. Wherever we went there were men hanging about, not scores of them but hundreds and thousands of them. The whole town looked as if it had entered a perpetual penniless bleak Sabbath. The men wore the drawn masks of prisoners of war. A stranger from a distant civilization, observing the condition of the place and its people, would have arrived at once at the conclusion that Jarrow had deeply offended some celestial emperor of the island and was now being punished. He would never believe us if we told him that in theory this town was as good as any other and that its inhabitants were not criminals but citizens with votes. The only cheerful sight I saw there was a game of Follow-my-leader that was being played by seven small children. But what leader can the rest of them follow?

After a glimpse of the river-front, that is, of tumble-down

sheds, rotting piles, coal dust, and mud, we landed in Hebburn, where we pursued, in vain, another man we wanted. Hebburn is another completely working-class town. It is built on the same mean proletarian scale as Jarrow. It appeared to be even poorer than its neighbour. You felt that there was nothing in the whole place worth a five-pound note. It looked as much like an ordinary town of that size as a dust-bin looks like a drawing-room. Here again, idle men – and not unemployable casual labourers but skilled men – hung about the streets, waiting for Doomsday. Nothing, it seemed, would ever happen here again. Yet oddly enough a great deal is happening here; more, in some directions, than has ever happened before. Its Council of Social Service possesses a particularly energetic secretary, and in this stranded hulk of a town there are courses on history and economics (an ironic course, this) and literature, an orchestra and ladies' and children's choirs, two girls' clubs for handicrafts, gymnasium classes, a camping and rambling club, and play centres for children. It is possible that Hebburn is coming nearer to civilization in its poverty than it ever did in its prosperity. Probably these cultural activities are breeding a generation that would not tolerate the old Hebburn, even though it offered them work and wages again. If this should be true, then at least in one direction there has been a gain. But consider the gigantic loss. It is not merely that two-thirds of the town is living on the edge of destitution, tightening its belt another hole every month or two, but that its self-respect is vanishing – for these are *working* towns and nothing else – and that it sees the sky forever darkening over it. We went down to the social centre, which after some difficulty we found in a couple of huts by the side of a derelict shipyard. A little gnome-like man, grandly proud of everything, showed us round. There were places for carpentering and cobbling, a tattered library, and a newly-finished hut for their twopenny whist drives and dances. (I had an odd feeling all the time that I was looking at a camp just behind the front line in some strange new war.) This centre possesses a boat of its own that has already achieved some fame, and our gnome-like friend offered to go down to the water's edge, where it was moored, to show it to us. To get there we had to cross the derelict shipyard, which was a fantastic wilderness of decaying sheds, strange mounds and pits, rusted iron, old concrete, and new grass. Both my companions knew about this yard, which had been a spectacular failure in which over a million of money had been lost. They had queer stories to tell of corruption in this and other yards, of lorry-loads of valuable material that were driven in at one gate and signed for, and then quietly driven out at another gate, of jobs so blatantly rushed, for show purposes, that in the last weeks wooden pegs were being used in place of steel rivets. As we came to the sullen waterfront, we could hear the noise of the electric riveting from the few yards working across the river; but both of them agreed that it seemed quiet now compared with the deafening din of the riveters in the old days. There was one ship in the yards now where there used to be twenty. Down the Tyne we could see the idle ships lying up, a melancholy and familiar sight now in every estuary round the coast. There is hardly anything that brings you more sharply into line with the idiotic muddle of our times than the spectacle of these fine big steamers rusting away in rows. We have these vessels doing nothing; we have coal for their bunkers; our ports are filled with ships' officers and men out of work; we have goods that other people need, and across every stretch of ocean are goods that we need; and still the ships are there, chained and empty, rusting in the rain, groaning in idleness night and day. But one boat is not idle on that river. That is the one we looked at now, as she creaked at her moorings. She was an old ship's boat and as she was in a poor shape, she was bought for the social centre for four pounds. The men themselves patched her up. She carries a sail and ten men usually go out in her, working three lines. The fish they bring back – and they have had some good catches, though the Tyne estuary is no Dogger Bank – is not sold but distributed among the unemployed men's families. She is called the *Venture*, and a better name could not be found for her. I do not know that anywhere on this journey I saw anything more moving and more significant than that old patched boat, which hung for years from the davits of a liner but is now the workless men's *Venture*, creeping out with the tide to find a few fish. The effort she represents is something more than a brave gesture, though it is that all right. It means that these men, who were once part of our elaborate industrial machinery but have now been cast out by it, are starting all over again, far away from the great machine, at the very beginning, out at sea with a line and a hook. And it will not do. These are not simple fishermen any more than this island of ours is one of the South Sea islands. They are the skilled children of our industrial system, artisans and men with trades in their fingers, and every time they go out and fumble frozenly with their lines and hooks, they declare once again the miserable bankruptcy of that system. This *Venture* may be their pride, but it is our shame.

Chilled and aching, I stood by the side of the river and looked at the mud and coal dust below, at the slimy and decaying wood piles on either side, at the tumble-down sheds above, and across at the motionless cranes and idle ships now fading in the mist; and as I looked about me, I remembered the miserable huddles of mean streets and dirty little houses behind me, and the grimy wilderness we had passed through during the morning; and I asked myself, with failing courage and hope, whether the whole Tyneside had not taken a wrong turning. There was a time when this must have been one of the prettiest of our green estuaries. With a clear sky above him and clear water below, a man could have been happy here in the old days, content to live in peace without cinemas and newspapers and racing dogs and betting slips or even without rambling clubs and musical societies and gymnastics and lectures on the Economic History of England. (He would not have known – the lucky fellow – that it had an Economic History.) I am not given to sentimentalizing the distant past, and have argued often and ferociously with those who do and have seemed to me to gloss over its ignorance and brutality and the narrow limits of its life. But I could see men reasonably content, if not happy, in this clean verdant river-sea country, with its fresh salt winds. Well, there is no more green estuary now. The whole river-side wears a black scarred face. It is not casually but ruthlessly ugly, as if every charm had been deliberately banished. But there was the new grimy fairy-tale of industry; there was work; there were rising wages. England would not be the England we know if the Tyneside were not the Tyneside we know. Coal, millions of tons of it, had been poured out down this channel; great ships had been built and repaired; engines had been constructed and sent away by the thousand; there had been enormous fortunes spent in wages and material, in profits and dividends. But still I wondered, as I stood there, shivering a little, whether it had all been worth while. Here was the pleasant green estuary, blackened and ruined, it seemed, for ever. Here was a warren of people living in wretched conditions, in a parody of either rural or urban life, many of them now without work or wages or hope, not half the men their peasant ancestors were. They seemed to have gained as little as the befouled river itself. And the fortunes, the piles of gold that the alchemy of industry had conjured from this steam and filth and din, where were they? What great work, I asked myself, owes its existence to those vast profits, those mounting dividends? What sciences and arts had they nourished? What new graces had they added to English life in return for what they had taken away from here? The ramshackle telephone exchange, at the back of my mind, put the call through, and I heard the bell ring and ring: but there was no reply.

On our way back from Hebburn to Gateshead, which was a journey among the very scrag-ends of industrial life, we passed no less than three funerals, each of them with a long black tail to it. Here, though you can no longer live well, you can still die and be buried in style. I had already noticed that although so many shops were closed in Jarrow and Hebburn, the shops that sold funeral wreaths were still open. True, the specimens they exhibited in their windows had a white waxiness that was now somewhat fly-blown, as if dissolution had anticipated their ultimate arrival at the grave or was becoming impatient and so setting its mark upon them. But there they were, and costing good money. It seemed as if Death provided the only possible spree left here. Once you had escaped from this narrow life your cold body was treated like an honoured guest and made a royal escape. There were flowers for the dead, if none for the living. All the neighbours turned out to witness this triumphant emigration. Here was something that asked for what was left of one's best clothes. Here was the remaining bit of pageantry. If you could no longer work and found it hard to play, you could still turn out and march to the cemetery. My companion told me that the district had always had a weakness for lavish funerals; its folk growing reckless and opulent in the presence of death. Years ago, he told me, his father, weary of seeing poor widows flinging their money away in this fashion, had had a few short sharp words with some of the local undertakers, who were not above encouraging the bewildered creatures to be lavish and outdo their recently bereaved neighbours. As we passed these long dragging funerals, I thought how hideously we have bedizened the face and figure of Death. The major events of our lives are unfortunate for our dignity: we come into this world to the accompaniment of shrieks of pain and the reek of disinfectant; we are married among idiotic ceremonies, and silly whispers, giggles, nudges, stares, and stale jokes; we leave this world in the company of wired flowers and dyed horses, commercial gentlemen with professionally long faces, and greeny-black suits that do not fit; and we can only say good-bye to the bodies we have loved in a monstrous atmosphere of black bogy-men on parade. 'Thou thy worldly task hast done,' I muttered to the last and grimmest coach. 'Home art gone and ta'en thy wages.' But there were probably no wages: home he had gone and taken his dole. And where was this home? Where was the fellow whose cold carcase had been screwed down inside that yellow tapering box? Was he in deep sleep for ever, or was he watching in amazement this procession, or was he already struggling into another life, perhaps not lacking so many elements of justice as this one, somewhere beyond Sirius?

Shotton, East Durham

THE country itself was very queer. Running across it, like great cracks, were the narrow valleys called 'denes', where there was usually a rushing stream, and perhaps some trees. These were pleasant enough, often quite picturesque. But as their charms were hidden away, well below most of the road levels, you did not see them but only saw what looked like a featureless and desolate plain, darkly studded here and there with pitheads and 'tips'. It did not seem an English landscape at all. You could easily imagine that a piece had been lifted out of the dreary central region of some vast territory like Russia or America, then dropped on to this corner of our island. True, I saw it on a dull November day, when nearly all the colour had been drained out of the world. The scene, as I remember it, was a brown monochrome, except where an occasional pithead brought a black stain into it, or a cloud of steam showed a distant little curl or two of white. I must go and look at that landscape again in a different light, in May or June; though it is hard to believe that the calendar up there ever reaches May or June. We passed through several villages that looked hardly more than slums that had been scattered along the road. This odd ribbon development is fairly common in colliery areas. The last village we visited, however, had been built on another plan. If there is a queerer village in all England than this, I have never seen it, and I do not know that I want to see it. Even in East Durham, this village of Shotton is notorious. It is not very long since I was standing in its one street; I have before me, as I write this, a sketch of it, now sadly smudged, that I did in my notebook, together with some notes that I made on the spot; but even so it seems incredible. I cannot help feeling that I shall be told that there is no such place, that I have invented my Shotton; and already I have examined no less than three good maps and have failed to find it. If I had been completely alone when I saw it I think that now I should be accusing myself of creating a weird Shotton fantasy, as a symbol of greedy, careless, cynical, barbaric industrialism. But my friend the lecturer was there, I know, and I can remember talking to several people; so some of it must be true. Imagine then a village consisting of a few shops, a public-house, and a clutter of dirty little houses, all at the base of what looked at first like an active volcano. This volcano was the notorious Shotton 'tip', literally a man-made smoking hill. From its peak ran a colossal aerial flight to the pithead far below. It had a few satellite pyramids, mere dwarfs compared with this giant; and down one of them a very dirty little boy was tobogganing. The 'tip' itself towered to the sky and its vast dark bulk, steaming and smoking at various levels, blotted out all the landscape at the back of the village. Its lowest slope was only a few yards from the miserable cluster of houses. One seemed to be looking at a Gibraltar made of coal dust and slag. But it was not merely a matter of sight. That monster was not smoking there for nothing. The atmosphere was thickened with ashes and sulphuric fumes; like that of Pompeii, as we are told, on the eve of its destruction. I do not mean that by standing in one particular place you could find traces of ash in the air and could detect a whiff of sulphur. I mean that the whole village and everybody in it was buried in this thick reek, was smothered in ashes and sulphuric fumes. Wherever I stood they made me gasp and cough. Out of one of the hovels there a queer toothless mumbling old fellow came pointing and peering and leering, first at the 'tip' and then at us, but neither of us could understand what he was saying. Perhaps he was the high priest or prophet of the belching black god up there. We retreated a few yards, into the roadway, where we found the landlord of the inn standing at his door. He did not know the height of the giant 'tip', but said that the atmosphere was always as bad as it was then and that sometimes it was a lot worse. And it had always been like that in his time. So it must have been, for a pile of smoking refuse as big as a hill cannot have grown in a year or two. There must have been a lot of labour put into the ground and a lot of wealth taken out of it before that 'tip' began to darken the sky and poison the air. I stared at the monster, my head tilted back, and thought of all the fine things that had been conjured out of it in its time, the country houses and town houses, the drawing-rooms and dining-rooms, the carriages and pairs, the trips to Paris, the silks and the jewels, the peaches and iced puddings, the cigars and old brandies; I thought I saw them all tumbling and streaming out, hurrying away from Shotton – oh, a long way from Shotton – as fast as they could go. But I did not stay long, staring, with my head tilted back. The giant 'tip' saw to that. I began coughing again, not being eruption-proof. 'Let's get out of this horror,' I said hastily, and out we got. In two or three minutes the wretched village had disappeared, but the 'tip' was still there, the hill that had come out of the deep earth. I hope it will always be there, not as a smoking 'tip', but as a monument to remind happier and healthier men of England's old industrial greatness and the brave days of Queen Victoria.

Morning City

THIS was one of those mornings when the smoke and the Thames Valley mist decide to work a few miracles for their London, and especially for the oldest part of it, the City, where Edward went to find Uncle Alfred. The City, on these mornings, is an enchantment. There is a faintly luminous haze, now silver, now old gold, over everything. The buildings have shape and solidity but no weight; they hang in the air, like places out of the Arabian Nights; you could topple the dome off St. Paul's with a forefinger, push back the Mansion House, send the Monument floating into space. On these mornings, the old churches cannot be counted; there are more of them than ever; ecclesiastical wizards are busy multiplying the fantastic steeples. There is no less traffic than usual; the scarlet stream of buses still flows through the ancient narrow streets; the pavements are still thronged with bank messengers, office boys, policemen, clerks, typists, caretakers, commissionaires, directors, secretaries, crooks, busy-bodies, idlers; but on these mornings all the buses, taxicabs, vans, lorries, drays, and all the pedestrians lose something of their ordinary solidity; they move behind gauze; they are shod and tyred in velvet; their voices are muted; their movement is in slow motion. Whatever is new and vulgar and foolish contrives to lose itself in the denser patches of mist. But all the glimpses of ancient loveliness are there, perfectly framed and lighted: round every corner somebody is whispering a line or two of Chaucer. And on these mornings, the river is simply not true; there is no geography, nothing but pure poetry, down there; the water has gone; and shapes out of an adventurous dream drift by on a tide of gilded and silvered air. Such is the City on one of these mornings, a place in a Gothic fairy tale, a mirage, a vision, Cockaigne made out of faint sunlight and vapour and smoke. It is hard to believe that somewhere behind this enchanting façade, directors are drawing their fees, debenture holders are being taken care of, loans are being called in, compound interest is being calculated, mergers are being arranged between a *Partaga* and a *Corona Corona*, and suggestions are being put forward for little schemes that will eventually bring revolution into Central America and mass murder into the Near East.

Arizona, Night

I LEFT the patio, where we were housed, for the little hut that was my working-place. I remember a particularly fine glitter of stars; with no moon; and with the desert hills so much starless indigo at the base of the sky. A freight train was clanking down the valley. It gave that long dissonant mournful cry of American trains, that sound which seems to light up for a second the immense distances and loneliness of that country. I had to do some lighting up myself, with a torch, in order to pick my way past prickly pear and cholla and cat-claw and other hooking and spiny growths, vindictive by day and devilish so late at night. The hut was in a little thicket. The sand between the curled dead leaves glittered in the light of my torch; and that would be the specks of fools' gold, with which all these dry river-beds and their banks are gilded. It looks much prettier than real gold. Some day perhaps it will be worth quite as much as real gold.

An enormous silence had followed the train; an ironical silence, like that which comes at the end of some noisy epoch. They kept early hours at the ranch, except when there was a dance at *El Recreo;* and there was nobody stirring anywhere; and not a sound even from the coyotes. In the silence, slowly picking my way, I thought about this Arizona country. The New World! It seemed to me the oldest country I had ever seen, the real antique land, first cousin to the moon. Brown, bony, sapless, like an old man's hand. We called it new because it was not thick with history, not a museum and guide-book place. Man had been here such a little time that his arrival had not yet been acknowledged. He was still some season's trifling accident, like a sudden abundance of coyotes or cotton-tails. The giant saguaro cactus, standing like a sentinel on every knoll, was not on the look-out for us, had not heard of us yet, still waited for trampling dinosaurs. There is no history here because history is too recent. This country is geology by day and astronomy at night. It offers a broad view of what is happening generally in the solar system, with no particular reference to Man. But it has a magnificent routine. The early mornings, in winter, are cold, very fresh and pure. Then, under the burning noons, the red cardinals and the blue-birds flash among the cotton-woods, as if nature had turned outrageously symbolic. The afternoons are simply so much sunlight and aromatic air. But at sunset, the land throws up pink summits and saw-toothed ridges of amethyst, and there are miracles of fire in the sky. Night uncovers two million more stars than you have ever seen before; and the planets are not points but globes. As I reached the door of my hut and switched off my torch, I looked up and noticed yet once again, with a shrinking sense of unfamiliarity, how all the constellations had been monstrously misplaced. I was far from home.

Hollywood

HOLLYWOOD is a long, long way from anywhere. That is why it has made so many good films, and why it has never made the best ones. True, Hollywood is a suburb of a large city, Los Angeles, but Los Angeles, too, is merely a place that is a long way from anywhere. Only a retired Iowan farmer would think of Los Angeles as a metropolis. It is a kind of boom town that has gone mushrooming itself for scores of miles. When you look down on its lights from the summit of Mount Wilson, you could imagine it was the capital of the world, for no city has ever before shown such lights, which blaze over a whole county. But when you travel along its immense boulevards, you feel you are looking at an immensely swollen small town. There seems to be miles and miles of unimpressive little bungalows and vacant building lots. Only at night does it lose its air of being determinedly third-rate. It has always seemed to me symbolical of an America I do not like, just as its rival, San Francisco, a real city with a sparkle and a charm of its own, has always seemed to me symbolical of an America I love, the large, hearty, devil-may-care, romantic America. Los Angeles has always appeared to me to be a city of boosters and boomers, Middle-Western farmers who have left their native shrewdness behind, bogus mystics and fortune-tellers, roaring publicity men, born comic-convention-attenders, all representative of an America I neither understand nor enjoy. I do not need to be told that there are plenty of nice ordinary sensible citizens there, because I have met numbers of them; but I cannot help feeling that it is not they, but the others who have created the atmosphere of Los Angeles, that the sprawling city does somehow suggest this new age of ours at its silliest.

This, then, is the city of which Hollywood is a suburb, almost the tail that wags the dog. Indeed, the truest as well as the wittiest description of Los Angeles is 'Six suburbs in search of a city'. And, I repeat, they are all six a long way from anywhere, down there in that corner of Southern California. There is something strange about that part of the world. It is a region in a moving picture. The hazy sea, the mountains that look like shabby brown skin-rugs, the crinkled desert, are not quite real. They do not take hold of the mind. They look more solid and enduring in photographs than they do in actuality. When I first entered this region, my mind may have been unconsciously dominated by the thought of Hollywood, but it did seem as if nothing down there was quite authentic. The orchards and gardens had been cunningly devised by an art director from Metro-Goldwyn-Mayer. The mountains beyond were by United Artists. The villages had come from Universal City. The boulevards were running through Paramount sets. Even the sunlight, which was pleasant but not quite the real thing, had probably been turned on by Warner Brothers. The picturesque Spanish bits had an operatic look about them, and I felt that somewhere round the corner was an operatic chorus of peasants, complete with cardboard flagons. The fruit so lusciously decorating the roadside was film fruit, meant to be photographed, not tasted. About all the little towns near Los Angeles there was a fancy fair and bazaar air, and it was impossible to believe they did solid business and that human beings were born or died in them. Even the ordinary people, coming from a queer mixture of races, did not seem like other Americans, but appeared to have developed an odd theatrical quality, as if they were all playing character parts. That is what I felt at first, and I do not feel very differently about it now. Except that now I feel there is also something disturbing about this corner of America, a sinister suggestion

of transience. There is a quality hostile to man in the very earth and air here. As if we were not meant to make our homes in this oddly enervating sunshine. I see the fine highways, the innumerable well-built townships, the nightly blaze of electricity along the coast, but I cannot believe that mankind has made a permanent settlement. It is all a *de luxe* camping. Or the most expensive film set possible to be devised. The people were not here yesterday and will not be here tomorrow. At any moment, I feel, the earth may give a shudder or two, and the towns will collapse like card castles, the coast will be rolled up like a carpet, and Southern California will be a silent desert again. It is all as impermanent and brittle as a reel of film. Nor am I alone with these fancies or premonitions. I doubt if any sensitive person who has ever stayed in this neighbourhood has ever quite escaped them. They help to explain many of the follies of the region. Nobody feels quite at home and at ease there.

Grand Canyon

HEAVY and hot about the eyes, I put on some clothes, then went blinking and shuffling out into the cold blue morning, a peevish passenger. The little station looked dreary. The young man waiting with the hotel bus did not look dreary, but he looked all wrong, for he wore a ten-gallon hat and an embroidered cowboy coat with English riding breeches and long boots, like a cowboy in a musical comedy. The bus turned two corners and landed us at the front door of an hotel that was so tremendously Western that it might have been created by a German scene-designer who had never been farther west than Hamburg. I felt grumpy about all this. A lot of nonsense. The interior of the hotel took my breath away, not because it was very beautiful, but because it was over-heated and seven thousand feet above sea level. I continued to disapprove of everything, but condescended to eat a large breakfast. After breakfast it was still snowing a little and there was nothing to be seen through the hotel windows but snowflakes and mist. I went panting up and down stairs several times, a man in a temper with a large breakfast getting at him, and then very soon it stopped snowing, so I went out. A few paces in front of the hotel there were some seats, a low wall, and then nothing. The world did not extend beyond that wall. Apparently it was a flat world, after all, and here was the edge. I stared over these battlements and saw a few last snowflakes fall into misty space. I walked a few paces through the slush, moving parallel with the wall, and it was wet and raw and there was nothing more to see. I might have been standing on the Thames Embankment on a foggy morning, except that the misty nothing over the edge here had a vaguely illimitable look about it. I decided that I had had enough of this. I threw a last glance over the wall, and then, down there somewhere, there was a swirling, a lifting, a hint of some early creative effort in the mist of Time. The next moment what breath I had left was clean gone. I was looking into the Grand Canyon.

Once I had made sure it really was like that, I hurried back to the hotel, shouted the good news, arranged to stay on, and cancelled the seats we had booked in the next train. There was to be no thought of trains. Even this one misty glimpse told me that a miracle had happened. At last, in all my travels, I had arrived and there had been no anti-climax, and my imagination, after weeks or months of expectant dreaming, had not cried: 'Is that all?' Reality, stung by my many jeers at its poverty, had gone to work to show me a thing or two. I thought I could imagine a better Grand Canyon, did I? Well, cried Reality, take a look at this – and – oh boy! – you ain't seen nothing yet. It juggled with all kinds of weather for us during that first short stay. We saw snow falling into that vast gulf, saw clouds stream below us, looked down on thunderstorms, stared at Nineveh and Thebes, rusty in the sunlight, coming through the mists, and watched rainbows arch and brighten and fade over the Painted Desert. We seemed to be witnessing, within a few hours, all the mad prodigality of Nature. One stupendous effect was piled on another; veils of mist and broken rainbows were caught in forests hanging in mid-air; the sunlight far below fell on ruined red cities; and to one hand, across the gulf, was a vertical Egypt, and to the other a perpendicular Assyria. There was in this immensity, although the weathers of four seasons and several climates seemed to chase one another down there, a silence so profound that soon all the noises from the life about us on the Rim were lost in it, as if our ears had been captured for ever, drowned in these deeps of quiet. We had only to walk a few hundred yards to find ourselves staring at new gigantic vistas, more forests hanging in the mists, more temples crumbling in the sunlight, more rosy peaks, green chasms, and cloud shadows like wandering stains. But it is useless to try and describe the Grand Canyon. Those who have not seen it will not believe any possible description; and those who have seen it know that it cannot be painted in either pigments or words. I have heard rumours of visitors who were disappointed. The same people will be disappointed at the Day of Judgement. In fact, the Grand Canyon is a sort of landscape Day of Judgement. It is not a show place, a beauty spot, but a revelation. The Colorado River, which is powerful, turbulent, and so thick with silt that it is like a saw, made it with the help of the erosive forces of rain, frost, and wind, and some strange geological accidents; and all these together have been hard at work on it for the last seven or eight million years. It is the largest of the eighteen canyons of the Colorado River, is over two hundred miles long, has an average width of twelve miles, and is a good mile deep. It is the world's supreme example of erosion. But this is not what it really is. It is, I repeat, a revelation. The Colorado River made it, but you feel when you are there that God gave the Colorado River its instructions. It is all Beethoven's nine symphonies in stone and magic light. Even to remember that it is still there lifts up the heart. If I were an American, I should make my remembrance of it the final test of men, art, and policies. I should ask myself: Is this good enough to exist in the same country as the Canyon? How would I feel about this man, this kind of art, these political measures, if I were near that Rim? Every member or officer of the Federal Government ought to remind himself, with triumphant pride, that he is on the staff of the Grand Canyon.

New Orleans

We met with much kindness and hospitality in New Orleans. We were drowned in Sazerac cocktails and smothered in delicious sea-food. If there is a city in England where a wandering American author and his wife would be instantly received with such warm hospitality, I am afraid I do not know where it is. Led by the charming Roark Bradfords, the citizens of New Orleans nobly entertained us. If I did not see everything worth seeing, that was my indolence and not their indifference. We began, of course, by exploring the *Vieux Carré*, the old French Quarter. Antiquity is purely relative. I exclaimed at the wonderful great age of these houses, clean forgetting that I had two houses in England both older than any of these. The charm of these crumbling tiny mansions, with their patios and iron traceries, has not been exaggerated; although I did not like the atmosphere of the quarter itself, for there was something fusty, secretive, desolating, rather sinister about it. Perhaps I had been reading too many unpleasant old stories of the quarter, but the fact remains I never took to it. The flavour somehow was queer. But of the antique grace of the streets and houses there can be no doubt. The Creoles built with an air. Nowadays, except with our aeroplanes and ships and automobiles, we have to make a severe effort to escape ugliness. If we want something graceful and handsome, we have to call in special designers and empty our pockets. But when the Creoles were building Royal Street, if you ordered an iron balustrade, a staircase, a chair, the trade calmly tossed back at you a thing of grace and charm. The workmen laboured in a tradition and as the tradition was good, the work was good. This explains why you can eat so superbly in New Orleans. The French have lived here and the French have a tradition of noble dining. The mysterious rich dishes they bring you at Antoine's, Galatoire's, Arnaud's or La Louisiane are not French and could not be obtained in Paris; they are as American as browned hash or deep dish apple pie; but the tradition behind them, like the ritualistic solemnity of the waiters, is French. When you eat (as you must) *huîtres en coquille à la Rockefeller* or *pompano en papillote* at Antoine's, you are making the best of two worlds, the Old and the New; for though the raw materials are American, the artistry and tradition are French. Not only is the food of these New Orleans restaurants magnificent, but the rooms themselves, so square and plain and sensible, like the elderly waiters in their alpaca coats, are at once homely and charming, like a good old host. They represent New Orleans at its highest pitch. If all the city and its life were on the same level as its restaurants, what a place it would be! What wisdom and nobility there would be in its public life! What art it would produce! What philosophies and sciences! What exquisite women and astounding men! The Mississippi would go curling round another and greater Athens of the golden age. But alas – there is nothing in the city to compare with its best food, nothing it has accomplished is fit to be mentioned with its *huîtres en coquille* or *pompano en papillote*. The spirit that flames around its *crêpe suzette* is perhaps the noblest it has known.

It was, I think, that Girod Street cemetery (which my wife firmly refused to see) which made New Orleans go all wrong for me. The city is largely built on a swamp, so the dead are buried above ground, in vaults or sometimes in brick tiers that look like gigantic ovens. The old burying place in Girod Street is not really very old. The dates on some of the vaults are quite recent. But that cemetery will remain in my mind, haunt my imagination, as a symbol of decay and dissolution. I saw it on a sticky warm morning, when the very sunlight seemed to be soggy and have weight, and I could almost taste the place for days afterwards. It terrified me. This is not an exaggeration. I never remember before being in a place that produced in me such a feeling of loathing and horror. It was uncanny. I might have been murdered or buried alive there in some previous existence. My feeling, which did not disappear for days, was out of proportion with what I actually saw there, but what I saw was bad enough. Everything in that cemetery was crumbling and rotting away. The very marble, I will swear, was turning to a damp grey pulp. Many of the vaults were cracking and bursting open, as if some slow and grisly resurrection were taking place there. If a rotten hand had made feeble motions at me, I would not have been much surprised. Probably nightmare creatures were feeding and breeding in the swampy soil beneath the vaults. A solitary midnight visit to that graveyard would be a test beyond my nerves. Poe would have been happy and creative in there. It had exactly the atmosphere, the elaborate pulpy rottenness, of his more characteristic charnel-house pieces. I could not help feeling that he and it belonged to the same world, and that it was not a world I knew or liked or wanted to explore more thoroughly. The House of Usher was still falling – or, rather, shredding away – there in Girod Street.

Call me a fanciful idiot, but I must confess that behind or mixed-in with everything I saw afterwards in or near the city were the flavour and atmosphere and general horror of that cemetery. We wandered round the solid American Quarter, built in the golden Fifties when this was the richest city in the Union; we looked at the newest garden suburb near Lake Pontchartain, the heavily bearded oaks of Chalmette, the last river steamer moving with pomp down the surprisingly narrow channel of the Mississippi; we stared at the animals and birds in Audubon Park; we caught glimpses of some remaining plantation houses, white ghosts among sad dark-green foliage; we dined with charming citizens and discussed with them the local trade and politics, manners and literature, climate and scandal. But I could not put that cemetery out of my mind. This is a city and a part of the world in which everything ages and decays at a frightful speed. A building fifty years old looks as if it were fighting a losing battle with the centuries. Gardens that were first made twenty-five years ago now look like antique wildernesses. The hothouse climate brings everything to a quick maturity and then condemns it to a shabby, sad, lingering death. At evening, outside the city, you see the sinister mists rising from the swamps. The sunsets are sudden, swollen, purple, as if the day had been suffering from a high blood pressure and had just had an apoplectic stroke. Men of our race find it difficult to thrive in such a climate. Our characteristic virtues cannot flower in this soil.

Rainbow Bridge

THE canyon itself turned sharply to the left, and as we looked down that way we caught our first glimpse of Rainbow Bridge. It looked disappointing, and for two good reasons: it was still about a mile away; and at that distance it was dwarfed by the giant bastions of rock on each side of it. So we pretended we had not seen it, and kept straight on to camp, which was in the shadow of the pink-and-cinnamon cave. Bill and Chance soon had a big fire going, and it was strange, then and for the next few hours, to hear the crackling of the burning sticks immensely amplified by the great overhanging walls into sounds sharper than pistol-shots. By the time the cowboy biscuits and the meat and fried potatoes and coffee were ready, daylight had gone, and as the vast curving walls, streaked with black, reflected the firelight, we seemed to be surrounded by giant specimens of primitive pottery. Afterwards, round the camp-fire, the children helped to ruin their eyesight by entering up their diaries, while the rest of us smoked and talked. Bill and Chance agreed that there were as many cowboys now as there had ever been, only now you hear little or nothing about them. The Wanderer, still sucking at his empty pipe, kept us informed as to the state of trade in East Texas, the mining activities in Southern Arizona, the canning plant in Phoenix, the condition of cattle between Kingman and Las Vegas, the fishing in the High Sierras, the winter feed in Idaho and Montana, the progress of the new dam on the Columbia River, with passing references to roads, bridges, trucks, snow-shoes, railroads, auto camps, and the history of the American Theatre between 1900 and 1927. When the children had finished with their diaries, they played noughts and crosses in the sand. The smoke went up to the firelit cliffs and then vanished into the indigo night.

Early morning was a miracle. Some of the cliffs were deep black and others were pale gold. The world, it seemed, had just been newly created for us. This was the blue air of Eden. We made our way after breakfast to the Bridge. The others were going farther along to the Colorado River, several miles away, but I was stiff and wanted an easy day. Moreover, I preferred to make the Bridge itself my farthest point of travel, the supreme goal, and I looked forward to having a few hours alone with it. So I remained in the silent blazing canyon, to smoke and dream in the shadow of the great arch. There was no disappointment now. This Rainbow Bridge is indeed one of the wonders of the world, and perhaps the last of them, for until 1909 no white man had ever set eyes on it, and even now only a comparative few have seen it. It is not really a bridge – if it were, it would be merely one of many – but a true arch, almost symmetrical, and though several hundred feet high, large enough to span most great public buildings, it has a noble grace and delicacy. The day was perfect. The sky, seen through the vast arch, was an indescribably brilliant turquoise, several shades darker than the shining stone of the Bridge itself. The view through the arch, with a patch of bright green vegetation below, brilliant sky above, and between them the burnished coppery cliffs and bastions of the canyon sharply framed, was an enchantment. You felt you had only to walk through that noble arch to find yourself in another and better world. Everything through there, beyond that magical frame, would be different. There, it seemed, as the Navahos cry at the end of their song prayers, 'All is peace, all is peace.' The Indians, who perhaps show a truer perception in these matters than we do, regarded this great rainbow of stone as a sacred thing, a sign set there by the gods. Their prayer to it, quoted by Mrs John Wetherill in her book on the Navahos, seems to me both appropriate and beautiful, with its invocation to the four winds – the Black Wind, the Blue Wind, the Yellow Wind, and the Iridescent Wind – with its repeated cry, which should find a terrible echo in our hearts: 'That it may be peaceful before me, that it may be peaceful behind me. All is peace, all is peace.'

As I loitered in that remote magical place, half-drowned in its sunlight and enchantment, I wondered how much wiser we are than those primitive singers. We have no prayer or song for the Bridge, but our geologists have worked out an explanation of how it came into existence. This gives us a temporary comfortable feeling of knowing the answer. Here's a neat trick in stone, we say, the handiwork of erosion. The fact that we can say that confirms our smiling superiority. Great scientists, from Newton to Einstein, do not talk and feel in this fashion, because in their powerful minds are the necessary elements of wonder and awe. But this is how knowing little minds behave, and we have millions of them. If they could see this noble rock, they would ask for and receive a geological explanation of its presence there, then go away and settle down to a hand at cards. There is nothing wrong with the geological explanation as far as it goes, but how far does it go? We are too apt to think that because we can understand how a thing came to be shaped, we know all about it. But an acoustic study of the workings of string, reed, and brass instruments does not explain the magic of a Beethoven symphony; it only explains the machinery of communication between Beethoven's rich passionate mind and ours. This will be admitted. But does erosion really account for the Bridge any more than acoustics explain Beethoven? How do we know that Rainbow Bridge, like the majestic, solemn Grand Canyon, is not itself a kind of symphony? I felt what the Indians felt, and a song to the gods would have expressed my feelings better than a short geological treatise. And it is good for a man to open his mind to deep wonder and awe. It is just as good for him to do that as it is for him to sharpen his intellect on the problems of science. In this matter we might learn a little from the Indians without forfeiting a jot of our science. For are we not living too exclusively in a narrow world of how-the-trick-is-done, with too much How and not enough Why? And may not this be at the root of our profound contemporary dissatisfaction? The Indians who sang and prayed here under this arch lived in a magical world, with the result that though they had emotional satisfaction denied to us, their way of life remained unchanged, at the mercy of wind and weather, and they were the fearful servants and not the masters of their natural environment. We who write geological treatises on the Bridge are compelled, because our science demands it, to live in a mechanistic world, and though this has given us enormous power over our environment, so that outwardly we are conquerors, it has dried up the springs and wells of deep emotion within, so that we live inside ourselves as in a desert. What we must do now, I thought as I stared at the great arch, is to live both as geologists and as Indian poets, not throwing away our science and the mechanistic view of things it necessitates, but retaining them as an instrument of power, a tool against the stubborn earth, while at the same time we live at heart like poets and priests, aware that this is still a magical world, moving with wonder and awe through a mystery. Without science, we are helpless children. Without poetry and deep natural piety, we are blundering fools, reeling in our new and terrible cocksureness into one disaster after another. That is what I learned beneath Rainbow Bridge, and though now, on a rainy morning in the Isle of Wight, I can hardly believe that I saw so great a shining arch of stone, I have not forgotten.

POLEMICAL

The Underground and the Future

THE other day I went by the Hampstead Tube to Tottenham Court Road and changed there for Oxford Circus, and it happened that there were very few people about, so that I was able for once to think about my surroundings. At Tottenham Court Road I was carried up an escalator, went along a passage and down some steps, found another train that shot me into Oxford Circus Station, and there, after more corridors, I mounted an escalator so long and high that it might have been Jacob's Ladder itself. It was while I was being carried obliquely upward by this astonishing thing that I suddenly thought, I am a creature who is carried about in this fashion. There I was; I had said good-bye to daylight on the summit of Hampstead, had stepped into a little box that had rushed me down a shaft to some passages and a platform somewhere in the middle of the hill, had boarded a vehicle, a thing as terrifying as a thunderbolt, that had hurtled me under half London, and after that I had been going up and down moving staircases. I remembered that years ago I had read a fantastic story by Bulwer Lytton called *The Coming Race*, but that nothing in that story was as fantastic as this journey from Hampstead to Oxford Circus. I wondered what Lamb or Hazlitt would have said if they had had a vision of these lifts, tiled corridors, thunderbolt trains, and staircases for ever moving up and down. They were wise men, but I swear they would have shuddered and cried: 'If this is what will happen, thank God we have not many years to live and will be dead long before life becomes so inhuman.' They would see us as people living in a nightmare of machinery, creatures as cold, strange, and remote as beings from the Moon. They would be astounded beyond measure to learn that their own works were still being read and admired – never so often read and never so widely admired – by these same queer beings. In short, they would feel what most of us have felt when we have read stories about the future, *When the Sleeper Wakes*, and the like. And I saw that what was wrong with such stories was that the sleepers never wakened properly, that they showed us a nightmarish life because they were still half in a dream.

The mistake, of course, is to deduce the inner from the outer facts of life, to imagine that the mere mechanics give the key to everything, to forget that the solid human core of thought and feeling remains. What was I doing – this man of buried tubes and moving stairways? Was I on my way to prostrate myself before some giant flywheel or piston and perhaps sacrifice a child or two to it, to take part in some awful rites suitable to such a being? That is what some horrified observer from the past might well have supposed. But you and I know very well that I was about to do nothing of the kind. As a matter of fact, your Lamb and Hazlitt would have been the first to appreciate the object I had in undertaking this nightmare journey, for I was simply on my way to do what they themselves had done hundreds of times, to see some friends and then enjoy myself in a cheerful playhouse. And the others, moving up and down those escalators, they too were on their way to look at hats and gowns, to be examined by the doctor, to try to sell 350 gross of what-nots at 35s. the gross, to listen to music, to meet their lovers. They were being haled up and down those escalators by motives that were hardly different from those in operation when Caesar landed in this island.

The English

I COULD think, and did, of many good things I had found in the course of this journey. For example, the natural kindness and courtesy of the ordinary English people. I have noticed more downright rudeness and selfishness in one night in the stalls of a West End Theatre than I have observed for days in the streets of some dirty little manufacturing town, where you would have thought everybody would have been hopelessly brutalized. And how often did I hear some wretched unemployed man and his wife say, 'Ay, but there's lots worse off than us.' What a desperate battle these people fight, especially the brave and stubborn North-country women, to preserve all the little decencies of life! Sometimes I feel like opposing the dictatorship of the proletariat simply because the proletarians I know are too good to be dictators. But then I do not like dictators. I came to the conclusion, however, that I should like to be dictator myself long enough to sweep away once and for all the notion that for the people who do the hard monotonous physical work any dirty little hole is good enough. As I thought of what the nineteenth century has left us in every industrial area, I felt at once angry and ashamed. What right had we to go strutting about, talking of our greatness, when all the time we were living on the proceeds of these muck-heaps? If we lived on some God-forsaken prairie, dusty in summer, frozen in winter, it might not matter, but we have ravished for unjustly distributed profit the most enchanting countryside in the world, out of which lyrics and lovely water-colours have come flowering like the hawthorn. And I saw again, clean through the fog that was imprisoning me, the exquisite hazy green landscape. I remembered the German in my hotel in Italy last year. He had lived and travelled all over the world; and I asked him which country he thought the most beautiful. He told me, England. Perhaps he did it to make me happy, but he sounded sincere enough. And now here I was, huddled in the fog, with memories reaching from West Bromwich to Blackburn, Jarrow to Middlesbrough, darkly crowding in on me.

I thought about patriotism. I wished I had been born early enough to have been called a Little Englander. It was a term of sneering abuse, but I should be delighted to accept it as a description of myself. That *little* sounds the right note of affection. It is little England I love. And I considered how much I disliked Big Englanders, whom I saw as red-faced, staring, loud-voiced fellows, wanting to go and boss everybody about all over the world, and being surprised and pained and saying, 'Bad show!' if some blighters refused to fag for them. They are patriots to a man. I wish their patriotism began at home, so that they would say – as I believe most of them would, if they only took the trouble to go and look – 'Bad show!' to Jarrow and Hebburn. After all, I thought, I am a bit of a patriot too. I shall never be one of those grand cosmopolitan authors who have to do three chapters in a special village in Southern Spain and then the next three in another special place in the neighbourhood of Vienna. Not until I am safely back in England do I ever feel that the world is quite sane. (Though I am not always sure even then.) Never once have I arrived in a foreign country and cried, 'This is the place for me.' I would rather spend a holiday in Tuscany than in the Black Country, but if I were compelled to choose between living in West Bromwich or Florence, I should make straight for West Bromwich. One of my small daughters, bewildered, once said to us: 'But French people aren't *true*, are they?' I knew exactly how she felt. It is incredible that all this foreign-ness should be true. I am probably bursting with blatant patriotism. It does not prevent me from behaving to foreigners as if they felt perfectly real to themselves, as I suspect they do, just like us. And my patriotism, I assured myself, does begin at home. There is a lot of pride in it. Ours is a country that has given the world something more than millions of yards of calico and thousands of steam engines. If we are a nation of shopkeepers, then what a shop! There is Shakespeare in the window, to begin with; and the whole establishment is blazing with geniuses. Why, these little countries of ours have known so many great men and great ideas that one's mind is dazzled by their riches. We stagger beneath our inheritance. But let us burn every book, tear down every memorial, turn every cathedral and college into an engineering shop, rather than grow cold and petrify, rather than forget that inner glowing tradition of the English spirit. Make it, if you like, a matter of pride. Let us be too proud, my mind shouted, to refuse shelter to exiled foreigners, too proud to do dirty little tricks because other people can stoop to them, too proud to lose an inch of our freedom, too proud, even if it beggars us, to tolerate social injustice here, too proud to suffer anywhere in this country an ugly mean way of living. We have led the world, many a time before to-day, on good expeditions and bad ones, on piratical raids and on quests for the Hesperides. We can lead it again. We headed the procession when it took what we see now to be the wrong turning, down into the dark bog of greedy industrialism, where money and machines are of more importance than men and women. It is for us to find the way out again, into the sunlight.

Equal Incomes and Privilege

I HAVE heard Bernard Shaw argue eloquently against the smallest inequalities in income, and demonstrate that anything short of a genuine equality of pay all round will keep us entangled in this sticky web of money and poison all our relations with one another. But Shaw appears to believe in privilege. And this will not do. He has never lived in a society in which money did not mean much but privilege meant a great deal. And I have. I served over four and a half years in the army, where money does not count for much and privilege, carefully adjusted according to rank and then very strongly enforced, counts for a lot. A wealthy private soldier is not allowed to be insolent to a poor officer. Money might bribe a little promotion, but that is all. Whereas there is a tremendous difference between what a private soldier is allowed to do and what a general is allowed to do. And to my mind this is far more galling than any difference of income, provided that that difference is above a certain level. Once the low level is raised, from starvation to decent comfort, the inequalities do not seem to me to matter very much. Henry Ford and the Duke of Westminster have more money than I can ever hope to have, but as I am not poor myself, have not to wonder where the next meal is coming from, I have never wasted a single second envying either of them. This does not mean that I cannot see that an immensely rich man may have far more power than any private person in a so-called democracy has any right to possess, just as if he owned an army or navy of his own. But that is a different argument, belonging to politics and economics. What I maintain is that as soon as everybody has a little more than enough to live on decently, we should be better off with what inequalities of income there may be left than we should be with equal incomes under a system of state privilege, organized with military precision. Thus – to take a small example – most seats at the opera are expensive, and it may be said that as conditions are now in America or England, attendance at the opera is one of the privileges of the rich. Smith has a passion for opera and is not rich. What can he do? The answer is that it is hard luck, but that it might be worse, for at least he can save enough to buy an occasional seat. But under an equal-income-and-state-privilege system, though opera seats might cost nothing at all, they also might be strictly allotted as perquisites to members of one or two privileged classes, and if Smith – who may be always out of luck – did not happen to belong to those classes, he would never get near the opera. In England during the War, when Smith was a private soldier, he was never allowed, when in uniform, to enter the more comfortable rooms in many taverns. Now that he is out of uniform, he can at least decide for himself whether the extra comfort is worth the extra penny or so he will have to pay for his drink in the better room. In short, equal income severely tempered by privilege would not enlarge but further restrict the liberty of the individual. What is needed is a juster distribution of wealth with as little privilege as possible.

The Good?

HERE, I have long thought, both the religious and those spiritual systems that occupy the place of religions take too narrow a view. They are too exclusively ethical. They concentrate upon the Good at the expense of the True and the Beautiful. Their spokesmen are not unlike the cobblers who cried 'Nothing like leather!' or those professors of philosophy who prove that the whole universe must have been designed to produce professors of philosophy. If many of these systems are to be believed, a touch of debility is a glorious asset. There is nothing in their theory to prove that any unselfish but sapless clerk or pious governess is not worth a dozen Shakespeares or Beethovens. No allowance is made for size and richness of mind and soul. It is all too negative. Spirit is associated not with the inmost flame of life, whose absence is real death, but with a tepid indifference or fierce opposition to the flesh, which is given a supreme reality of its own. This may be because such systems come to us from the East, where good men were compelled to retreat from the glare and confusion and sensual riot of common life, in order to meditate at all. It is this retreat that is still being sounded. These last few years I have been snowed under with pamphlets and booklets, Christian, Buddhist, Theosophical, New and Higher Thought, in which mere rejection or a negative attitude of mind is assumed to be the beginning of a spiritual life. You are asked to lead the existence of a ghost, a feeble and attenuated parody of a life. Not one of them tells you to live eagerly and ardently like a poet. They turn the universe into a kind of boarding-school for debilitated little prigs. There is no place in their worlds, whether the material and fleshly here or the 'spiritual' hereafter, for those battle-scarred giants of our race who have swung between passionate rebellion against the gods and agonies of pity and tenderness for their kind. Their authors do not understand that spirituality does not mean some tepid ghostly business round the corner, but the light in the mind and the flame in the heart. Even Aldous Huxley, in his *Ends and Means*, seems to me altogether too negative. Nobody will march far under his banner of 'non-attachment'. I do not say that some persons ought not to withdraw, to refuse to join in, to save their souls neatly and quietly in seclusion, to acquire virtue by turning down a friend's dinner; but what I am tired of are systems in which only this type of temperament is allowed to flourish – if the term is not too flamboyant – and we are given to suppose that the universe is so contrived that no other persons will make any progress in it. There are more kinds of excellence in the spirit than they appear to understand. It is a house, as we know, of many mansions, and not every room is occupied by an ascetic examiner. That only the good can enter, I am willing to believe, but who are the good ...?

Patriotism

We should behave towards our country as women behave towards the men they love. A loving wife will do anything for her husband except to stop criticizing and trying to improve him. That is the right attitude for a citizen. We should cast the same affectionate but sharp glance at our country. We should love it, but also insist upon telling it all its faults. The dangerous man is not the critic, but the noisy empty 'patriot' who encourages us to indulge in orgies of self-congratulation. This game is now played, in every country, by certain sections of the Press. The late Arthur Brisbane, who had a daily column printed in all the Hearst newspapers and was said to be the most highly-paid journalist in the world, gave the Great American People a dose of flattery every morning, and everything he saw, heard, touched or tasted only proved to him all over again the immeasurable superiority of this Great People. That is the trick; and a bad one. Mistrust any newspaper that is for ever showering compliments on its public. Journalists are not by temperament given to wondering admiration of the mass of their readers. Somebody must be cheating. In 1931, when there was more duplicity in high places and stupidity in low ones than I ever remember before, some of our newspapers almost foamed with praise of the British Character. While we were still on the gold standard, we were praised for our steadiness, courage, determination, good sense. When we suddenly went off the gold standard, we were equally praised for our realism, enterprise, courage, good sense. The fact is, of course, that such newspapers are now manipulated with an unscrupulous cynicism that regards all these paragons of steadiness, courage, good sense as so many million half-wits. There is about as much real love of country here as there would be conjugal love in a wife who encouraged her husband to go to the nearest saloon-bar and there stand rounds of drinks from morning till night. And everywhere, in every country, as the people are regarded with more contempt, so the tide of public flattery rises.

The New Urban Life

YOU see a new kind of urban life now in the natty suburbs of the provincial cities and near all the main roads leading out of London. In theory and on paper it looks a pretty good life. It is very much of our time, bang up to date, with its neat labour-saving contrivances, and a lot of ingenious machines working for it. The life, like most of the contrivances and machines, was imported from the United States. It ought to be much more fun, far more rewarding in every way, than the sort of existence my parents led just off Toller Lane, Bradford, in the early years of this century. It ought, but I do not think it is. Only in theory is it a great improvement on the older kinds of bourgeois life. There is less daily worry and work for the housewives, who, in consequence, look prettier after a few years of marriage than they used to when I was a boy. But on the other hand, these modern suburban young wives have to keep paying visits to the doctor, not because they are really sick in body, but because they are a trifle sick in mind. The trouble is that they feel depressed, dreary, and terribly lonely. Now people like my parents lived in a real society, were members of a community, whereas a great many of these young flat-and-bungalow couples do not live in a society and are not members of a community. They are young people eating and sleeping and trying to enjoy themselves in a certain place, with no interest in or feeling of responsibility for that place. They are nearly as far removed from the main stream of civic life as those melancholy souls who exist perpetually in hotels. There is something thin, brittle, mechanical about their life. It lacks richness, human variety, sap and juice, just because it has no real social background. Higher wages, shorter hours, more labour-saving devices, bigger garden suburbs, though excellent things in themselves, will not greatly improve this way of living. What they cannot restore to it is the social background, the civic feeling, the deep sense of being a member of a community. The people do not really *belong* to the place they are in, but are camping in it. They are nomads without a tribe.

Then this new urban life we are developing, after the American pattern, differs from the old one I knew in the significant fact that it is far more dependent on money. My parents spent about fourpence on a tram and then went walking, probably every fine Saturday. These young people have to run a car, and that costs money. To go to the films, to dine in restaurants, to go out and dance, these pleasures all cost money, whereas it is very cheap to talk to your friends and give them a bite of supper at home, to sing in a choir, to attend political meetings, to search for wild flowers or look at birds. Although I am in favour of money being briskly circulated and believe that once we are free of a faulty and cramping financial system we shall have more to spend, I think it is dangerous to be too dependent on money. Many of the most satisfying things in life cost little or nothing. And our new way of living tempts us to overlook this important fact. Again, that old life was far more active than this new one. People did things themselves instead of allowing others to do everything for them. There is nothing essentially wrong with our new popular amusements, such as films and the radio, both of which have done much to brighten people's lives. But they should be enjoyed actively and not passively, attended to eagerly and critically and not used as a kind of mild dope. Chesterton once observed shrewdly that there was a great difference between an eager man who wanted to read a book and a tired man who wanted a book to read. It is the difference between active and passive amusements. Now we have too many tired persons who merely want a book to read, a film to stare at, a wireless programme to listen to, and to be smothered in a stuffy comfort while they are doing it. There is too much of this: 'You can do it from your own armchair.' This is all right for the elderly, but younger people should get out of their armchairs and do something more than turn on a switch. I was brought up among people who could amuse themselves, could play instruments and sing and devise games and argue half the night, and I distrust this passive drowsy crowd we are creating who can do nothing for themselves and will not have anything unless it is handed to them almost on a plate while they bury themselves in their armchairs or their velvet theatre seats. We used to storm gallery doors and sit jammed on wooden benches, with our heads only a few feet below the roof or perhaps less than that from the side-walls with their caged gas-jets, to see the plays of my boyhood; but now these young suburban folk will tell you that they do not want to come near your theatre unless you can guarantee them a velvet-covered seat booked over the telephone for two or three shillings. I do not want theatres or any other places to be uncomfortable; I am no Spartan myself; but I dislike this insistence upon comfort and convenience before everything else. We do not want a whole population behaving as if they were malingering, rich, spoilt old women.

'Going in for' Politics

It is about time, if there is to be a real democracy in this country, that we tried to understand what we mean by 'politics'. Now, ever since I can remember people have been said to be 'going in for' politics. This 'going in for' politics never suggested any particular enlargement of the mind and its interests but only a certain definite direction given to a person's activities. Generally you 'went in for' politics by joining one of the parties, making yourself useful at the local party headquarters, offering to speak at party meetings, and making yourself familiar with and rather voluble about the party programme and the party gossip. The next stage was to acquire a good platform manner, and after that a good electioneering manner and an easy way with the reporters, and perhaps after that a good committee manner. Finally, the budding politician, now a member, would acquire a good House of Commons manner. The rest might depend on ability, cunning, and luck.

There has long been to my mind something very unimpressive about this political progress, just as there is something unimpressive about most of our contemporary political figures, who can rarely live up to the newspaper fuss about them. Most men of mark have a definite contribution of their own to make to their times, and as a rule it is not difficult to discover in them the rare qualities that have enabled them to make that contribution. But most of our politicians do not give the impression of possessing any unusual qualities. (There are of course some notable exceptions.) They exhibit neither breadth of knowledge nor depth of insight. There is not even any particular richness of character in them. Compared with the distinguished men of letters, artists, scientists, scholars, engineers that one has known, these men, looming so large in the public mind, mostly seem rather commonplace fellows. It will be said that I, a democrat, can hardly object to ordinary men representing ordinary men. I have no objection at all, but the point is, that these politicians are not ordinary men, although their abilities may be nothing out of the ordinary. What sets them apart from ordinary men is not their ability but their way of life. They have, you see, 'gone in for' politics, and having succeeded, they have almost disappeared from ordinary life. What probably makes them seem, at close quarters, even more commonplace as figures than they really are is the mysterious remoteness of their way of life. They themselves are almost shockingly unimpressive, but their mode of living, their detachment, their mystery, are too impressive. And that is probably what is wrong with our politics.

Put it another way. What is wrong with our politics is that political life is thought of as a career. It should never be regarded as a career. In a few exceptional instances, with those rare minds who have a genius for statesmanship, it should be regarded as a vocation. For the rest it should be regarded as an ordinary civic duty. We are all living politics, whether we like it or not. Every hour we are making political statements, whether we are aware of the fact or not. We all adopt political attitudes, whether we know it or not. And a truly democratic state should consist of a few real statesmen and several million politically-minded citizens, and not of a thousand politicians and several million sheep. The fact that politics can be regarded as something apart from the ordinary citizen, therefore something to be 'gone in for', proves that we have drifted away from the democratic idea.

The Community and the State

WE must take care not to confuse the community with the state. They are not at all the same thing. The community consists of living persons, and without it we should merely be so many Robinson Crusoes. Some of us would go so far as to declare that the community is something more than the sum total of the people in it. A community might have a sort of mind or soul of its own, which would explain the strange sudden flowering of genius in ancient Athens, medieval Florence, Elizabethan London. We owe most of our life to the community, and it repays tenfold everything we give it. Again, a person becomes still more of a person by living intimately in and with a community. That is why democracy, which insists upon the individual worth of persons, has never denied but has always affirmed the value of the community.

Now nearly all the hocus-pocus of Fascism, some of which it took over from official Prussian philosophy, is bent on persuading its victims that the state is the community. We have seen how the trick works. Hitler, we will say, has a complex or phobia about Jews. Having arrived at a position of supreme power, like some mad Oriental despot, he decides that none of his subjects shall inter-marry with the Jews, just as he might have decided that all bald-headed men should go about on all-fours every alternate Thursday. This monstrous decision is now, by all manner of verbal and quasi-legal flummery, translated into an expression of the will of the state, which is not shown as an organization for compelling Germans to obey Hitler and his friends, but is said to be a gigantic, mystical super-person in whom all good Germans have their being. First it is proved that you owe everything to the state, without which you are nothing at all, and at the same time it is proved that the dictator himself, by some mystical identification, is really the state. Thus any gangster who moves in and manages to control the army and the secret police is given the sanction of divine authority, and his smiling approval is as necessary to your well-being as sun and air and water. This is impudent cheating on a really magnificent scale.

No matter how much common ownership you think desirable or how much collective action we should take, no matter how many schemes of electoral reform you have in mind to make representation more just and flexible, it seems to me essential that you must not allow yourself to confuse the state, which is one organization among many and can never be anything else, and the community, which is unique and a living society. It is as dangerous as mistaking a machine for a person. Some enthusiastic reformers write and talk as if just round the corner there was waiting for us a magic state, quite unlike any state that has ever existed. It is as if they believed that the average policeman could suddenly be transformed into an exquisite, wise, and gracious hostess. We shall be well advised to take a very sceptical view of these rosy visions of the state of the future. The state is an organization, an instrument, a machine, and will always have the limitations of such things. No matter how it is reformed, it will always tend to be slow, cumbersome, rigid in its workings. Even if it began to recruit the most brilliant and swiftly creative minds, it would still contrive to take the edge off them. All this seems to me inevitable, and any talk of the coming of a fairy-tale state is a mere waste of time. Moreover, by making artful use of this confusion of the state and the community, reactionaries may find it easier to create here some form of Fascism.

The state can never be the perfect expression, in political and economic action, of the community. It will always be necessarily rough-and-ready, and lag behind. It will, in short, behave like the vast cumbersome machine it is. But of course a democratic community can make good use of this machine. It should be regarded neither as something sacred nor as something fundamentally hostile but as the general boss organization among other organizations. And it should take charge of these organizations when they become so big and important and urgently necessary to the public well-being that they cannot be left to private ownership and control, just as armed forces cannot be left to private control. Again, any enterprise that feels justified in demanding a subsidy from public funds, or that has to be constantly controlled by the authorities, should be taken over by the state. If the state is the organization of the community in terms of power, which it is, then it should have complete control of power, as it has had for a long time in the obvious case of power by way of armed forces. But it is still possible for individuals to wield economic power so great that they are like commanders of private armies, and it is obvious that the state must be able to control them, otherwise they may be able to control the state, which is of course what such individuals often have done. Whatever it may masquerade as, this is really racketeering and brigandage, and the state exists to abolish all such crimes against the community. It is of the essence of democracy that no one person should have enormous power, and clearly this applies to economic as well as political power. To control one and not the other is now seen to be a mockery. ('In America to-day,' as a wit over there recently observed, 'the rich want liberty and the poor want ham and eggs.') No man, or group of men, has any more right to make hay of two thousand other men's economic life (and social life and personal life), for greed or a whim, than he or his group has to enlist a band of toughs and beat up the neighbourhood. The state exists to restrain such antics.

POSTSCRIPTS

The Little Ships

HERE at Dunkirk is another English epic. And to my mind what was most characteristically English about it – so typical of us, so absurd and yet so grand and gallant that you hardly know whether to laugh or to cry when you read about them – was the part played in the difficult and dangerous embarkation – not by the warships, magnificent though they were – but by the little pleasure-steamers. We've known them and laughed at them, these fussy little steamers, all our lives. We have called them 'the shilling sicks'. We have watched them load and unload their crowds of holiday passengers – the gents full of high spirits and bottled beer, the ladies eating pork pies, the children sticky with peppermint rock. Sometimes they only went as far as the next seaside resort. But the boldest of them might manage a Channel crossing, to let everybody have a glimpse of Boulogne. They were usually paddle steamers, making a great deal more fuss with all their churning than they made speed; and they weren't proud, for they let you see their works going round. They liked to call themselves 'Queens' and 'Belles'; and even if they were new, there was always something old-fashioned, a Dickens touch, a mid-Victorian air, about them. They seemed to belong to the same ridiculous holiday world as pierrots and piers, sand castles, ham-and-egg teas, palmists, automatic machines, and crowded sweating promenades. But they were called out of that world – and, let it be noted – they were called out in good time and good order. Yes, those 'Brighton Belles' and 'Brighton Queens' left that innocent foolish world of theirs – to sail into the inferno, to defy bombs, shells, magnetic mines, torpedoes, machine-gun-fire – to rescue our soldiers. Some of them – alas – will never return. Among those paddle steamers that will never return was one that I knew well, for it was the pride of our ferry service to the Isle of Wight – none other than the good ship 'Gracie Fields'. I tell you, we were proud of the 'Gracie Fields', for she was the glittering queen of our local line, and instead of taking an hour over her voyage, used to do it, churning like mad, in forty-five minutes. And now never again will we board her at Cowes and go down into her dining saloon for a fine breakfast of bacon and eggs. She has paddled and churned away – for ever. But now – look – this little steamer, like all her brave and battered sisters, is immortal. She'll go sailing proudly down the years in the epic of Dunkirk. And our great grand-children, when they learn how we began this War by snatching glory out of defeat, and then swept on to victory, may also learn how the little holiday steamers made an excursion to hell and came back glorious.

Local Defence Volunteers

A NIGHT or two ago, I had my first spell with our Local Defence Volunteers or 'Parashots'. I'd been on the muster for the previous fortnight – but I'd been away, busy with other work, so I hadn't been able to see how our village was keeping watch and ward. Ours is a small and scattered village, but we'd had a fine response to the call for Volunteers; practically every able-bodied man in the place takes his turn. The post is on top of a high down, with a fine view over a dozen wide parishes. The men I met up there the other night represented a good cross-section of English rural life; we had a parson, a bailiff, a builder, farmers, and farm labourers. Even the rarer and fast disappearing rural trades were represented – for we had a hurdle-maker there; and his presence, together with that of a woodman and a shepherd, made me feel sometimes that I'd wandered into one of those rich chapters of Thomas Hardy's fiction in which his rustics meet in the gathering darkness on some Wessex hillside. And indeed there was something in the preliminary talk, before the sentries were posted for the night, that gave this whole horrible business of air raids and threatened invasion a rustic, homely, almost comfortable atmosphere, and really made a man feel more cheerful about it. In their usual style, these country chaps called every aeroplane 'she'. They'd say: 'Ay, she come along through the gap and over along by Little Witchett – as I see with me own eyes. Then searchloights picks her up – moight be Black Choine way or farther along, over boi Colonel Wilson's may be – an' Oi says to Tarm: "Wont be long now, you'll see, afore they gets her" – and then, bingo, masters, down she comes!' They have the sound countryman's habit of relating everything intimately to their own familiar background. Now of course this doesn't take away any of the real menace, but what it does do is somehow to put all this raiding and threatened invasion in their proper places. The intellectual is apt to see these things as the lunatic end of everything, as part of a crazy Doomsday Eve, and so he goes about moaning, or runs away to America. But the simple and saner countryman sees this raiding and invading as the latest manifestation of that everlasting menace which he always has to fight – sudden blizzards at lambing time, or floods just before the harvest.

I think the countryman knows, without being told, that we hold our lives here, as we hold our farms, upon certain terms. One of those terms is that while wars still continue, while one nation is ready to hurl its armed men at another, you must if necessary stand up and fight for your own. And this decision comes from the natural piety of simple but sane men. Such men, you will notice, are happier now than the men who have lost that natural piety.

Well, as we talked on our post on the hilltop, we watched the dusk deepen in the valleys below, where our women-folk listened to the news as they knitted by the hearth, and we remembered that these were our homes and that now at any time they might be blazing ruins, and that half-crazy German youths, in whose empty eyes the idea of honour and glory seems to include every form of beastliness, might soon be let loose down there. The sentries took their posts. There was a mist coming over the down. Nothing much happened for a time. A green light that seemed to defy all black-out regulations turned out to be merely an extra large and luminous glow-worm; the glow-worms, poor ignorant little creatures, don't know there's a war on and so continue lighting themselves up. A few searchlights went stabbing through the dusk and then faded. The mist thickened, and below in all the valleys, there wasn't the faintest glimmer of light. You heard the ceaseless high melancholy singing of the telegraph wires in the wind.

So we talked about what happened to us in the last war, and about the hay and the barley, about beef and milk and cheese and tobacco. Then a belt of fog over to the left became almost silvery, because somewhere along there all the searchlights were sweeping the sky. Then somewhere behind that vague silveriness, there was a sound as if gigantic doors were being slammed to. There was the rapid stabbing noise of anti-aircraft batteries, and far away some rapping of machine-guns. Then the sirens went, in our two nearest towns, as if all that part of the darkened countryside, like a vast trapped animal, were screaming at us.

Two Ton Annie

ON the second day of this war, I wrote an article called 'Two Ton Annie'. I'd been watching some invalids from mainland hospitals being evacuated to the Isle of Wight, and among these invalids was a very large elderly woman, who was sitting upright on her stretcher and being carried by six staggering, sweating, grinning bearers, who called her 'Two Ton Annie'. She exchanged cheerful, insulting remarks with everybody.

She was a roaring and indomitable old lioness, and wherever she was carried there was a cheerful tumult; and as she roared out repartee she saluted the grinning crowd like a raffish old empress. Yes; she was old, fat, helplessly lame and was being taken away from her familiar surroundings, a sick woman, far from home. But she gave no sign of any inward distress, but was her grand, uproarious self.

She did all our hearts good that day, and I said then that although Britannia can put up a good fight, Two Ton Annie and all her kind can put up a better one. I said that if it comes to a struggle between them and worried, semi-neurotic, police-ridden populations for ever raising their hands in solemnly idiotic salutes, standing to attention while the radio screams blasphemous nonsense at them, these people will emerge victorious, because their sort of life breeds kindness, humour, and courage, and the other sort of life doesn't.

Kindness, humour, and courage are mightily sustaining qualities. They prevent that breakdown inside upon which our enemies with their screaming bogy-machines always depend.

Well, that was Two Ton Annie, who gave me such a heartening glimpse of our folk at the very beginning of the war. Since then, I'll confess, I've had glimpses that were much less heartening – in fact were even depressing. For weeks, perhaps months, somehow Two Ton Annie and her uproarious stretcher-bearers and admirers disappeared, and instead I encountered another set of figures who might be described as Complacent Clarence, Hush-Hush Harold, and Dubious Departmental Desmond. These gentlemen have their places in our war-time scheme of things: this is not an attack upon them and their like; but often I couldn't help feeling, as a man who'd tried for years to understand our national character, that there was a real danger of these pundits and mandarins creating a rather thick, woolly, dreary atmosphere in which that national character of ours couldn't flourish and express itself properly.

The war, to which we have brought a unity of feeling never known before in our island history, was somehow not quite our war. Nobody told us right out to mind our own business, but often something of the sort was implied. There were too many snubs and cold shoulders about. That was before the Blitzkrieg began. Since then, and especially since the danger crept nearer and the screaming threats grew louder and louder, I feel that that fog and its whispering figures have almost vanished, and that at any moment now I may encounter again my old friend Two Ton Annie.

The Duck

It was rather late the other night, and we were coming home to Highgate Village by way of High Street, Hampstead, and the Spaniards Road, which run, you might say, on the roof of London. We had to pass the Whitestone Pond. Now I like the Whitestone Pond. On fine afternoons, boys sail their toy boats on it, and when there's a wind blowing across the Heath the toy boats have to battle with enormous waves – about three inches high. At night, this pond is like a little hand-mirror that the vast, sprawling, yawning London still holds negligently; and you see the stars glimmering in it. Well, the other night was one of those mysterious nights we've had lately when there seems to be a pale light coming from nowhere, and the sky has a pure washed look. The dim lights of a few cars could be seen in the dusk round the pond, and some people, late as it was, were standing and staring.

We stopped, and heard a solicitous quacking and a great deal of faint squeaking. Then we saw on the pond, like a tiny feathered flotilla, a duck accompanied by her minute ducklings, just squeaking specks of yellow fluff. We joined the fascinated spectators; we forgot the war, the imminence of invasion, the doubts about the French Fleet, the melancholy antics of the Bordeaux Government.

Our eyes and ears, and our imagination were caught and

held by those triumphant little parcels of life. This duck hadn't hatched her brood here; she'd hatched them in some hidden corner – nobody knows where – and had then conveyed them – and nobody knows how – to swim happily in the dusk on this summit of the city. She hadn't asked anybody's advice or permission; she hadn't told herself it was too late or too difficult; nobody had told her to 'Go to it' and that 'it all depended on her'. She had gone to it, a triumphant little servant of that life, mysterious, fruitful, beautiful, which expresses itself as a man writes a poem – now in vast galaxies of flaming suns, now in a tiny brood of ducklings squeaking in the dusk.

Margate

THERE we were at last – on the front at Margate. The sun, with a fine irony, came bounding out. The sea, which has its own sense of humour, winked and sparkled at us. We began to walk along the front. Everything was there: bathing pools, bandstands, theatres and the like; gardens blazing with flowers, lido, and miles of firm golden sands all spread out beneath the July sun. But no people! – not a soul. Of all those hundreds of thousands of holiday-makers, of entertainers and hawkers and boatmen – not one. And no sound – not the very ghost of an echo of all that cheerful hullabaloo – children shouting and laughing, bands playing, concert parties singing, men selling ice-cream, whelks, and peppermint rock, which I'd remembered hearing along this shore. No, not even an echo. Silence. It was as if an evil magician had whisked everybody away. There were the rows and rows of boarding houses, the 'Sea Views', and 'Bryn Mawrs' and 'Craig-y-dons' and 'Sans Soucis' and the rest, which ought to have been bursting with life, with red faces, piano and gramophone music, and the smell of roast beef and Yorkshire pudding, but all empty, shuttered, forlorn. A most melancholy boarding-house at the end of a row caught my eye – and that one was called 'Kismet'. Kismet, indeed!

In search of a drink and a sandwich, we wandered round, and sometimes through, large empty hotels. The few signs of life only made the whole place seem more unreal and spectral. Once an ancient taxi came gliding along the promenade, and we agreed that if we'd hailed it, making a shout in that silence, it would have dissolved at once into thin air. An elderly postman on a bicycle may have been real or yet another apparition.

At last we found a café open, somewhere at the back of the town, and had no sooner had our roast mutton and green peas set in front of us, than the sirens began screaming. But after all this strange ghostliness, an air-raid warning didn't seem to matter much; and we finished our mutton and had some pancakes. The 'All Clear' found us in a small bar about two miles away, where one of the patrons – a fat man in his shirt-sleeves – observed placidly: 'Well, I fancy there ought to be another one just about six.' After noting this evidence of the 'terrible panic' among the remaining inhabitants of the south-east coast of Britain, we returned to contemplate, still under its strange spell, this bright ghost of a Margate. I remembered so vividly a day I'd spent here ten years ago, when the whole coast was crammed and noisy with folk and it was all a jolly, sweaty pandemonium. Had that been a dream? – or was this strange silent afternoon a dream? It seemed impossible that they should both be real. Yet here we were, alone, hearing our own footfalls on the lifeless promenade. The evil magician had muttered the enchanted phrase – and a wind had come from Hell and blown away all the trippers and paddlers and pierrots and hawkers – all that perspiring, bustling, rowdy, riotous holiday-making.

The Pie

THE pie-shop and the pie were still there. I must explain about these. Ever since I could remember there'd been just at the back of this draper's a small eating-house that specialized in meat and potato pie; one of those little Dickensy places that still survive in provincial towns. I remembered it well, though I was never one of its customers, because there'd always been on view in the window, to tempt the appetite of the passer-by, a giant, almost superhuman, meat and potato pie with a magnificently brown, crisp, artfully wrinkled, succulent-looking crust. And not only that – and now we approach the marvellous, the miraculous – out of that pie there came at any and every hour when the shop was doing business a fine rich appetizing steam to make the mouth water even as the very window itself was watering. There it was, a perpetual volcano of a meat and potato pie.

And that steaming giant pie was to my boyish mind – and, indeed, to my adult mind, for we never forget these things – as much an essential part of my native city as the Town Hall and its chimes.

Now, I'd heard that this shop and its famous steaming pie had been destroyed in the raid, and so when I went to see what had happened, I'd made up my mind that I would stand in the ruins of that shop, catching perhaps a last faint lingering whiff of that steam, and would compose some kind of lament or elegy. But, I found that the shop hadn't finished, but was there, wide open, and doing business. True, it was showing a few scars, and instead of the window, it had been neatly boarded up, but there was a square opening in the middle of the painted boarding and there, seen through the opening, framed perhaps a little narrowly but in itself as magnificent as ever, was the great pie, still brown, crisp, succulent, and steaming away like mad. Every puff and jet of that steam defied Hitler, Goering, and the whole gang of them. It was glorious.

Now, the owner himself, an elderly man with one of those folded-in Yorkshire faces, and character written all over him, was standing just inside the doorway. So I asked him, in my delight and relief, what had happened. He replied shortly, and, indeed, rather grumpily, that the shop had had its front blown out but was now open, as I could see, and that the famous pie hadn't been damaged at all, because it was his habit when closing the shop to remove this noble trade mark to a place of safety. As he said this I could feel his hand on my back and a distinct sensation of being gently but firmly pushed into the street, where, the hand hinted, I belonged. Rather grieved by this suspicious reception, I went farther along to have a closer look at the neighbouring ruins. I had not been there more than a minute or two before I was clapped on the shoulder, and there was the pie-man again, this time wearing his coat and not wearing his apron, holding out a hand and beaming at me. It seems that his wife recognized my voice. I am not telling this for my own glory, though I must say it's one of the most handsome compliments I ever received. And so after doing a quick change with his apron and coat, he came round after me. He didn't admit as much; indeed, we never went into the question, but I think that he'd imagined that I was some trade rival – no doubt I have a look of the younger ambitious pie-man about me – who was anxious to discover after years of unsuccessful fifth-column work the secret of the famous steaming pie.

Now, this secret was revealed to me, without my even asking, by its owner, all smiles and friendship and confidence, but, of course, I can't pass it on to all you people, but I will say this: that suspicions I'd entertained ever since the age of fourteen about that giant pie, for ever jetting forth its fragrant steam, were now amply confirmed. 'Ai,' said the pie-man proudly, 'it's a secret, that pie is, and a rare lot 'ud like to know how it's done. I've had it five and forty years, that same pie, and luckily I'd put it away in a good safe place same as usual, so as soon as we got started again, and we wasn't long I can tell you, and I gets window boarded up, I got pie out again. There's only one thing,' he added wistfully, 'that 'ole I'd left in the centre of the boarding to see the pie through. Ai, well, it's not quite big enough.' I wanted to tell him that that was a national fault of ours. We have the pie, and nobody's going to take it from us, but we do have a habit of boarding it up a bit too closely and we need to open out and to give the people a better look at the pie, and give the pie a better sight of the people.

And now, I suppose, all my more severe listeners are asking each other why this fellow has to go on yapping about his pies and nonsense at a time like this when the whole world is in a turmoil, the fate of empires is in the balance, and men, women, and children are dying terrible violent deaths; to which I can only reply, that we must keep burnished the bright little thread of our common humanity that still runs through these iron days and black nights; and that we are fighting to preserve and, indeed, I hope to enlarge that private and all-important little world of our own reminiscence and humour and homely poetry in which a pie that steamed for forty-five years and successfully defied an air-raid to steam again has its own proper place.

PROCEEDINGS

Battalion Reunion

NEVER have I seen a tavern stairs or a tavern upstairs so crowded, so tremendously alive with roaring masculinity, as I did that night. Most of the faces were strange to me, but here and there, miraculously, was a face that was not only instantly familiar but that at once succeeded in recalling a whole vanished epoch, as if I had spent long years with its owner in some earlier incarnation. We sat down, jammed together, in a dining-room that can never have held more people in all its existence. It was not full, it was bursting. We could hardly lift the roast beef and apple tart to our mouths. Under the coloured-paper decorations, we sweated like bulls. The ale went down sizzling. But we were happy, no doubt about that. We roared at one another across the narrow tables. The waiters, squeezing past these lines of feasting warriors, looked terrified and about half life-size. The very bunting steamed. I was between two majors, one of whom was the chairman and (no cool man at any time, except no doubt at a crisis in the front line) now quite red-hot. With him I exchanged reminiscences that seemed almost antediluvian, so far away were those training camps and the figures that roared commands in them. The other major, unlike most of us there, was not a West Riding man at all, but a South Country schoolmaster, known to all his men as 'Daddy', and whose character and reputation were such that through him the whole affected tittering South Country was forgiven everything. In short, he was amazingly and deservedly popular. Rarely have I observed such waves of affectionate esteem rolling towards a man as I did that night. Those rough chaps, brought up in an altogether alien tradition, adored him; and his heart went out to them. I caught a glimpse then – and I am not likely to forget it – of what leadership can mean in men's lives. I had seen it, of course, in the war itself; but long years of a snarling peace, in which everybody tended to suspect everybody else, had made me forget almost its very existence. And I do not suppose that in all the years that had passed since the war any of those men had found themselves moved by the emotion that compelled them that night to rush forward, at the earliest opportunity, and bring themselves to the notice of 'good old Daddy'. In other words, they had known this endearing quality of affectionate leadership in war but not in peace. It is more than sentimentality that asks, urgently and bewilderedly, if they could not have been given an outlet for this deep feeling just as easily in a united effort to help England as in a similar effort to frustrate Germany. Are such emotions impossible except when we are slaughtering one another? It is the men – and good men too – who answer *Yes* to this who grow sentimental about war. They do not seem to see that it is not war that is right, for it is impossible to defend such stupid long-range butchery, but that it is peace that is wrong, the civilian life to which they returned, a condition of things in which they found their manhood stunted, their generous impulses baffled, their double instinct for leadership and loyalty completely checked. Men are much better than their ordinary life allows them to be.

The toast in memory of the dead, which we drank at the end of the dinner, would have been very moving only unfortunately when we were all standing up, raising our glasses and silent, there came from a very tinny piano in the far corner of the room what sounded to me like a polka very badly played. I tried to think, solemnly, tenderly, about my dead comrades, but this atrocious polka was terribly in the way. I sat down, bewildered. 'Damn fool played it all wrong,' growled the major, our chairman, in my ear. 'Should have been much slower. Regimental march, y'know.' That little episode was just like life; and I suppose that is why I am at heart a comic writer. You stand up to toast your dead comrades; the moment is solemn and grand; and then the pianist must turn the regimental march into something idiotically frivolous, and ruin the occasion. I am certain that if my friends ever want to drink to my memory, something equally daft will happen; and I shall murmur 'What did I tell you?' from the great darkness. Now more men came in; the temperature rose another fifteen degrees; the waiters shrank another six inches; and there were songs and speeches. The chairman made a good speech, and in the course of it told the lads that the last battle in which the battalion had been engaged, on the Italian Front, was the greatest pitched battle in the whole history of the world. As he talked about this battle and its momentous consequences, I stared at the rows of flushed faces in front of me, and thought how queer it was that these chaps from Bradford and Halifax and Keighley, woolcombers' and dyers' labourers, warehousemen and woolsorters, clerks and tram-conductors, should have gone out and helped to destroy for ever the power of the Hapsburgs, closing a gigantic chapter of European history. What were the wildest prophecies of old Mother Shipton compared with this!

I had arranged to meet, in a little ante-room, the survivors of my original platoon, and as soon as I decently could I escaped from the press of warriors in the big room, to revisit my own past. There were about eight of us present, and we ordered in some drinks and settled down to remember aloud. I had not seen any of these fellows for seventeen years. I knew them all, of course, and they seemed little older. The difference was that before they had all been soldiers, whereas now their respective status in civilian life set its mark upon them, and now one was a clerk, another a tram-conductor, another a mill-hand, and so forth. Nearly of all them remembered more than I did, although I have an exceptionally good memory. Details that had vanished for ever from my mind were easily present to theirs. Why? Was it because a defensive mechanism in my mind had obliterated as much as it could from my memory; or was it because much more had happened to me since the war than had happened to them and, unlike them, I had not gone back over and over again to those war years? (A third explanation, of course, is that, living in the same district and often running across one another, they had talked over those years far more than I had.) As figure after figure, comic and tragic, came looming up through the fog of years, as place after place we had been in caught the light again, our talk became more and more eager and louder, until we shouted and laughed in triumph, as one always does when Time seems to be suffering a temporary defeat. Frensham, Aldershot, Folkestone, Maidstone, Bully Grenay, Neuve Chapelle, Souchez – how they returned to us! Once again the water was rising round our gum boots. We remembered the fantastic places: that trench which ran in front of a graveyard, where the machine-gun bullets used to ricochet off the tombstones; that first sight of Vimy Ridge in the snow, like a mountain of despair. We recalled to one another the strange coincidences and dark premonitions: poor melancholy B. who muttered, 'I'll be lying out there to-night,' and was, a dead man that very night; grim Sergeant W. who said to the draft, 'This is where you can expect to have your head blown off,' and had his own head shattered by a rifle-grenade within three hours. And little Paddy O., who had always seemed such a wisp of a chap, with everything about him drooping, who looked the same as ever, ready to drop at any moment, though he never had dropped and the Central Powers must have spent hundreds of thousands of marks trying to kill him, little Paddy, I say, came close to me, finished his beer, and asked me, stammeringly as ever, if I remembered sending him from the front line for some water for the platoon, on a summer morning in 1916. 'Nay,' he stammered, 'I wasn't gone more than t-ten minutes, and when I c-come back, where you'd been, Jack lad, there was n-nobbut a bloody big hole and I n-never set eyes on you again till to-night.' And it was true. I had sent him away on a ten minutes' errand; immediately afterwards a giant trench mortar had exploded in the very entrance to the little dug-out where I was dividing up the platoon rations; I had been rushed away, and was gone before he returned; and it had taken us more than seventeen years to find one another again.

Lecturing in America

By now I have in my head a composite picture of a large Middle-Western university. I see myself arriving at a smallish station, being met by two or three pleasant young fellows, who drive me through an uninteresting town to where the university looms on the hill. We cross an enormous campus, like a young battlefield. I am shown the hall in which I shall speak, which is usually the big hall of the union building. It looks about the size of Waterloo Station. This union building is buzzing and crackling with students of both sexes, who are playing basket-ball or the piano, practising tap-dancing, painting scenery, eating ice-cream and looking at *Life* and *Time*. There are thousands of them. Then there is always a keen spectacled girl who interviews you for the university magazine. There is nearly always a sort of demigodlike young man, who is the captain and leader of everything. When you walk round with him, the honours are divided. He is secretly in awe of you, and though he knows nearly everything he does not know that you are secretly in awe of him too. He hands you over to a member of the faculty, who takes you to dine with the president or the dean or whoever it is. The trouble about this dinner, which is probably excellent, is that it comes too early in the evening, for at six-fifteen you are not hungry, and even if you were, you would not stuff yourself before lecturing. Because this is a closed little community, with its own intrigues and scandals and politics and excitements, you have the feeling that although you are an Event you are not very real and important to these people; although they ask you questions and would be delighted if you held forth, especially about people, Great Names, for that is what they really miss out there, not ideas, which they can find in books, nevertheless, the real urgent life of the dinner-party, of which you catch frequent glimpses, swirls all round you, but does not touch you, for you have no part in it. The people themselves vary, of course, but I have a composite picture of them too. First, your host and hostess, very grand, very solemn, and a bit inhuman, not because they are really like that, but because they are overdoing the occasion. Then there is usually some dean or professor of senior rank who thinks he is as good as, if not better than, the host, and so to show us that a dinner at the president's does not impress him, he talks in a loud confident tone in a waggish style. If his wife does not adopt the same tactics, then she is usually a grim silent woman, whose every glance is a complete and damning inventory of the whole room. Then there are several safe dependable senior members of the faculty, nice dullish men, with vaguely apologetic wives who have all had their hair done that afternoon by the same assistant and so look more alike than they really are. Of these the only couple that stands out is the one – and there always is one – that went to Europe last summer. Then among the younger guests there is the Rebel-Who-Will-Not-Be-With-Us-Much-Longer, and indeed there was probably some discussion as to whether he should be invited to-night. (It is with him that you have already made a secret pact to meet after the lecture and drink a little Scotch and talk treason.) And there is nearly always one younger wife who is prettier and livelier and less amenable to discipline than the rest and is thought to be no better than she should be. If she should be the wife of the Rebel, then you may assume they will be thrown out very soon. To counter-balance the Rebel is the still-younger assistant professor who has worked like mad and agreed with everything anybody has ever told him, has nearly ruined his eyesight and poured out his youth as if it were dish-water, just to be a member of this faculty and to attend such dinner-parties and to agree eagerly and catch the president's eye. His wife, a dim girl, is nearly fainting under the importance of the occasion. And through-out the dinner, you are thinking that these are very nice people, but that it is a pity they are so dull and pompous and humourless and that there is so little fun in them. And most of them are wondering why the British are so heavy and pompous and humourless and go through life with so little sense of fun. The table is weighty, not only with chicken and salad and layer cake, but also with the gravest misunderstanding.

The Museum Meeting

THE rector took the chair. He was a large, pink, very clean gentleman with a booming voice, which made him sound as if he were broadcasting himself. He was full of congratulations. He congratulated the ladies and gentlemen of the committee on turning up in such numbers, on their being able to meet in this historic Dunbury Hall, and on their having as a fellow member no less a person than Lady Foxfield herself, upon whom he would call first.

Lady Foxfield was quite unlike her son in appearance. She was a soldierly-looking woman with big craggy features that had been heavily powdered, so that she looked not unlike a whitewashed sergeant-major. She had a hoarse and masterful voice. A frightening woman. 'Now you all know why you're heah,' she told them, looking about her scornfully. 'We've already decided that the town should have a museum. We've had estimates and we know it wouldn't cost very much to make the necessary alterations to the Market Hall to turn it into the right kind of building. We also have a promise of some contributions. Dunbury,' she went on, as if the others there had only just arrived in the place and would want to know something about it, 'is a very ancient and historic borough. All of us heah are proud of its – er – historical – er – associations. We wish to show othahs that we are proud of our – er – ancient history. I understand that there has been some talk in the town about selling the Market Hall to – er – a commercial – er – enterprise. Disgraceful talk, in my opinion. It's not to be thought of.' She looked about her sternly, daring one of them to think of it then and there. 'I needn't remind any of you heah that the Market Hall originally belonged to the Foxfield family, who made a very generous gift of it to the townspeople on the condition – on the condition, please remembah – that the townspeople made a propah use of it. As we all know, the townspeople have shown themselves unfit to use it properly, and the sensible membahs of the council have already agreed that the Hall should be turned into a museum. I have promised to loan such a museum some Foxfield family heirlooms of great historical interest.' She graciously allowed the applause to subside. 'In addition, I am able to announce that the Lord-Lieutenant has expressed great interest in our scheme. Also, that our friend Mr Finningley has promised a very handsome donation to the Museum Fund.' More applause, in the middle of which a little man with a long moustache popped up and bowed. Lady Foxfield now held up her hand and looked very stern indeed, as if about to give the whole battalion an extra half-hour's drill. 'We must all stand togethah, not only for the sake of our ancient borough but also in ordah to preserve the great traditions of our country. A museum will show the people what those traditions are. It will prove a bulwark against dangerous tendencies. It will tell the people that our motto is still what it always was – For King and Country.'

To enthusiastic applause Lady Foxfield sat down and immediately closed her eyes, giving the impression that in her opinion the real meeting was now over. The rector warmly thanked Lady Foxfield for her public-spirited and inspiring speech, and called upon Colonel Hazelhead, their treasurer, to address them.

A very tall, thin man, who looked like some kind of bird that had found its way inside a tweed suit much too large for it, shot up in the front row. It was difficult to catch what the colonel said, for not only was he very staccato but he seemed to swallow half his words, so that only a brief précis of the speech that was somewhere in his head, which was much too small for the rest of him, reached his audience.

'*Um-yah* Chairman ... *um-yah* Lady Foxfield ... *um-yah* great pleasure ... *um-yah* considerable progress ... *um-yah* some opposition ... *um-yah* commercial people ... newcomers to town ... *um-yah* no real stake in town ... out for what they could get *um-yah* ... understand some new trouble last night ... *bolshie* fellows ... *um-yah* prompt action by police ... quite agree with Lady Foxfield ... *um-yah* bulwark against subversive tendencies ... glorious history ... *um-yah* gone out from Dunbury to ends of earth ... cause of Empire ... wished to present as own contribution valuable Indian and Burmese objects and *um-yah* ... prove education in itself ... *um-yah* patriotism ... museum fund small but rich in promises ... *um-yah* friend Mr Finningley ... final remarks ... stand no nonsense ... police to be relied upon ... *um-yah* stiff sentences ... *um-yah* ... *um-yah* ... *um-yah* ... listening so patiently thank *um-yah* ...'

The rector, now sounding more like a national broadcasting station than ever after the colonel's vague barking, boomed his thanks and asked if anybody would like to ask the colonel a question. Mrs Hathersage? Yes, Mrs Hathersage?

The woman who rose in the second row wore a floppy hat that seemed to rest on the bridge of her nose, which was enormous and really all that could be seen of her. Her voice was monstrously out of proportion to her nose, and she might have been a mouse squeaking behind the wainscoting. 'Tweedle,' said Mrs Hathersage, 'tweedle-eedle-eedle-eedle-eedle – tweedle –?'

The colonel replied to this with three *um-yahs*, which appeared to satisfy Mrs Hathersage and everybody else down there. Meanwhile, Hope and Sir Reginald were still standing between the two suits of armour, invisible in the dusk that was gathering in the upper part of the hall.

The rector now broadcast that Lady Shepshed, who, although not a Dunbury resident, had shown such interest in their project that she had been co-opted, would give them her views. 'Lady Shepshed,' he concluded, smiling and beckoning and looking quite idiotic, 'please come to the front so that everybody can hear you.' And somebody – ten to one it was little Mr Finningley – cried very earnestly: 'Hear, hear!'

Lady Shepshed coming to the front was not unlike a revival of the old-fashioned May Day processions with prizes for the best cart-horses. She was not really a very large woman; actually she was short though very broad; but she was wearing so many coats and scarves and was so hung about with furs and jangling chains and took up so much room and made such a commotion, that it was just as if a procession were coming into the place, accompanied by sleigh bells and a drum and fife band. As a speaker, however, she was not noisy and imposing. Her line was the ultra-feminine, the arch and coy line, as if at one time she had played heroines in the old-fashioned musical comedies. She tilted her head, she smiled and pouted, she closed her eyes and then opened them very wide, and at the end of every sentence seemed to wait for the orchestra to give her the note for the big waltz song. Hope enjoyed Lady Shepshed, who was a really good turn.

'Thank you so very much,' she cooed at them all. 'So very sweet of you to allow me to be one of your committee. As your dear rector has told you –' and here she gave him a look that invited him to drink champagne out of her slipper at midnight – 'although I don't live in this part of the county, I like to think of dear Dunbury as my town too – *so* many friends here –' she opened her eyes very wide now, and implored every man present to join her in the second act in Monte Carlo by moonlight – '*such* a dear little town if we don't allow it to be spoilt – and there the museum – *such* a splendid idea – will help enormously. *Such* a pleasure to be with you. Lady Foxfield *so* right in saying it will preserve the great traditions of our country. I do *feel* that the people must be taught to respect those traditions. And now *such* a delightful surprise. Mr Churton Talley, the great art critic and expert and everything, who knows *all* about museums, has been doing some work down here and is now staying with me, and I've explained *everything* about our museum plan to him, and he's *most* kindly come along to tell us what an *expert* feels about it all.' She waited for the round of applause, then led it herself. Then she threw an enormous smile clean over six rows, crooked her forefinger and beckoned with it in a manner that suggested unmentionable things, and said: 'Mr Churton Talley, come along.'

The rector, to show that the meeting had not been taken out of his hands, rose to his full height and boomed: 'I know we shall all be delighted to hear what Mr Churton Talley has to say.'

Mr Churton Talley proved to be a slender, wavy-haired youth of about fifty-five, with enamelled pink cheeks, a cherry lip, and the eye of a dead codfish. He was wearing a delicious confection of pale blue. He came mincing forward, almost swooned at the sight of those staring faces but bravely recovered himself, and then began delicately hissing at them like an outraged serpent. He was very difficult to hear from above, where half the time, with those long drawn-out sibilants of his, he merely sounded like an escape of gas. Hope began giggling at him and nearly gave away her presence on the landing. He said something about being sure they were working on the right lines, and something about 'plenning for aesthetic es well es hissstorical sssignificance,' and something about the importance of getting really expert advice when the time came to choose the exhibits (he was trying to touch for a job), and went on yammering and hissing for quite a time. He did not go down too well. In fact, as Hope whispered to Sir Reginald, Mr Churton Talley was a flop.

Not so Mr Finningley, the little man with the long moustache, who was known to have promised a fat cheque for the fund. It was clear that Mr Finningley was socially on the make. ('Awful little squirt,' whispered Sir Reginald. 'Only recently settled here. Made a pile in Borneo or Africa or one of those places.') But his very eagerness to please, supported as it was by real money, gave him a good audience. He was, as he said, no speaker. But not only did he want to please, but he was himself, as he said many times, very pleased. Yes, he was very pleased to be there at the meeting, very pleased to be called upon to say a few words, very pleased to be allowed to contribute towards the museum fund, very pleased to hear such good speeches, especially from *the ladies* (he was one of those men who insist upon referring to the ladies in italics), very pleased to know that the Market Hall was to be put to proper use at last, very pleased with the progress that was being made; and he gave the impression that he would have been equally very pleased to have blacked the boots of anybody present. At the end it was evident that his fellow members thought well of Mr Finningley, who might now expect social promotion at any moment.

The rector enquired if anybody had a question, some points that ought – as is the strange habit of points at meetings – to be raised. Someone had. A large lady in purple had a question, and gave the impression she was about to make a contralto solo of it. 'Several of us,' she sang, 'are not very clear as to the exact position at present. Have we received a definite promise from the Borough Council that when the – er – various legal matters are settled – we shall be given the exclusive use of the Market Hall? If not, what is the position at present? I am sure we should all know.' She took a low *A flat* for her final note, and received a murmur of approval.

Major Shiptonthorpe, who was also a solicitor in the gentlemanly interests, was called upon to reply to that question, and to show that he was not trifling with them he unfolded some eyeglasses and put them halfway down his nose, and then looked gravely at the meeting over the top of them. He was glad to have this opportunity of explaining the exact position with regard to the Market Hall. The property was held in trust, and the trust was of an unusual kind. The first step, that of refusing to grant any further licence to the Hall, had been simple enough. ('And I bet you've been doing some wangling,' Hope told him under her breath.) There would be no great difficulty, though certain legal complications would have to be unravelled, in the town turning the Hall into a museum, so long as there was no opposition. But unfortunately there was considerable opposition, for some members of the council, for reasons best known to themselves, wished to accept the offer that *United Plastics* were making for the property, and there were even a few – whose political views encouraged them to make as much trouble as possible – who declared that the Hall should be kept for its original purpose, overlooking the fact that the people were no longer interested in that purpose. 'Now, ladies and gentlemen,' Major Shiptonthorpe continued, removing his eyeglasses and sawing the air with them, 'no decision of the council can be legal, according to the terms of the trust, unless three-quarters of the members at least are in favour of that decision. Thus, at the moment, there is a deadlock. Yes, Mr Chairman,' he added, as if the rector would find this a special treat, 'a complete deadlock.' He put his eyeglasses back, turned himself from a major into a solicitor again, and waited for another question and presumably another fee before replying to it.

The rector played up manfully. 'Well, Major Shiptonthorpe,' he boomed, 'we all feel this is an impossible state of affairs. What happens if this deadlock continues?'

Lady Foxfield was plainly heard to snort and mutter 'Preposterous! Time these people had a sharp lesson!'

'I quite agree with Lady Foxfield,' said Major Shiptonthorpe. 'Fortunately, I've made some enquiries – I was up in London yesterday and the day before – and the position is not as bad as it would first appear. Unless the *United Plastics* people have something up their sleeve. There's a meeting of the council to-morrow – and if it's still impossible to obtain this three-quarter majority and the deadlock continues, then we can ask for government arbitration. An arbitrator – somebody, of course, of recognized position and authority – will be appointed, and then the decision will rest with him. I may add – again, I must point out, unless *United Plastics* steal a march on us – that I have reason to believe that any such arbitrator, if only by reason of his background and training, would favour our side of the question.'

There was a murmur of approval and self-congratulation. Hope had a strong desire to throw something at them. They sat there like a lot of enormous stuffed frogs. If there had to be a museum, then these creatures ought to go in it, all in glass cases. But there wasn't going to be a museum. She had promised Uncle Fred that much. And even if she hadn't, she'd want to take a hand now, if only to stop Major Shiptonthorpe and company being so pleased with themselves. Just quietly pinching a large hall, that's what they were doing!

There was a stir below. Somebody had arrived. The rector looked across and nodded: 'Ah! – Commander Spofforth. Well, better late than never, eh, commander? And I'm sure we'd like to hear the commander's views.'

'Certainly,' said Lady Foxfield loudly. Evidently the commander, a burly dark fellow, was one of her favourites. And it was soon obvious why he should be.

'Tough guy, huh?' whispered Hope.

In his bluff sailorlike fashion, Commander Spofforth said he didn't understand why so much hanky-panky was going on. Didn't care a great deal about museums himself, and didn't pretend to, but if the best people in the town wanted the Market Hall as a museum, as they obviously did, then the sooner they took it the better. Inspector Parkin had just told him there was some sort of hanky-panky in the Little Hall last night, with that fellow Largs mixed up in it, as usual. Fellow Largs was an agitator, and probably well paid for it. Latest trick was to bring in a bunch of Reds to take possession of the Hall. Soon put a stop to that sort of thing. Guarantee to do it himself in a jiffy.

'Quite so,' said Lady Foxfield in a loud approving tone.

'Thanks, Lady Foxfield,' the commander continued. 'So let's have no more shilly-shallying, I say, but set to work, take what we want, and incidentally clean up the town a bit. Could do with it – what? So could the old country. Too much arguin' an' beefin', majority an' minority nonsense, talkin' shop stuff. What we want's a bit of direct action – a few people to give orders an' the rest to obey 'em – eh?'

'Heil Hitler!' cried Hope, who found the commander so exasperating that she could keep silent no longer. At the same time she made a sudden impatient movement, sent a suit of armour toppling against the rail, which brought it up with such a jerk that the headpiece flew off and fell with a startling clang into the hall below, only just missing the large lady in purple. Everybody jumped up.

Sir George Arbitrates

THERE was quite a little crowd outside the entrance to the Guildhall, which was a fairly old but not very imposing building, just off the market square. At the door were two policemen.

'Tell you one thing,' said Sir George, as he climbed out. 'I'm going to be devilish thirsty. Feel it coming on now, and this affair may last hours – though not if I can help it. Ought to have brought something with me.'

'It's here,' cried Daisy, appearing as if by magic at that moment. 'Take it.'

'Thoughtful of you, very thoughtful indeed. Many thanks.' Sir George glanced down at the paper-covered bottle he was now holding. 'What is it?'

'Good old malt whisky. Looks nearly like water. But it's thirty years old.'

'By Christmas, what a woman!' roared Sir George, to the delight of the whole crowd. 'You're a little miracle. Well now, in we go.'

'Beg pardon, sir, 'as all your party got business inside?' asked one of the policemen.

'Yes, officer,' replied Sir George, with immense dignity. 'They are all with me, Sir George Denberry-Baxter.'

'Yes, yes, that's all right. This way, please, Sir George. Everything's ready. Everybody's waiting.' This was from little Mr Orton, from the Town Clerk's office and late of the Dunbury Harriers. He was in his best suit and a great state of fuss.

'And that's where you're wrong, young man,' said Sir George severely. 'Everything is *not* ready and everybody is *not* waiting. I am not ready and I am not waiting. Now, lead on.'

The rest of them followed him in, hardly noticed in his shadow. The hall was not very large; it had a narrow gallery running round three sides, about twenty rows of little cane-bottomed chairs on the ground floor, and a rather high platform; and it was nearly full, not with ordinary townsfolk but with councillors, privileged persons, members of the groups that were claiming the Market Hall. Hope noticed nearly all the people she had seen at the museum committee meeting at Lady Foxfield's. And Tom Largs was there, with his daughter and the young solicitor, still wearing the same dark blue shirt. While the five from the 'Dog and Bell' found seats for themselves in one of the middle rows, Sir George, still carrying his bottle, rolled gigantically towards the platform, where the mayor, two senior aldermen, and the town clerk were already installed behind a long table. Young Orton, pale and damp with anxiety, appeared to be acting as something between a master of ceremonies and an usher. There was a round of applause as Sir George, who now looked a most picturesque and imposing figure, settled himself in an immense high-backed chair in the middle of this platform group. He acknowledged the applause by a nod and a wave of the hand, and then busied himself with arranging the decanter of water, the glass, and his bottle of pale old whisky, within easy reach. The mayor, the two aldermen, and the town clerk all looked terrified, as if a cat had suddenly arrived to take the chair at a meeting of mice. Young Orton laid some documents in front of the great man, who now produced a giant-size pair of folding *pince-nez* and clapped them on the end of his nose at an odd angle. He looked now like a scholarly pirate.

The mayor, a thin earnest man in the furniture trade, opened the proceedings. He seemed to have learnt his speech by heart, and spoke it as if he were a foreigner who could produce the sounds but did not really know what the words meant. 'We Are Met Here,' he told them, 'To Decide The Future Of Our Old Market Hall As We Have Not in Accordance With The Law Been Able To Secure The Necessary Majority In Our Borough Council Meetings Therefore In Accordance With The Law We Are Met Here To Decide By Arbitration The Decision Of The Arbitrator To Be Final Such Arbitrator Having Been Appointed By His Majesty's

Government Namely Sir George Denberry-Baxter.' Then he added, dropping into ordinary Dunbury speech: 'And I 'ope that you will all keep good order as there's been enough trouble in the town already.' And this was received with a few gentlemanly *hear-hears* and some mild applause.

The town clerk now rose to explain how the Market Hall came to be in the possession of the town, but he had a squeaky little voice, read his speech very rapidly, and only told his audience what nearly all of them knew already, so nobody took any notice of him. Sir George regarded him with some astonishment, as if he were a talking insect, helped himself to whisky and water in an extremely dignified manner, and then only partly stifled a vast yawn.

'He's 'as bottled now,' whispered Timmy to the Professor, 'as when we first met him. You'll see.'

The *United Plastics* people were to present their case first. The manager, the two assistant managers, the head of the sales department, with a secretary or two, were there, looking extremely worried, as well they might, for they had a strike on their hands, neither the new system nor the old one was working at all, and cables that became more and more intelligible, the angrier they were, had been arriving from New Jersey at all hours. But they were not presenting their case themselves, however, but had imported a haughty young barrister from the Middle Temple, who now came forward, coughed twice, made a little bow to Sir George, coughed again, then began: 'On behalf of my clients, *United Plastics* –'

Sir George stopped him. 'What are they?'

'I was about to explain, sir. *United Plastics* is a very prosperous company, of American origin, that has its English factory here in Dunbury, and it is easily the largest employer of labour in the district. On behalf –'

'What is this stuff they manufacture?' asked Sir George, breaking in again. 'Is it the stuff they make these little coloured ash-trays and bowls out of?'

'Yes, sir, it –'

'Loathe the stuff. Never did like it, never shall. But, of course, I'm old-fashioned, clean out-of-date – eh? Anyhow, lot of other people do like it, I suppose, eh? Firm makes money, eh?'

'Yes, sir. I have here the figures of the annual expenditure of the company in wages –'

'Keep 'em. Don't want figures. No use addling our wits with a lot of nonsensical figures.' He took another pull at his whisky and water. 'Go on. What do these people want to do?'

'It is their desire, sir, to acquire the Market Hall and use it as a showroom for their products and, of course, as a central warehouse, offices, and so forth. They are willing to pay a good price to the town for the purchase of the building, considerably more, in fact, than it could command in the ordinary way.'

'Why? What's the point of it?'

'Er – I should like to consult my clients before I answer that question, sir.' And he went into a huddle with the manager, the two assistant managers, the head of the sales department, while Sir George helped himself to more whisky and then mopped his brow.

'It seems, sir, that the policy of the parent company in America has always been to try and associate its products in the public mind with places or buildings of historical or strongly aesthetic interest. Thus, the parent company has recently acquired the birthplace of a well-known public figure, Senator Jenks, and is using it as a showroom –'

'What, a whole town?' roared Sir George. 'Oh! – I see – one house. So their game is somehow to persuade the idiotic public that their plastic stuff is very new and yet very old all at the same time. Cowardly, I call it. If you're new, *be* new, I say. Not new myself, don't pretend to be. Almost an anachronism, I am. But I'd respect these people a bit more if they didn't go and pretend to be Senator Jenks's grandmother. Not that I care who Senator Jenks's grandmother is, because I never heard of the fella.'

'Quite, sir,' said the young barrister very smoothly. 'That was merely an example of the policy. But what I should like to emphasize is that my clients are ready to pay a handsome sum to the town for a building that is no longer useful –'

'What's the town going to do with the money?' asked Sir George, staring about him masterfully. 'Anybody know? Not decided yet, eh? What do you say?' This to the unfortunate town clerk, blushing and squeaking. 'Can't hear you. Never mind, let it pass.'

'By establishing their factory here, my clients have brought a great deal of money into the town – and –'

'And made a very nice thing out of it, I'll bet my boots. And if they hadn't, they wouldn't still be here. No, don't think much of that argument – never did. It's a little shopkeeper's point of view, that. Won't pass it. Eh?' he added, to the mayor, who was saying something. 'Speak up, Mr Mayor, speak up, and let us all hear you.' There was some applause at this.

'I just wanted to say,' said the mayor, who clearly did not know what to make of Sir George, 'that some of us – who've been for many, many years in the service of the Borough, senior members of the Council, and so forth – feel that this offer by *United Plastics* should be given very serious consideration.'

'Ah!' Sir George made this sound very significant. 'Ah! You do, eh? Senior members of the Council, eh? Well, well, well!' He shook his head, looking like a distressed red-and-white lion, refreshed himself again, and then stared down in surprise at the place where the young barrister had been standing a minute before. The man there now seemed to be a different size and shape. 'What,' enquired Sir George slowly, 'is the idea of this?'

'I'm the manager of the sales department of *United Plastics*,' he began, in an ingratiating tone, 'and I feel that our counsel hasn't perhaps put forward our claim as it –'

'Sit down, sir,' Sir George thundered. 'Let's have none of your sales department tricks here. No salesmanship! No pedlar's artfulness! Just a quiet, straight-forward discussion of this little problem. So sit down, sir,' he bellowed.

The mayor and the two aldermen, who had been exchanging timid and bewildered glances, now trotted off the platform, and received a scattered round of applause, led by T.

Tiverton. Sir George completely ignored this sudden retreat, but looked very fiercely at the little town clerk, who, perhaps because he was feeling lonely and afraid, beckoned to young Orton. Sir George did not like this, glared at the town clerk, waved young Orton towards him and said loudly: 'Come along, young man, don't stand dithering there. Who are the next claimants?'

Young Orton scampered round like a rabbit to the museum group, from which Major Shiptonthorpe emerged, a legal man but also a gentleman representing the gentlemanly interests, and as he came forward he took off his eyeglasses so that he would be ready to saw the air with them at any moment. Major Shiptonthorpe's manner said very plainly: 'These commercial people having got what they deserved, you will now see how we do the trick, all in a neat, gentlemanly fashion.' All the museum party watched him with a proud confidence. The arbitrator himself did not observe this approach, being busy mixing more whisky and water.

'Sir George, I represent the Dunbury Museum Committee – Major Shiptonthorpe – and –'

Sir George stopped him. 'Any relation to Tubby Shiptonthorpe who used to be out in Johore?'

Major Shiptonthorpe smiled. 'My cousin.'

'You know he came a nasty cropper, poor old Tubby,' said Sir George, striking a rich vein of reminiscence. 'No brains, of course, not a glimmer of 'em. But I didn't mind him. The last time I saw poor Tubby – it was in a filthy little rest house during the rains – he'd got the idea in his muddled head that there was a whole secret society of Malays after him. All nonsense, of course. Wouldn't leave the little brown girls alone, that was Tubby's trouble. You fellas,' he added sternly, 'think you can do what you like out there, and it doesn't work, y'know, Shiptonthorpe, it doesn't work. Well, glad to have had a word with you, Shiptonthorpe. Never forget poor old Tubby. Now let's get on.'

Major Shiptonthorpe smiled again, but this time very faintly. 'As I said, Sir George –'

'Look here, Shiptonthorpe,' said Sir George severely,

'I've a good deal to do, y'know. Can't gossip here all the afternoon. Some other time, if you please. Now then, who's representing these people who want a museum?'

'I am,' shouted Major Shiptonthorpe, losing his temper. 'I've said so already.'

'Don't take that tone with me, my dear sir,' and Sir George, purple with fury, thumped the table and set all the papers dancing. 'Coming up here, chattering about your cousin! Now then, sir, what have you to say?'

'A number of – er – influential residents, headed by Lady Foxfield, have formed a Museum Committee, and the proposal of this Committee is that the Market Hall, which is no longer needed for its original purpose, should be placed at the disposal of the Committee in order that it should be turned into a museum –'

'Yes, yes, yes,' said Sir George irritably. 'You sound to me as if you're going round and round in a circle. What sort of museum?'

'With your permission, sir, I should like to call upon Lady Foxfield to answer that question. Lady Foxfield!'

The lady came forward in a grim purposeful manner. She nodded to Sir George. 'How d'you do?'

'How d'you do?' he replied glumly, staring down at her with some distaste. He decided to refresh himself before listening to what this grim-looking female had to say.

Lady Foxfield, who had a strong rather than a fertile mind, began the same speech she had made at the meeting at her house. 'Dunbury is a very ancient and historic borough. All of us heah are proud of its – er – historical associations. We wish to show othahs that we are proud of our ancient history –'

'Why?' asked Sir George, rather quietly for him.

'Why?' she repeated, looking at him as if she could hardly believe either her ears or her eyes. 'Surely it's important to preserve the great traditions of our country?' And her friends applauded this and one or two of them, including Mr Finningley, cried 'Hear, hear!' Which was unwise of them, for Sir George glared in their direction and then when he returned to contemplate Lady Foxfield again, he looked at her with more distaste than ever. But he did not reply at once, and now Lady Foxfield rashly assumed that she had the moral superiority and began to hector him. 'There is no need to point out to one who has served his King and Empire in many parts of the world, that these traditions must be preserved, that a museum will show the people what those traditions are, and that – er – therefore – it will prove a bulwark against dangerous tendencies.' And the whole museum group clapped hard and Mr Finningley cried 'Hear, hear! Bravo!'

'Quiet!' shouted Sir George angrily. He was now very ripe indeed. As he half-rose to his feet and leaned over the table, he swayed slowly, and his enormous face shone with sweat. Then, to everybody's astonishment, he suddenly cried: 'Is my friend Dr Krudiebacker, late of Vienna, still here? If he is, I now ask him to step forward.'

The Professor, more astounded than anybody else, discovered that he was being propelled out of his seat and along the row by Timmy. He did not go right down to the platform, however, but stood against the wall at the side, where his height made him immediately conspicuous.

'Ah, there you are,' shouted Sir George, still leaning on the table and swaying. 'Now, Dr Krudiebacker, you're a man of intellect and learning, a foreigner but one who knows something about this country – so I want you to tell us – very simply, very clearly – what you think are the great traditions of this country. Now listen, everybody, listen carefully – especially that fella down there who keeps shouting "Hear, hear!" like an idiot. Dr Krudiebacker?'

'The great traditions of this country,' cried the Professor in a loud clear voice, 'are these. First, the liberty of the individual. So long as they do no harm to others, men must be allowed to develop in their own way. Second, that which goes with liberty – toleration. Third, voluntary public service. Fourth, a very deep love, a poetical love, rooted deep down in the unconscious, of England and the English way of life, of the fields and woods, flowers and birds, of pastimes, of the poets and story-tellers. Fifth, which you find everywhere among the common people, humour and irony and along with these a profound depth of sentiment. You may say some of these are characteristics and not traditions, but here in England, where everything is hazy, nothing clearly defined, characteristics of the people and traditions of the race melt into one another and cannot be separated. That is all, I think – except to say, as a foreigner, that I love these traditions very much and that the world would be much poorer without them.' And the Professor gave the company a short stiff bow, then marched back to his seat.

Sir George shook his white mane. 'Thank you, Dr Krudiebacker,' he roared. 'And now, at last, you've heard something worth listening to, after all this drivel about selling ash-trays and Senator Jenks and Tubby Shiptonthorpe and museums that are bulwarks against dangerous tendencies. I like dangerous tendencies, and I hate bulwarks.'

'One moment, please!' called Lady Foxfield sharply.

'Certainly not, madam, you've had your moment, and told me I didn't want to preserve the great traditions of our country. And with all due respect to you, madam – and with none at all to your idiotic friend down there who keeps shouting "Hear, hear!" – I say you're talking a lot of nonsense. And bad nonsense too. I love our traditions. I want the English to be more English every year, so that Dr Krudiebacker keeps coming back to admire us more every year. And I can't see that a public building taken over by fellas who shout "Hear, hear!" like idiots and all manner of old busybodies, who stuff the place full of warming-pans and broken old horse pistols and moth-eaten bonnets and shawls and a lot of other junk –'

'Really!' shouted Lady Foxfield, in a fury. 'Really, this is quite –'

'Don't try to bully me, madam. Either resume your seat or leave the building.' Sir George stood erect now, though still swaying dangerously, and waved her away. As she went, he took a tremendous drink, gasped for air, then returned to his discourse, which was wilder and louder than ever. 'Museums? Nothing wrong with 'em in their place. Sent lots o' things to museums myself, wonderful stuff. Still got plenty left. But this little town doesn't need a museum. Ridiculous idea! Only persons who could seriously entertain such an idea ought to be in museums themselves. Put them in a museum, and then let the other people wake up. I believe you people here,' he added, with some dim recollection of what the Professor said to him at the 'Dog and Bell', 'are all going to sleep. Music now? Where does music come in? Comes in somewhere, I know.' He stopped at this point because he found that the little town clerk, who was desperate, was tugging at his sleeve. 'Don't do that, man. Detestable habit. If you've anything to say – say it.'

'I'm afraid,' stammered the town clerk, 'that is – I really think – we ought to adjourn – as you're not feeling well –'

'Not feeling well?' roared Sir George, glaring at him. 'Never felt better in my life. Must be the air. Half a mind to come and live here. As for adjourning – that is a most improper suggestion, my dear sir –'

Here Major Shiptonthorpe, who was still standing near the platform, took courage. 'I agree with the town clerk. Under the circumstances, we cannot possibly accept the arbitration –'

Sir George thumped the table again. 'I'll reply to you when you've answered three questions. What are these circumstances you talk about? Who are you – apart from being Tubby Shiptonthorpe's brother – and we know what that's worth? And how can you refuse to accept an arbitration award when it hasn't yet been offered to you? And another question. Is it necessary to stand there flapping your eyeglasses about like that? If not, then go and do it somewhere else. Now we'd arrived at music. Why? Where did music come into this? It didn't, I suppose.'

'Really preposterous!' This came, quite clearly, from Mr. Finningley.

'Put him out,' thundered Sir George to young Orton. 'Fella who's been making nuisance of himself all afternoon – with his "hear, hear!" – getting worse now – put him out.'

Young Orton moved slowly in the direction of the museum group, from which came cries of protest. Mr Finningley was standing in the middle of them crying: 'No, no, no, no, no!' Several of them were for leaving in a body, as a protest against these monstrous proceedings, but Lady Foxfield, having now returned to her seat, shouted grimly that she didn't propose to leave it when nothing had been settled. Young Orton somehow never arrived at Mr Finningley, but that did not matter now because Sir George's attention was elsewhere.

Tom Largs had decided that it was their turn. 'You see,' he told Sir George, 'this Market Hall they're trying to take away from us was given to the people in the first place as a kind of musical headquarters. They used to be famous for their music round here.'

'They did, eh? Well, why aren't they still famous for their music?'

'Oh – they let it go,' replied Largs. 'Even the town band winked up a few months ago – I think some of these people you've heard helped to kill it so that they could say that nobody wanted the Hall for music any more – but now I've just revived it.'

'You have? You the conductor, eh?'

'Yes. Try to be.'

'Come up here, my dear fella,' roared Sir George with the most astonishing enthusiasm, 'and let me shake you by the hand. Now we're getting to something, after all this Jenks and Tubby Shiptonthorpe and warming-pan nonsense. What's your name? Largs, eh?' They were shaking hands now, and there was considerable applause from the back seats and the little gallery. 'What is it you've got – an orchestra?'

'No, not yet. Just the military combination – brass and wood-wind.'

'Ah! – pity about that. If you'd had strings now, by thunder! – I'd have played for you myself. Think – think into what a heaven you can wander, with a full orchestra! Bach, Mozart, Haydn,' shouted Sir George ecstatically, 'Beethoven,

Schubert, Brahms. But what,' he continued, coming down to earth again, 'can you do with a military band?'

'You'd be surprised,' said Largs, settling down beside him.

'Have a drink?' Sir George took a good pull himself.

'No, thanks,' said Largs. 'But nearly everything's arranged for this combination nowadays. It's not the same thing, of course, without the string tones, but you'd be surprised what we can do. We've a rehearsal at half-past six to-day, you ought to come and hear us, so long as you realize we're only just beginning again. Now what about this Market Hall of ours, which was given to the people of Dunbury for their music?'

'It's yours,' declared Sir George, with passionate emphasis, 'and, so far as I'm concerned, it stays yours.' He turned to the crowd. 'My decision is – that the Market Hall is not to be used as a show-room or a museum or for any other nonsense. It must remain the property of the people of Dunbury so that they can play in it and sing in it –'

'Let the people sing!' cried a tremendous voice in the gallery.

'And a damned good idea!' roared Sir George. 'The best I've heard for months. Let the people sing!' There was some cheering at the back, and several cries of protest from the front rows. Sir George now turned to the town clerk. 'If the Hall is open for the people to sing in, then keep it open. But if it isn't open, then see that it's opened at once.'

'Do nothing of the kind,' cried Major Shiptonthorpe.

'The Hall is closed,' said the town clerk, screwing up his courage and his face with it, 'and I shall take care that it remains closed. I cannot possibly accept this decision.'

'You're quite right,' Lady Foxfield called out. 'Whole thing's preposterous.'

'Hear, hear!' from Mr Finningley.

Feeling that he had the best people with him, the town clerk grew bolder, looked Sir George in the face, and said loudly: 'We cannot accept this arbitration.'

Instead of exploding, Sir George was now surprisingly calm, though it was not a reasonable and sober calm, but one that might be found in some moon-haunted stratosphere of lunatic high spirits. He did not address himself to the little protesting group near him, but to the whole audience. His manner had immense dignity; all his words were quite clearly pronounced, as they had been throughout the afternoon; he swayed a little and his gestures were perhaps a trifle florid; but there was not much outward evidence to suggest that Sir George Denberry-Baxter was now governor-general of some distant dominion of Cloud-Cuckoodom.

'No doubt you have heard,' he began, in the broad oratorical style with its frequent grave pauses, 'that my arbitration in this matter of the Market Hall has been refused. I came here to do my duty to you people of Dunbury, without prejudice, with no desire but to see that justice should be done. A man of ripe experience in government, grown old in the service of the Colonial Office of His Majesty's Government, I was invited, I accepted the invitation, I came. And here I am.'

This statement was loudly applauded, and, muttering something about 'an old throat trouble', Sir George seized the opportunity and had another large whisky. He emerged from this whisky more dignified than ever, almost regal, although there was now a very wild glitter in his eye.

'I have listened – I trust with reasonable patience – to some of the most astounding rubbish that has ever afflicted my ears. I need only mention ash-trays, salesmen, Senator Jenks, Tubby Shiptonthorpe, warming-pans, and bulwarks, to refresh your memories of these incredible speeches.' He now stared with great severity at Mr Finningley. 'The fact, too, that we have here several little men with long moustaches who cry "Hear, hear!" at every fresh piece of idiocy, has not made things easier. Whether these same little men, with the noisy women they have brought with them, many of whom, to their shame, bear old and not entirely undistinguished names – though if the Foxfields ever did anything of any importance, it's the first I've heard of it – I say, whether these men and women have plotted and intrigued to deprive the citizens of this borough of their music, for which, let me remind you, though I didn't know it myself – damn it, a fella can't know everything! – I say, for which they were once famous, and could be famous again, though I have no hesitation in saying that my friend here is completely wrong in simply using a woodwind and brass combination, because the string tone – so clear, so vibrant, capable of such exquisite modulation – is essential. You must have strings,' he told them, with great earnestness. 'First and second violins, violas – a difficult but very beautiful instrument, 'cellos and double-basses. Without them your band can make a loud and cheerful noise – excellent, excellent, I've no objection to it in its place – but it will never achieve the true singing tone –'

'Let the people sing,' cried a man in the gallery, probably because he had had enough of this bewildering oration.

Sir George accepted it as a cue. 'Certainly let the people sing, my friend. Not only that. By thunder, the people are going to sing – and in that Hall too – before I leave this town. Neither the freemen of Dunbury, the singing freemen of Dunbury, nor George Denberry-Baxter can be dictated to by a lot of drivelling solicitors and clerks and salesmen and retired shopwalkers with overgrown whiskers. It can't be done. Follow me,' he shouted, rolling along the platform, then turning and pointing at Tom Largs, who was still on the platform: 'Come along – oh! – and bring that bottle with you, it's not quite empty yet.' He descended gigantically to the floor level and came rolling forward, shouting: 'Dr Krudiebacker, Tommy Tupperton, all my party there, rally yourselves, rally yourselves, and prepare for action –'

One of the policemen had come in to see what was happening. 'Now then, sir,' he called out, with an attempt at severity, 'we can't have all this noise.'

'My good man, this isn't a noise,' said Sir George, smiling wickedly upon him. 'These are merely a few observations and high-spirited exclamations. The *noise* hasn't begun yet. But it will – it will.'

ENSA in the Canteen

At the far end of the canteen, across one corner, was a small stage. It was a very small stage and this was a very large canteen. And once again, Dolly – of 'that well-known variety act, Dolly and Dan' – pointed out these facts to her husband, Dan Croly. They were now making-up in a tiny curtained space at the side of the stage.

'And another thing,' continued Dolly, who was a plump, sharp-tempered woman in her fifties, and now, with an auburn wig and a dazzling crimson-and-white make-up and an emerald-green frock, looked like an Edwardian charmer remembered in a delirium, 'another thing – just you remember, Dan Croly, that before we open, about five thousand helpings of cottage pie and ginger pudding will be on them tables.'

'Well, what of it, what of it?' asked her husband, who was busy reddening his nose and making his battered ugly face still uglier.

'What of it?' she cried in derision. 'Anybody'd think you'd never been in the profession. What of it! We've got to play to 'em, that's what of it. And you might as well try to get up and do a turn in Waterloo Station, that's all.'

'I told you – didn't I? – I told you there's loud speakers all over the place. They'll hear us all right.'

'Well, even if they do – and I doubt it – they won't see us. I'll bet half of 'em won't know we're here.'

With the weary resignation of a man condemned to argue with a woman, he replied, as he tried on a bright green bowler: 'We wouldn't have been sent here if it didn't work, would we? If you'd listened to that "Workers' Playtime" like I told you, you'd have heard for yourself. I tell you, these shows – they're a riot.'

'I've seen riots before,' retorted Dolly darkly.

'Oh cheese it!' He was annoyed now, chiefly because he himself was not as self-confident as he pretended to be.

'And cheese it yourself! If you think you're going to be

funny, at half-past twelve in the morning, to two acres of cottage pie and ginger pudding, then all I can say is – you'll have to be a lot funnier than you sounded to me last night. And give me a cigarette.'

'Be careful of your voice.'

'A pound of shag in a clay pipe couldn't spoil my voice here – that is, if I've still got any voice to spoil.' And Dolly, feeling that she had won handsomely on this exchange of views, lit her cigarette and enjoyed it in silence.

Dolly and Dan Croly had had more than thirty years on the variety stage. They had never been top-liners, and indeed had never seen much of the Number One towns, but for years they had never been short of bookings, including some good pantomime engagements, until the years just before the war. Then their age and lack of good new material, which cost more to buy than they could afford, began to tell against them. They struggled along until the war came, and then Dolly, who was tired of digs and travelling and wanted a home of their own and regular money, asserted herself and declared that they must retire. Her sister, a widow, ran an hotel in Reading that did a very good bar business, and, finding himself short of staff, she offered Dolly and Dan both regular employment and a home there. It was not quite like having a home of one's own, but it seemed to Dolly (who had ideas about keeping an hotel herself) the first step towards one, and so off they went to Reading, where they had remained, busy as bees, for the last two-and-a-half years. Dolly had been quite willing to stay there, at least until they had a chance of managing an hotel for themselves. She liked the life. But Dan had never settled down to it. He was an artiste, not a barman. The evenings found him restless. When he ran into old friends of the Halls, their talk left him even more dissatisfied. And from what everybody said, it was easier now to get bookings than it had been. Some people even declared that there was now a shortage of talent. He was advised to try ENSA. He listened to several broadcasts of shows given by the B.B.C. and ENSA to these factory workers in their canteens. He heard, with envy and regret, the uproarious applause. Without saying anything to Dolly, he wrote to ENSA and then paid them a visit at Drury Lane.

It took him a month, with many quarrels and much sulking on the way, to persuade her to give the plan a trial. Now they had their three months' contract, to give these factory shows, at fourteen pounds a week for the pair of them, which was very nice money and more than they had seen for several years, as even Dolly had been compelled to admit. This was their very first show. And now, not twenty minutes before they would be doing their act, she had gone and turned sour, and was crabbing the whole thing as hard as she could, against every tradition of the profession, not caring if they went on and got the bird, perhaps hoping they would. She had never been like this in the old days, of course, just the opposite, in fact; it was this hotel business that had done her in. And now, just when he was not feeling too confident himself, for all this was new and after nearly three years away from show business he could not help feeling rusty, she was doing everything she could to take the heart out of him.

The other performer, the accordion-playing girl who called herself Gipsy Violet, all made-up and ready, was at the other side of the stage, talking to the pianist and Mr Proscot of the factory. Dolly had taken an instant dislike to this girl, who clearly fancied herself, so Dan decided it would be a good thing to bring her in as a subject of their talk, so Dolly could let steam off that way.

'How's Gipsy Violet looking?' he therefore enquired, with a sarcastic inflection.

'About as much like a gipsy as you do,' replied Dolly, who could always express her dislikes. 'Gipsy from Whitechapel, that's what she is. And telling me she'd always been a single turn and appeared mostly at high-class concerts, when I know very well I saw her with these very eyes as one of the Six Merry Midgets on the bill with us at Devonport, twelve or fifteen years ago. Wouldn't have it, of course. Looked me straight in the eye and denied it. But I *know*.'

'I believe you're right too, Dolly,' said her husband, relieved to hear the talk taking this line.

'I know I'm right. Old Mrs Farthing was runnin' 'em – the *Six Merry Midgets* – and they used to come on first, so what those six kids got, when Mrs F. had taken her whack, you can just imagine. High-class concerts indeed! Why not Buckingham Palace an' have done with it? But I expect she'll be just right for this mob, screaming her head off with that accordion. It's about what they'll want.'

The conversation was moving towards dangerous ground again, so Dan said nothing, and pretended to be busy giving final touches to his make-up. However, this did not work well.

'What you're bothering like that for about your make-up, I can't think,' she cried. 'Just take a look at what we're playing in. A shed half a mile long. Anybody'd think you were going on at the Palladium, the way you're touching up that old mug of yours.'

'Oh, for Christ's sake!' he burst out, glaring at her.

She glared back. 'Don't start swearing at me, Dan Croly.'

He stopped glaring at her now, but looked steadily for a moment or two, and then said very quietly: 'Listen, Dolly. I want to have a sensible word or two before they start coming in.'

'They're coming now,' she said. And there was the sound, rapidly drawing nearer, of a great chattering, clattering tide of folk. It was rather frightening, and even Dolly was affected by it. She drew back from the stage, came closer to him. 'Well, what is it?'

'I'm sorry I lost my temper then, Dolly. I'm nervous, that's why. Yes, I'm nervous. And you're quite right about the make-up, but I was trying to give myself confidence – see?'

'Yes, I see, you silly old fool.' But she said it with more affection than contempt.

'Old fool's right, Dolly,' he continued, regarding her earnestly. 'I'm over sixty, don't forget. And I've been out of the business for nearly three years. And this is all new to me. For me – I don't know about you, Dolly, I'm talking about me now – a lot depends on how we go down today.'

She tried to say something, not angrily by the look of her, but with a quick apologetic gesture he stopped her.

'No, dear, let me finish. I never said much, but I never liked that hotel game – specially where we were, for your sister never took to me – and showed it – and I never fancied her much, nor most of her pals neither. I'm a pro. Always have been. Can't be anything else. This is my life. If it doesn't want me, then I'm finished. Better dead.'

'Now don't start talking silly, Dan,' she said, more moved by his earnest manner than she cared to show.

'It's not silly. It's God's truth. And there's another thing. I've always wanted to do my bit in this war, the way all these people here are doing theirs. If I can make 'em laugh a bit, forget their troubles, help to make it seem not such a long day, then I'll be glad an' proud. In fact, I'll feel better than I've felt for years. But if they don't want me, I don't know what I'll do – honest to God, Dolly, it's as bad as that. Now you've been a good wife to me –'

'Why, you silly old fathead, of course I have,' she cried, very much moved now.

'Yes, yes, I know. Well, even if you don't like it here, wish we'd never taken the engagement, give it a chance, love – just for my sake.'

'Give it a chance! Why, what d'you take me for? Haven't I been in show business nearly as long as you have? And haven't we got a reputation to keep up? Why, Dan, just because I grumbled a bit, you've no need to talk to me like that. As if I'd let you and the act down! The very idea! And don't you start worryin' yourself sick neither. You know your work, nobody better, and I'll bet you'll make 'em eat it – along with their pie and ginger pudding. And what's this? Haven't we played Saturday nights in Glasgow, and Southsea and Devonport with the Fleet in? Why, this is easy. Leave it to me, Dan.'

And she gave immediate proof that she was on his side, because at that moment the pianist and Mr Proscot came across to tell them that they were opening the programme after a short announcement by Mr Proscot. Dolly caught a look of alarm in her husband's eye, and knew instantly what it meant, for the noise now in the vast canteen was colossal and terrifying. There seemed to be a solid wall of sound out there. Her own heart was racing now.

'Now just a minute, Mr Proscot,' she cried urgently. 'That won't work. We're new to this, and Miss Violet isn't. Besides she's a musical act, which is always easier to get across quickly. We don't want to take anything away from her, even if we are old-established favourites. But let her go on first, do half her act, then she can come on again after us and finish it, getting the big final round. That's best, isn't it, Dan?'

Dan swallowed hard, and said that it was.

The pianist, who knew his Gipsy Violet, hesitated, but Mr Proscot, who seemed a nice obliging gentleman, agreed that it would be best, and the pair of them went back and could be seen arguing with the girl about it. Finally, she nodded.

'Thank God for that,' said Dan.

'Thank me, you mean,' said Dolly.

He put a trembling hand on her arm. Feeling closer to him than she had done for many a year, she put her other hand over his.

'I am thanking you, love. And I won't forget it, whatever happens.'

'All that's going to happen is that we'll give 'em a good little show. You'll see.'

Mr Proscot was now at the microphone, and in an easy confident style, getting a laugh or two as he went along, he announced the show. The applause that followed was strangely different from the applause they had heard six nights a week for thirty years, as different as the great lighted eating-place was from the cosy little auditoriums they had known. But after all, it was applause, and meant that those mysterious thousands sitting at the tables were ready and waiting to be amused. What more could an old Pro. want? The pianist rattled off a popular tune or two. Then Gipsy Violet swept on, playing her accordion and wriggling and ogling like ten Gipsy queens rolled into one, sang a passionate, broken-hearted number, sang a rollicking light-hearted number, and got a hand that was like a gigantic hailstorm on a corrugated-iron roof. Whether she had graduated from the Six Merry Midgets or high-class concerts, there was no denying that Gipsy Violet could slam across her stuff. And she warmed them up for Dolly and Dan. Or had she? Perhaps they only wanted gipsies with accordions.

'And now, friends,' Mr Proscot was shouting, 'that well-known variety act, Dolly and Dan, in comedy numbers. Dolly and Dan.'

'Go on, boy,' yelled Dolly, above the applause, to the shaking elderly man, white beneath his clown's paint, by her side. For he always made the first entrance. 'Go on, they'll eat it.'

For days now, Dan had been living with a Woolworth notebook, into which he had entered, after much reflection, various new topical gags – about Hitler and Mussolini, Lord Woolton and ration cards, war work and so forth – just to show them that he was a bright up-to-the-minute comic. And now, stumbling out shakily into that glare and din, on that little stage, with no footlights between him and the crowd, no painted street-scene behind him, reminding himself desperately that he must make straight for the microphone to be heard at all, now he could not remember a single word of these topical gags. Every syllable of them had vanished. He had nothing to say. He was sunk.

He managed to get to the microphone, a wide foolish grin on his face, his fingers frantically interlocking and unlocking themselves. But that was enough for the audience, so far. They thought he looked funny, so they laughed. Then they waited for him to say something. And he couldn't. He had completely dried up.

Dolly saved him again. Putting her head round the curtain at the side of the stage, she bellowed at the very top of her formidable voice: 'How you doing, love?'

'Terrible,' he replied, not knowing what he was saying but involuntarily speaking into the microphone. 'I've dried up.'

A week's rehearsal could never have given him such a comical terrified tone. It seemed to the audience very funny indeed, and a massive yell went up, giving him time to pull himself together. It was all right. They liked him. And it didn't matter about the new gags, the old ones would do. They returned to his memory, as if drawn by the familiar sound of laughter, without any further effort on his part; and now thirty years of touring sprang to his aid; he slammed across one old gag after another; began to remember quite miraculously some of the new topical ones, and tried them out with increasing success; and then, after five minutes, with every minute better than the last, Dolly, whom they were ready to like after that droll interruption of hers, came charging on, as if she had been playing factory canteens for years, an emerald-green, crimson-and-white battle-cruiser going into action; the pair of them, plunging into a well-tried old routine and playing it as fast and broad as they knew how, flung genial insults at each other, sang hoarsely and confidently, stopped their singing for more insulting back-chat, and triumphantly piled up the laughs and the applause.

So there is the scene, at this midday pause in the grim task of war production. A fat middle-aged woman, most unsuitably dressed and raddled, and an elderly painted buffoon, shouting and posturing, yelling in coarse accents their stale old jokes, busy vulgarizing the sex instinct, performing without grace or wit. Gaping at the tiny stage, staring and nudging, guffawing and screaming, there are the thousands of workers of all ages, making what seem animal noises that yet no animal has ever made, and seeming all mindless eyes and ears, wide loud mouths, and clapping hands. A strange and no doubt a deplorable scene. Yet there was about it an air of release and innocent happiness; a kind of struggling goodness in it; a mysterious promise, not mentioned, not tried for, not even understood, but there somewhere all the time, of man's ultimate deliverance and freedom, a whisper of his home-coming among the stars. Nobody there was consciously aware of this, yet nearly everybody there, beneath the surface of the mind – that crackling surface where the jokes exploded, because of the absurdity of this life of ours – somewhere in the deep communal recesses, in the dark river of racial being, felt all this, and was refreshed and restored by it. 'Cheers you up a bit,' they told one another; or agreed: 'It makes a change.' And so uttered profound truths.

'Carm, carm, I want yew eo-eonl-y,' sang Gipsy Violet, in her final, grand, give-me-your-applause number.

And behind the curtain, at the side of the stage, where nobody could see them, Dolly and Dan were hugging each other, not knowing whether to laugh or cry, still shaken, battered, and intoxicated by their glorious reception.

'You did it, old girl, you did it,' Dan was saying.

'We both did it,' she told him. 'And you were right after all, Dan. They're all right. They're nice. They deserve all we can give 'em. And we're goin' to enjoy this engagement.'

'We are, we are,' said Dan. 'I wonder if we take a final call?'

PURELY PERSONAL

My Father

My father was a schoolmaster, and a very good one, with an almost ludicrous passion for acquiring and imparting knowledge. He was not a born scholar, but he was a born teacher. Outside his school, he did a great deal of useful public service – speaking, helping to organize, working on committees, and so on – not because he was a busybody or was socially ambitious, but because he was essentially public-spirited, the type of citizen that democratic theorists have in mind but rarely in actual view. But there was nothing of the smooth committee humbug about him. He was very brisk, humorous, stout-hearted, not to be patronized or bullied. I am commonly supposed to be pugnacious, but he was at heart ten times more pugnacious than I am, and if you went one step too far with him, his ruddy face turned scarlet, his eyes were electric blue, and he came roaring at you like a little lion. He had the only sensible way of dealing with money, and I am glad to say that he bequeathed it to me. This is to realize as soon as possible what kind of life you can lead with the money at your disposal (and he had never much, yet was never dissatisfied), then within that circle to live at your ease, never worrying about money. He deliberately shut out one sort of life – the more expensive life of hotels, restaurants, cabs, theatre stalls, Havana cigars, liqueur brandies – and then lived like a king in the dominions left to him. To think hard and realistically about money, then to forget it, that is what neither spendthrifts nor misers can do, and it is the only way to be merry and wise. He was not a romantic figure, did not pretend to be. His world lacked glitter and glamour. I never remember seeing him either in ecstasies nor yet defeated by despair. But he never failed a duty, left the world better than he found it, was loved by his friends and respected by his army of acquaintances, and had a lot of fun. Beneath the rather droll surface peculiarities – his love of making acquaintances, of asking questions, of imparting information; his fear of minor social criticism; his distrust of the picturesque, romantic, grandiose things of this life; his odd mixture of patience and explosive hot temper – he was a living rock of good solid human nature. If I was picking a team to go and colonize another planet, I would choose his kind first. Years ago, when my first scribblings were achieving print, he was proud of me; and now, too long after we exchange our last words, I think I am prouder still of him.

My Face and I

WHEN I first entered adult life I imagined, like the young idiot I then was, that I had complete control of my face. I was convinced that I could permit myself to feel anything behind that bland disguise. When I went out for the evening and found myself becoming more and more bored by the company, I was sure that nobody but myself was aware of the fact. I set my face, as best I could from behind, to register a polite or even eager interest; I put on a smile and kept it there, left my eyes to sparkle away, and so forth; and then felt, even though the smile seemed rather stiff towards the end of the evening, that I could relapse with safety into comfortable boredom. As I never saw myself, it was some time before I was disillusioned. We never lose any of our illusions about ourselves in the company of strangers. But I made friends, and in this, as in other matters, they very quickly disillusioned me as they strolled, in the usual friendly fashion, through the house of my mind and casually opened a few windows here and there to let in the east wind. One would say: 'Dullish at the So-and-so's the other night, I thought. You looked dreadfully bored.' A succession of such remarks soon revealed to me the true state of things, and I realized that I had been deceiving myself. It was not for me to try to look one thing when I was thinking and feeling another. The idea of myself as one of your smooth fellows, made for diplomacy and the best society, for ever charming yet secretly tired of it all, would no longer hold, and, bearing in mind my newer and truer relations with my face, I was compelled to revise my estimate of myself.

There was, however, nothing alarming or even really disappointing in the situation. I was not sorry to be free from the strain of a diplomatic bearing, and congratulated myself on the fact that the higher types of human beings do not wear a smooth and impassive front. There is nothing better than an open, honest countenance, frankly expressing to the world its owner's feelings. I thought so then and I think so still, though now my opinion is worth more if only because it is more disinterested. I imagined then that mine was one of those open, honest faces, and was happy in this belief until the cumulative effect of a series of misunderstandings, of which that one last night is a good example, compelled me to take stock of myself once more, with the result that I was disillusioned once and for all. I found that people were always telling me not to be so angry when, in actual fact, I was only slightly annoyed, were for ever asking me why I was so jubilant when in truth I was only mildly pleased, were constantly suggesting that I should not glare furiously at strangers when I was only conscious of feeling a little curious. At last I realized the truth. My face did not even honestly reflect my mind but grossly caricatured it. I was carrying into all companies a monstrous libel of myself. It was as if I were compelled to wear a set of features that did not belong to me at all but to some other and very different kind of man. Small wonder, then, that I should be so frequently misjudged, for it is not unnatural that people should imagine that these facial antics, for which I am held responsible though they seem to be entirely beyond my control, are an indication of my state of mind. How are they to know that my face has apparently an independent existence, setting to work merely on a hint from my mind and then going on in a fashion of which I strongly disapprove?

That is the irony of the situation. My face would seem to belong to a type of man I dislike. It is a theatrical, temperamental affair, for ever rushing out to extremes, whereas I am all for moderation. I do not pretend to absolute philosophic calm and detachment, but – whatever my acquaintances, the deluded audience of this face, may say to the contrary – I am certainly not a man of strong feelings, one of those people who must be excited about something, who are not happy unless they are in the depths of misery or find all existence wretched because they do not feel ecstatic, who must be always yearning and burning, loving and hating, laughing and crying. Not only have I a contempt for such persons, but I could not imitate them if I would. Such emotions as I have are small and safe and never likely to get out of hand. Ecstasy and despair do not come my way and are never likely to be encountered in the easy rambles that my mind takes every day. My attitude towards my fellow creatures is one of timid goodwill, tempered here by tranquil affection and there by a faint hostility. Even the kind of man who ought, at this moment, to be wearing my face only arouses a dislike that stops very far short of definite hatred. When, let us say (for last night still rankles), I win a game, I am only conscious of feeling a slight pleasure, spiced by just the slightest sense of triumph; and when I lose, as I do very frequently, I am certain that I am visited by nothing stronger than a tiny feeling of disappointment, a mere mental sigh. I have been guilty, in my time, of some meannesses and may have contrived, here and there, to do a kindness, but never yet have I played either the villain or the hero. If life is a melodrama – and sometimes it has every appearance of being one – then I am certainly a very minor character. In short, I am a well-fed, comfortable, calm, and not entirely unphilosophical adult male, with no desire for raging emotions and with precious few to rage.

That is what I am really like inside. Outside, apparently, everything is different, thanks to a set of features that totally misrepresent me. So far as I can gather, my face pounces on the least whisper in my mind, as it were, and transforms it into a shout. It grins insolently and sickeningly with triumph over a mere hand at cards. It scowls ferociously at inoffensive strangers, screams 'You're a bore!' at prattling callers, and twists and writhes, lights up or fades out, falls into a sodden mass of depression, glitters with mischief, gapes or grins or glares, at every fresh turn the conversation takes. It transforms every hour into a benefit performance by a bad actor of the old school, strutting and mouthing insanely in the limelight. A talking ape with a megaphone could not produce a worse caricature of its master. While the company I am in is staring at this monstrous show, I sit there innocently behind it all, an unassuming fellow with nothing but a pleasant little rise and fall of emotion, entirely forgetting that this awful travesty of my mind is taking place until some strange misunderstanding bids me remember how grotesquely and unhappily I am situated. Am I alone in my trouble or has there been a general misdeal of faces? Perhaps there are other unfortunates for whom the situation has been reversed, who find themselves possessed of the most towering emotions, yet cannot make their passion felt because their faces refuse to express anything beyond a slight feeling of annoyance or a tranquil pleasure. If there are any such persons, I should like to meet one of them for the purpose of comparing our baffled sensations and of finally forming and consolidating a friendship. We could at least enjoy one another's faces.

The Grumbler

I HAVE always been a grumbler. All the records, going back to earliest childhood, establish this fact. Probably I arrived here a malcontent, convinced that I had been sent to the wrong planet. (And I feel even now there is something in this.) I was designed for the part, for I have a sagging face, a weighty underlip, what I am told is 'a saurian eye', and a rumbling but resonant voice from which it is difficult to escape. Money could not buy a better grumbling outfit.

In the West Riding of Yorkshire, where I spent my first nineteen years, all local customs and prejudices favour the grumbler. To a good West Riding type there is something shameful about praise, that soft Southern trick. But fault-finding and blame are constant and hearty. The edge of criticism up there is sharpened every morning. So the twilight of Victoria and the brief but golden afternoon of Edward the Seventh discovered Jackie Priestley grumbling away, a novice of course but learning fast. A short spell of the Wool Trade – and in no trade do you hear more complaints and bitter murmurs – developed my technique. Then came the First World War, in which I served with some of the dourest unwearying grumblers that even the British Army has ever known, and was considered to hold my own with the best of them. After that, a rapidly ripening specimen, I grumbled my way through Cambridge, Fleet Street, and various fields of literary and dramatic enterprise. I have grumbled all over the world, across seas, on mountains, in deserts. I have grumbled as much at home as abroad, and so I have been the despair of my womenfolk.

Not that they ever understood what I was up to. We have always been at cross-purposes here. The feminine view appears to be that grumbling only makes things worse, whereas I have always held that a fine grumble makes things better. If, for example, an hotel gives me a bad breakfast, I have only to grumble away for a few minutes to feel that some reasonable balance has been restored: the grumble has been subtracted from the badness of the breakfast. So it is no use crying to me 'Oh – do be quiet! It's bad enough without your grumbling.' My mind does not move along these lines. If I have not had a good breakfast, I argue, at least I have had a good grumble. Thus I have always been innocent of the major charge – that of trying deliberately to make things worse.

Another point for the defence is that I have always looked and sounded much worse than I felt. When I am displeased – but not when I am pleased, I gather – for some reason, still hidden from me, I tend to overact my part. Often when I am feeling merely annoyed, a little put out, I appear to be blazingly angry or lost in the deepest sulks. The appearance is larger than the reality. And I have suffered much from this suggestion of the theatre or the public platform in my private behaviour. Time and again my real feelings have been misinterpreted. I may not have been enjoying myself, but at least I have not been suffering as intensely as the rest of the company imagined. (When rehearsals are going badly, I am often rushed out of the theatre, given drinks, flattered, cajoled, simply to keep me out of sight of the players, those pampered creatures.) Once, years ago, at a large party, when I was grumbling as usual, a young woman who was a stranger to me turned on me fiercely and told me I had better go home instead of trying to spoil other people's pleasure. I was taken aback, and may be said to have stayed aback ever since.

Shrewd Reporter?

WHEN I had first stayed on the ranch, the winter before, I had found it hard to work in my bedroom in the patio, where people were always moving about and calling to one another. What I needed was a little place of my own to work in, well away from the main ranch buildings. So as soon as I came back, for a longer stay, up went this shack, and within a day or two it had its bookshelves, stove and electric light. Nothing very wonderful about all this. It was easily erected, and of course I paid for it. But I feel that in any European country there would have been endless palavers and fusses, whole crops of difficulties raised, before one would have had a brand-new place to work in; if indeed one would have persisted in the face of a mountain of objections. Here, in the Far West, it was done so casually and quickly. 'You bet!' they cried, and went ahead. Perhaps it is sheer space that makes the difference. What seems obvious and easy in the vast crystalline spaces of Arizona may well appear a tricky enterprise in shuttered Europe. This shack was built on the very edge of a river I have never yet seen, the Hassayampa, which only appears – as a sudden yellow flood – towards the end of summer. If you drink its waters, they say, you are for ever afterwards incapable of telling the truth. But the winter visitor does not even see them. This had been a good place to work in. I asked for nothing better. Sometimes in the mornings, before the sun commanded the scene, it had been rather cold and cheerless; and often later in the mornings and during the blazing afternoons, it had been too warm, for there was only one layer of thin boards between me and the weather. But it had been my own place, and quiet, except for an occasional bird that would come to the window, knock with its beak, and stare at me as if we were meeting in Eden. The little hut had served me well.

I had spent most of my time in there writing a novel about London. With the door and the two windows wide open; a thin curtain drawn to dull the bright shaft of sunlight; wearing nothing but a shirt, old flannel trousers, and slippers, I would sit in a sweet cloud of American tobacco smoke, peer through it at my script, and tap-tap away at my account of life in the rain and fog of London streets. There in the middle of my hut, with Arizona glittering round it for hundreds of miles, was a tiny dark London, into which I popped every morning about ten. When people tell you how lucky you are to be a professional writer, they enumerate advantages that you know very well are things not worth having; but they never mention this genuine bit of luck, that you can sit in Arizona and build for yourself a London that has just the people, streets, houses, and weather you need, and can then, months afterwards, sit in Highgate on a dark wet Monday morning and conjure for yourself the bright illimitable spaces of the Arizona desert. True, other people can do this, but they must do it in their own time, for their own amusement; they are not at liberty to call it work. And it is a dark wet Monday morning this morning, and I am sitting in Highgate – working.

When I had gone out there, I had meant to spend the winter writing a novel, but I had had only the vaguest notion of the form it would take, and so I had not a single note. I had to remember and invent the London of my story. Since then, these chapters have been described by reviewers as so many pieces of 'brilliant reporting'. They were not intending to be very complimentary: the inference was that reporting was my level. They may well be right when they hint that the higher, grander, subtler forms of imaginative writing are quite beyond me; I have never made any great claims myself for my fiction, beyond protesting once or twice that there might be a little more in it than met the top-speed reviewer's eye, and that because I wrote one jolly, hearty, popular novel it does not follow that everything I have written since is exactly the same. But they use words very loosely. To report is to narrate, describe, and repeat as an eye-witness. The reporter is the man on the spot, or he is nothing. Now anyone less on the spot, less of an eye-witness of what he was describing, than myself in that hut can hardly be imagined. A man in Arizona who attempts to describe, with some wealth of detail, what it feels like to be a waitress or a parlourmaid in London, using not one single note, may be a good, bad or indifferent novelist, but he will certainly not be much of a reporter. He has removed himself far from the scene; he has not prepared himself to describe it; and only by a fairly violent use of his imagination can he identify himself with characters so entirely different from himself. If this is reporting, then I no longer understand the English language.

For truth's sake, and not from any desire to appear a dashing figure of genius, I now put it on record that I would have made a wretched reporter. I have not the energy, the conscience, the trained observation, to report well. I am not sufficiently extroverted. How oddly we are estimated! How fantastic the monsters in public processions, like those in French carnivals, that are carried above our names! Time after time, I have seen myself described as an astute, supremely observant, hard fellow, shrewd and pugnacious, smashing his way into best-seller lists. Intelligent people no longer expect to find all Irishmen imaginative and combative, all Scots dour and grasping and given to theological argument. Yet these same people will easily assume that a Yorkshireman must necessarily be shrewd and hard, and that if he goes into authorship, it must be in the same spirit in which a bluff West Riding gambler sets about cornering the Australian wool market. All this seems to me so ludicrously false that I cannot be angry about it. I have as much self-knowledge as the next man, and probably more than most, and I am ready to declare under oath that I am not very astute nor very observant, am inclined to be timid, irresolute, melancholy, am easily influenced and frequently humbugged, and have neither the enterprise nor the determination to be a hard careerist. I take no thought whatever about a career, make no plans far ahead, but do whatever I want to do, with no reference to its possible dignity or lack of it. I have a restless nature, easily bored, and so I flit from one kind of work to another, partly sustained by a very genuine interest in the technical problems of all forms of writing. I have always wanted vaguely to be an all-round man of letters on the Eighteenth Century plan, which allowed or commanded a man to write essay or poem, novel or play, just as he pleased. This is good fun, but it may not be good business. If you want to play for safety, keeping the career on a steady course, you will do the same thing over and over again – painting two cows in a field, two cows in a field – until at last they write, for the school books, 'Nor can we omit a consideration of the leader of the two-cows-in-a-field group ...' And there you are in your pigeon-hole, and not unlike a stuffed pigeon.

Why the Theatre?

WHY had I suddenly changed course, and gone from miscellaneous writing and novels into the Theatre? Sitting there in that hut in Arizona, feeling very much alone in the sleeping desert, I put this question very seriously to myself and did my best to find an honest answer. We have often been told by dramatists, who like us to think they are masters of a Mystery, that novelists envy them their noisier and more glittering successes. But I knew at once this would not do. The Theatre, for all its noise and glitter, is a tiny world. Most of the people who work in it do not realize how small it is because they never take the risk of stepping outside it. But the writer of books, whose post may bring him letters from the ends of the earth, knows what a miniature world the dramatist lives in. He knows too that he has only to begin writing for the Theatre to vanish completely from the minds of thousands of his readers, who may not be at the ends of the earth but actually living within sight of the theatres where he is working. He also knows that once a book is in print, sooner or later it will find a way to its readers, whereas a play is at the mercy of circumstance, the chance of finding the proper players, the right theatre. A dramatist always is in the position of a novelist who, on completing his book, finds that now he has to go round looking for a likely compositor and printer, a paper merchant to be flattered into friendliness, a bookbinder caught in the right mood, booksellers that have to be treated like hysterical babies. The novelist who has written his novel has finished. The dramatist who has finished his play has hardly begun; he is still in fair possession of his nervous energy and self-esteem; but by the time the dramatic critics, looking sulky, have sunk into their seats for the first night, he will be a wreck, a shadow. So much was known to me before I made a move towards the Theatre. I have my illusions, but they are not of this kind. So much for the noise and the glitter.

Nor was it money, though the very successful dramatist can make more than even the most successful novelist. But the dramatist who is not extremely lucky can have years of dead loss, impossible to the novelist who has good health and a firm of publishers behind him. Unlike readers of books, the theatrical public has no loyalty to its authors, only to its actors; and Shakespeare could return from the grave next week and have a flop. As a dramatist, you can burn up months of your life, and have no return for them but charred nerves. I have met a few disappointed and permanently soured novelists and essayists, but I know far more disappointed and permanently soured dramatists. They have years and years of work hopelessly awaiting production. I have yet to meet a novelist with any name who had cupboards filled with unpublished stories. And long before I pencilled in my first cast, I knew all this. What then was the compulsion, the force that hurled me towards these barriers? It was the ancient witchery of the work itself, the eternal fascination of the Theatre. And by the Theatre, I do not mean Shaftesbury Avenue and Broadway, for I am not too fond of the metropolitan theatrical world, with its smart hangers-on, its mysterious financial gentlemen, its supper-room exhibitionists, its 'You were marvellous, darling' nonsense. No, I mean the essential Theatre, wherever it may be. Indeed, I believe I should be happiest working with some stock company in an unfashionable town, if the actors were reasonably good and the audience not too hopelessly dull. The Theatre seems more glamorous to me when it suddenly pops up in the side-street of some dreary industrial town than it does when there are rows of it, blazing with neon signs, in one of the capitals. My heart leaps up when I behold the Theatre Royal, Coketown.

After years of working alone, as the writer of books must do, there is a deep satisfaction – no matter how much wrangling there may be – in working with other people, as the dramatist does. Even now I know a man may tire of it, may return in relief to his study. But even the temporary loyalties and team work of the Theatre of today, with its too flimsy organization, are a welcome break. That, however, does not explain the fascination. I have to go back to my teens to find the real explanation. As a youth I was a passionate playgoer, and for some time was determined to go on the stage myself. (A good comic actor was lost in me, or almost lost.) Then other ambitions came, sweeping me away from the Theatre, through poetry and journalism, the barren interlude of the War, then afterwards through criticism, essays, and fiction; but the movement was circular, and after twenty years or so I found myself thinking hard about the Theatre again; but this time, being a professional writer, as a dramatist. And I did not hesitate to turn manager for myself too, learning a good deal in the rather grim process. The witchery still remained; but now it was more than an unreasoning adulation of histrionics. I came to see that the Theatre, though much of its appeal may be childish, is an institution that cannot be safely despised even by the philosopher. It is indeed one of the few common meeting places of the child and the wise adult. It is rich in symbols. The actor himself is such a clearly symbolic figure that I always find it hard to resist the temptation to write about him. His sharply-coloured, ironic life is a parody of all our lives. There is more in 'All the world's a stage' than first meets the eye. Where there is self-consciousness, there – you may say – the Theatre has set up its platform and curtains. We all play character parts, day and night. We are haunted by a feeling that we are acting in a gigantic masque. It is significant that in the ancient world the Theatre was a religious institution. I am not sure that the link between Religion and the Theatre has been broken for ever. One of our few contemporary prophets, George Bernard Shaw, has chosen to work in the Theatre. Now, some of the most earnest of our young poets are obviously being attracted towards it. Perhaps we may have a new serious Theatre that will be the servant of a religion that has not yet taken shape. To many of our contemporaries Communism is a substitute for religion, and, for all its austerity, Communism seems to turn instinctively towards the Theatre. With intelligence and sincere emotion behind it, a theatrical production, that mimic piece of life coloured and contrived to the wink of an eyelash, is a very rich, four-dimensional kind of creation, a tiny epitome of the universal drama of creation. Thus we could enlarge the meaning of Hamlet's description of the players as 'the abstracts and brief chronicles of the time'. They may paint their faces to take part in a Mystery. And I suspect that it may be some obscure but deep-seated apprehension of this, and not simply the glitter and applause, the possibility of easy fame, the erotic atmosphere, the escape through exhibitionism, the whole glamorous bag of tricks, that leads men and women to sacrifice their time, their health, their peace of mind in the service of the Theatre. Not Broadway, not Shaftesbury Avenue, but the essential Theatre, the place round the corner where they are doing a play tonight.

Too Simple?

AT the end of a long talk with a youngish critic, a sincere fellow whose personality (though not his values) I respect, he stared at me and then said slowly: 'I don't understand you. Your talk is so much more complicated – subtle – than your writing. Your writing always seems to me too simple.' And I replied: 'But I've spent years and years trying to make my writing simple. What you see as a fault, I regard as a virtue.' There was now revealed to us the gulf between his generation and mine. He and his lot, who matured in the early 'thirties, wanted literature to be difficult. They grew up in revolt against the Mass Communication antics of their age. They did not want to share anything with the crowd. Writing that was hard to understand was like a password to their secret society. A good writer to them was one who made his readers toil and sweat. They admired extreme cleverness and solemnity, poets like political cardinals, critics who came to literature like specialists summoned to a consultation at a king's bedside. A genuine author, an artist, as distinct from hacks who tried to please the mob, began with some simple thoughts and impressions and then proceeded to complicate his account of them, if only to keep away the fools. Difficulty was demanded: hence the vogue of Donne and Hopkins. Literature had to respond to something twisted, tormented, esoteric, in their own secret natures. In all this there was no pose; and here their elders went wrong about them. They could be accused not unjustly of narrowness and arrogance, but not of insincerity. They were desperately sincere in believing that the true artist must hide from the crowd behind a thicket of briers. They grew up terrified of the crowd, who in this new Mass Age seemed to them to be threatening all decent values. But I was born in the nineteenth century and my most impressionable years were those just before 1914. Rightly or wrongly, I am not afraid of the crowd. And art to me is not synonymous with introversion. (I regard this as the great critical fallacy of our time.) Because I am what is called now 'an intellectual' – and I am just as much 'an intellectual' as these younger chaps – I do not feel that there is a glass wall between me and the people in the nearest factories, shops, and pubs. I do not believe that my thoughts and feelings are quite different from theirs. I prefer therefore a wide channel of communication. Deliberately I aim at simplicity and not complexity in my writing. No matter what the subject in hand might be, I want to write something that at a pinch I could read aloud in a bar-parlour. (And the time came when I was heard and understood in a thousand bar-parlours.) I do not pretend to be subtle and profound, but when I am at work I try to appear simpler than I really am. Perhaps I make it too easy for the reader, do too much of the toiling and sweating myself. No doubt I am altogether too obvious for the cleverest fellows, who want to beat their brains against something hard and knotty. But then I am not impressed by this view of literature as a cerebral activity. Some contemporary critics would be better occupied solving chess problems and breaking down cyphers. They are no customers of mine, and I do not display my goods to catch their eye. But any man who thinks the kind of simplicity I attempt is easy should try it for himself, if only in his next letter to *The Times*. I find it much easier now than I used to do, but that is because I have kept this aim in view throughout years of hard work. I do not claim to have achieved even now a prose that is like an easy persuasive voice, preferably my own at its best; but this is what I have been trying to do for years, quite deliberately, and it is this that puzzled my friend, the youngish critic, who cannot help wanting something quite different.

The Lonely Author

I DO not mind being alone like this, though that does not mean that I do not like having the rest of the family or a friend or two here. But I have to spend a great deal of my time alone, far more than most men. Except during the actual production of a play, I work alone, which means that a great part of nearly every day I spend isolated from my kind. I have never objected to going to plays and concerts and films by myself. When I am travelling in order to describe what I see – as, for example, when I was writing *English Journey* – I always prefer to be alone, for it is my experience that one notices more and is really more sensitive to the look and sound and flavour of things when solitary than one is with company. After a few days of this lonely travelling there descends upon me a mood of boredom mixed with melancholy, rather like that of Jaques in the Forest of Arden, and out of this has come some of my best work. Company makes me cheerful or aggressive, acting upon me instantly as drink does upon many men. But my habitual mood when alone is rather sombre and brooding, inclined far more to pessimism than to optimism. That does not mean that I fake my writing when it takes on, as it so frequently does, a hearty, bustling, zestful manner. I am not trying, for ethical or commercial reasons, to cheer up the reader. But the thought of the reader, who has in fact arrived to keep me company, cheers me up. Nevertheless, if you are quick you can catch a glimpse of the rather melancholy background. I never have press cuttings sent to me and so am no authority on what has been written about me, but the only reviewer I ever remember who seemed to penetrate to my real self was the late Gerald Gould, in the very last review he wrote of a book of mine, towards the very end of his life, when his gentle, witty soul had almost ceased to concern itself any longer with our affairs. It was then that he wrote a sentence or two that flashed a lantern. And how rarely that happens! Thousands of sentences, stuffed with praise, blame, admiration, condescension, approval, patronage, but hardly ever a flash of the searching lantern or a ring of the bell!

Illusion

THERE are mornings even now when I arrive in my study like a demi-god who has been given a planet to play with. Outside my high windows the sunlight falls lovingly on all green and growing things. The paper on my desk looks as if it could be conjured almost without effort into a masterpiece. The keyboard of the typewriter glitters invitingly. The old tin box of paper fasteners, which somehow has survived all moves and changes, looks like some battered faithful sergeant who has been at my side in a hundred battles and sieges. The work, when we get down to it, will be wonderful. And brighter than the gilt along the bookshelves are the illusions of the moment ... critics are kind and wise ... readers and audiences are enchanted ... Income tax is sixpence in the pound ... the United Nations consists of united nations ... and high and shining in the regard of all good folk everywhere is that sagacious, witty, tender, profound writer ... who, now waking from his day dream, sits down, a fat grumpy fellow, to slog away until lunchtime.

The Secret Dream

THE secret dream: the hunger that can never be fed. All my adult life I have been more or less a Socialist Intellectual. I have tried to make myself – and other people – aware of the harsh economic and industrial realities of our time. Again and again I have taken my notebooks and typewriter to the factories, the mines, the steel mills. I denounced or jeered at those colleagues who would not look. I wrote some of the first detailed accounts of the depressed areas. Having been brought up on the edge of it, I knew what life was like 'back o' the mill'. I did not discover the proletariat at Oxford or Cambridge, for the West Riding working-class was in my blood and bones. I grew up among Socialists. I watched the smoke thicken and the millionaires who made it ride away. I saw broken old women creep back to the mills, and young men wither because there was no work for them to do and nobody wanted them. I knew the saddest waste of all, the waste of human beings. If Socialism was the way out, then Socialism we must have. If it meant more and bigger factories, then we must have more and bigger factories. If it meant larger and larger cities, more and more bungalows, cinemas, football grounds, greyhound tracks, motor roads, personal appearances of film stars, boards and committees, hostels, organizations for the right use of leisure, clinics, identity cards, radio night and day in every home, press officers and propaganda, party bosses arranging all our lives – very well, we had to have them. At the worst they were still better than the grey misery I had seen, the deep cancer of injustice. But there was never anything here for my own secret delight. Nothing for the hunger of the heart. Perhaps, for all my pretence of being up to the minute, I was not even living in the right age; and when I looked for my own enduring delight, I became an anachronism. When I caught myself off guard, last thing at night after too long a day, huddled in a train and too tired to read, coming out of a dress rehearsal into a wet Sunday midnight in Manchester or Sheffield, I would remember what I wanted, and it was always something quite different from what we were all demanding. Sometimes it seemed as if the capital of a tiny German dukedom, round about 1830, were nearer to my desire than anything my friends were planning or that I could help to bring into this world. I wanted a place with the dignity and style of a city, but reasonably small and clean, with genuine country only half an hour's walk from its centre, its single but superb theatre, its opera house, its symphony orchestra, its good restaurant always filled with friends. One little civilized place full of persons, with no nameless mob, no huge machinery of publicity, no glaring metropolis. To be myself in this one dear place, with a position as comfortable as an old slipper in a tiny sensible society; and not a caricature of myself in several continents. To come out of a late rehearsal and smell the lilac. To have a play done as well as it could be done, by tried colleagues, by friends, in the one familiar theatre; and not indifferently produced in a hundred different theatres, for large sums of money hastily removed from me by accountants and tax collectors. Not to be caught up and lost in the machinery of existence – as most of us are now – but to live simply and directly, like an artist, a philosopher, and in such a way that feeling, thought, action, were always closely allied, and last year's inspiration would be this year's achievement. No rushing about, no long-distance telephone calls, no expensive mountebanking, no losing touch with friends and admired colleagues, no running a career as if it were a damned great factory. Everything small but of fine quality, cosily within reach, and means and ends in sight of each other. Poky and provincial? Why, almost all the world's best work has been done in these conditions. Think of Athens, Florence, Elizabethan London, Weimar. And what has come out of Megalopolis but rubbish and hysteria? But if I should be told – and my candid friends will be on to it before you can say *knife* – that now there never can be such a place outside a daydream left over from adolescence, then I can only nod and look away. But perhaps something like it, at least more like it than what we – no, no, I see. Fall in, comrades! Quick march! But one of us, as we go, still hugs the notion of something quite different, the delight that never was, on sea or land.

The Birds and the Flame

THERE is a kind of dream that is very rare but has been known to men since history began. That is the clear wise dream, which even a psycho-analyst, if he ever had such a dream, would have to consider far removed from ordinary dreams, for instead of a confused reflection of ordinary experience it seems to offer us a new and superior type of experience. When the wise old ancients in the desert said that God had appeared to them in a dream, undoubtedly this was the kind of dream they had had. Instead of the familiar confusion, there is a crystal clearness, and things are not out of focus but are more sharply observed than ever before. It is as if, returning to Dunne's theory, we were for once able to maintain a concentrated four-dimensional focus on four-dimensional presentation. Or, alternatively, that for a brief while we had been attached to a mind infinitely richer and greater than our own. And in these rare dreams there is not only delight but wisdom.

Just before I last went to America, during the exhausting weeks when I was busy with my Time plays, I had such a dream, and I think it left a deeper impression upon my mind than any experience I had ever known before, awake or in dreams, and said more to me about this life than any book I have ever read. The setting of the dream was quite simple, and owed something to the fact that not long before my wife had visited the lighthouse here at St Catherine's to do some bird-ringing. I dreamt I was standing at the top of a very high tower, alone, looking down upon myriads of birds all flying in one direction; every kind of bird was there, all the birds in the world. It was a noble sight, this vast aerial river of birds. But now in some mysterious fashion the gear was changed, and time speeded up, so that I saw generations of birds, watched them break their shells, flutter into life, mate, weaken, falter, and die. Wings grew only to crumble; bodies were sleek and then, in a flash, bled and shrivelled; and death struck everywhere at every second. What was the use of all this blind struggle towards life, this eager trying of wings, this hurried mating, this flight and surge, all this gigantic meaningless biological effort? As I stared down, seeming to see every creature's ignoble little history almost at a glance, I felt sick at heart. It would be better if not one of them, if not one of us all, had been born, if the struggle ceased for ever. I stood on my tower, still alone, desperately unhappy. But now the gear was changed again, and time went faster still, and it was rushing by at such a rate, that the birds could not show any movement, but were like an enormous plain sown with feathers. But along this plain, flickering through the bodies themselves, there now passed a sort of white flame, trembling, dancing, then hurrying on; and as soon as I saw it I knew that this white flame was life itself, the very quintessence of being; and then it came to me, in a rocket-burst of ecstasy, that nothing mattered, nothing could ever matter, because nothing else was real, but this quivering and hurrying lambency of being. Birds, men, or creatures not yet shaped and coloured, all were of no account except so far as this flame of life travelled through them. It left nothing to mourn over behind it; what I had thought was tragedy was mere emptiness or a shadow show; for now all real feeling was caught and purified and danced on ecstatically with the white flame of life. I had never felt before such deep happiness as I knew at the end of my dream of the tower and the birds, and if I have not kept that happiness with me, as an inner atmosphere and a sanctuary for the heart, that is because I am a weak and foolish man who allows the mad world to come trampling in, destroying every green shoot of wisdom. Nevertheless, I have not been quite the same man since.

Recent Penguin Fiction

THE MAN OF PROPERTY

John Galsworthy

831

The first – and perhaps the best – of the trilogy of novels which ultimately became known as *The Forsyte Saga.* Its characters are that celebrated family of English fiction whose members represent in their various ways the complex pattern of the affluent middle class two generations ago. It is a composite portrait drawn with profound observation, social sense and delicate irony. (2s 6d)

A TREE GROWS IN BROOKLYN

Betty Smith

834

The New York Times described this book as 'a poignant and deeply understanding story of childhood and family relationships'. It concerns the Nolan family – principally the daughter, Francie – and their hard, eventful life in the slums of Brooklyn. Many film-goers will remember the recent very successful screen version of the story. (3s 6d)

THE GRAPES OF WRATH

John Steinbeck

833

The story of a dispossessed community, driven from its bit of land in Oklahoma by the implacable march of industrial progress.

'I have no hesitation in saying that *The Grapes of Wrath* is one of the most vital stories that I have read for some time ... This is a terrible and an indignant book; yet is not without passages of lyrical beauty, and the ultimate impression is that of the dignity of the human spirit under the stress of the most desperate conditions.' – *Manchester Guardian.* (3s 6d)

A New Penguin Classic

CHAUCER: THE CANTERBURY TALES

Translated by Nevill Coghill

L 22

The Canterbury Tales is one of the great books of the world, and is certainly the liveliest, wisest, wittiest presentation of the human comedy in our language. The passage of time has, however, in the course of five and a half centuries, obscured it a little from us, and what were once the freshest colloquial Chaucerisms seem at times archaic, quaint and even difficult to understand to-day. Notes and glossaries are necessary, yet they impede the eager reader plunging for pleasure among the tales. And pleasure there is in plenty, whether in the sharp portrayal of a lively and varied human nature that does not seem to have changed much since the fourteenth century, or in the tales that are told; tales that range from noble romances of love and warfare to the ruderies of millers and cooks. Nevill Coghill's translation or modernization, passages from which have been read and later dramatized on the B.B.C.'s Third Programme, has given the easy fluency of a modern conversational idiom to Chaucer's work, while remaining faithful in scholarship to the original texts, without expurgation; readers who have hitherto found Chaucer too difficult will here become easily and happily acquainted with him and the rich legacy he made to them and to England. (3s 6d)

New Books On Art

CONTEMPORARY BRITISH ART

Herbert Read

A 250

The aim of this Pelican is to give a survey of British painting and sculpture at mid-century. The text attempts to isolate and account for a specifically British element in the general confusion of styles, and to trace significant movements and groupings. The leading artists of the modern school are dealt with, and their influence on their younger contemporaries is estimated. The seventy plates, six of which are in colour, illustrate the work of as many artists, and these, together with the accompanying biographical notes, make the volume the most convenient and comprehensive guide to the subject yet published. (3s 6d)

PAINTINGS FROM AMERICA

John Walker

E 39

Paintings from America has been written and edited by John Walker, Curator of the National Gallery of Art in Washington. It includes reproductions of some of the famous American pictures which have been on loan exhibition at the Tate Gallery and many examples from the most important private and public collections in the United States, making 40 black-and-white and 8 colour plates in all. It is a survey of two hundred years of painting, beginning with some of the little-known American 'primitives' and representing such international artists as Benjamin West, John Singleton Copley, George Innes, and the expatriates, Whistler, Mary Cassatt and John Singer Sargent. A special publication measuring 9¼ by 6½ inches. (7s 6d)